A SURGEON'S LIFETIME

A SURGEON'S LIFETIME

Evolution in General Surgery
1959–2001

David Watkin

Surgeon, Leicester Royal Infirmary

Troubador Publishing Ltd
Unit E2 Airfield Business Park,
Harrison Road, Market Harborough,
Leicestershire LE16 7UL
Tel: 0116 279 2299
Email: books@troubador.co.uk
Web: www.troubador.co.uk/matador

ISBN 9781805140818

British Library Cataloguing in Publication Data.
A catalogue record for this book is available from the British Library.

Printed by Printed and bound in Great Britain by CMP UK
Typeset in 11pt Adobe Caslon Pro by Troubador Publishing Ltd, Leicester, UK

Matador is an imprint of Troubador Publishing Ltd

CONTENTS

FOREWORD

The history of medicine and its practice in the United Kingdom in the second half of the 20th century is of particular interest owing to the vast number of changes that took place during this period, many of them undoubtedly beneficial – others, questionably, less so. There was change in the method of training consultants and change in consultant practice with the rise of specialism. Concurrently there were new diagnostic methods and treatments with the development of so-called high-tech medicine. The organisation of hospitals changed as a result of diminished hours of work for trainees, successive reorganisations of the National Health Service and change in the expected lifestyle of professionals. All are examples of events that make medicine at the turn of the century and beyond hugely different from that of the 1950s.

David Watkin, who began his medical career as a student at Christ's College, Cambridge in 1953 and retired from clinical practice as a distinguished consultant surgeon in 2001, lived through these changes and actively participated at local and national level in the many adaptations that became necessary so far as they affected surgery. In this engrossing memoir he details the story of his life from childhood to retirement against the background of change as it affected his own practice. This makes for fascinating reading, not only for his family (who were his intended audience when he began) but also for those professionally involved in surgery as well as social historians and interested members of the public. Throughout the book he writes with precision and candour about the sometimes difficult choices that had to be made and emphasises the importance of family life which has sustained and supported him throughout his career. It is a life story that deserves a wide readership.

Sir Barry Jackson MS FRCS FRCP
Past President, The Royal College of Surgeons of England

SOURCES AND ACKNOWLEDGEMENTS

I held appointment diaries for the latter part of my working life and retained a selection of committee minutes. Otherwise, I have relied on memory and accordingly apologise for the inevitable inaccuracies. I mention various surgical documents and government reports, but have not burdened the text with their references, which can be found using a search engine.

My thanks go to the numerous patients and colleagues with whom I have been associated, I'm grateful to Rachel Barnes for my photograph and the general design of the front cover. My wife Elisabeth has been a great support throughout our lives together and in the production of this book. Our daughter Sally, a former journalist, kindly advised about the text.

INTRODUCTION

This is an account of my life and times, how I became a surgeon and the many and varied activities during my career. Apart from advances in surgical practice, I discuss how changes in hospital management and the supervision of training affected clinical services. It is not a 'blood and guts' story of surgery, though there is a sprinkling of clinical anecdotes. Threading through this is family life, and finally retirement.

There was no medical background to my upbringing. My father was keen that I should be educated in the private sector but this was only possible courtesy of a generous award from his employers. The glories and idiosyncrasies of the schools are discussed, and I had several other career plans before opting for medicine when in the sixth form. The next section describes my time on the pre-clinical course at Cambridge and then clinical training at the old Westminster Hospital Medical School. During the latter I decided on a surgical career and met Elisabeth, my future wife.

My surgical training is considered objectively. After house officer and SHO posts at the Westminster and Kingston-on-Thames, we married and I started surgical training in Bristol. There followed two years as a general surgical registrar in Leicester and then a senior registrar post in Derby rotating to Sheffield. On the 'see one, do one and teach one' basis, I acquired great clinical and operative experience but by modern standards little training. I enjoyed opportunities to teach my juniors and medical students. A lack of research and paucity of publications was corrected by my last post as a lecturer in Sheffield. While we were there, Elisabeth trained in radiology.

Moving to a consultant post in general surgery in Leicester in 1971, I describe starting my practice, which initially included urology and neonatal surgery. I opted for two sessions in the private sector. Almost immediately, I was tasked with setting up training for intensive care nurses and then a course for the new grade of operating department assistants. I was glad that a new medical school was to open in Leicester in 1975 and was delighted to be asked to be the first clinical sub-dean, responsible for organising the clinical course.

Chapters on my consultant career are arranged thematically, the topics ranging from clinical teaching, hospital building, and my wife's career as a consultant radiologist, to the management of emergency admissions. General surgery changed as its subspecialties gradually separated and I became a large bowel surgeon. Support for juniors particularly in emergency work improved and their hours were brought under control. This section ends with brief accounts of some memorable clinical cases, emphasising errors. I report my personal involvement with duodenal ulcers, in research, in operative surgery and as a patient, exemplifying the changes over more than 30 years.

The next two sections describe my part in local management and then in national surgical affairs. Chairmanship of the Leicestershire Medical Committee, with membership of the District Management Team, was revealing and prompted me to review the changes in management of the NHS since its inception. At that time the excessive hours for junior doctors were beginning to be corrected and I recount our efforts to implement that.

I was elected to represent the Trent Region on the council of the Association of Surgeons and as Regional Adviser in Surgery, leading to involvement in the development of surgical audit and the introduction of the new FRCS (General Surgery) exam taken at the completion of training. I became a member of the Specialist Advisory Committee responsible for training in General Surgery and then served as its chairman. Throughout this period, I remained busy in clinical practice, including being on the emergency rota. Finally, I was elected President of the Association of Surgeons for 2000–2001.

The last section describes our adjustment to retirement, expanding our interests, travelling and finding roles in the management of local societies. Our family life is reviewed and we each had experience as surgical patients. I allow myself some comments on changes in the NHS. The account ends in 2019, avoiding consideration of the Covid-19 pandemic.

The pace of change accelerated throughout my career, and I describe evolution in general surgery, with implications for the service and for training. Surgical techniques advanced, particularly after the introduction of video-laparoscopic operating. Gastro-intestinal endoscopy and cross-sectional imaging increased the power of investigation. Lengths of hospital admission shortened, and many more procedures were carried out as day cases. Hospital management was repeatedly re-organised. The one constant feature was our family, continuing into retirement.

CHILDHOOD

1

ANCESTRY

My grandparents had vastly different origins and attitudes. Great grandfather Edward Watkin was the son of a Montgomeryshire farmer, who occupied a property of about 100 acres, a reasonable size for those days. He was for many years the landlord of The (Green) Dragon in Montgomery. Originally a coaching inn, it had lost that business when the railway arrived in 1861, and as the station is over a mile from the town it did nothing for the inn's prosperity. A cutting from the local newspaper, displayed in The Dragon, records that Edward Watkin's funeral in 1893 attracted seventy mourners including the Lord Lieutenant!

Edward's son, Thomas Lloyd Watkin, initially worked at the hotel. Then he took the tenancy of The Hem at Forden, some two miles north of Montgomery. Many years later my father, visiting the Welshpool branch of Barclays Bank to assess the damage after the strongroom was flooded, found an entry in a ledger recording his father opening an account in 1887. The Great and Little Hems were farmed as one, employing several workers. Thomas married Hannah Maria Vaughan, youngest sister of a successful farmer and haulier based at Court Calmore near the railway station. They had four children: the eldest, Percy, died aged 31, Letitia (Letty) married Cecil Coleman and more will be mentioned of them later, my father and Nita, the youngest.

My father was born at The Hem in 1901. He was christened Francis (Frank) John Lloyd Watkin, but his uncle Arthur Vaughan was displeased not to have been mentioned, so Arthur was added, between Lloyd and Watkin, allegedly at a further christening but more likely just at the register office. This indicates that Arthur Vaughan was the most successful member of that generation, farming, winning championships at the Royal Welsh Show and building a terrace of neo-Georgian houses in Montgomery.

My father said that his father 'liked to do the big stuff' and was 'very generous to the men at Christmas'. However, the early 20th century was difficult for farmers and Thomas gave up the farm in about 1909.

The family next moved to The Pigot Arms at Pattingham, near Wolverhampton, where Frank sang treble in the church choir. It is not clear why they moved again in 1911, this time to The Seven Stars in Wolverhampton, but it may have been a larger pub. Only months later they moved yet again, to Birmingham, and then back to The Garrick's Head in Wolverhampton. My father recalled that, as was then widespread practice, they brewed their own beer. Pubs did good business during the First World War, and they decided to modernise, installing new steel vats. The beer produced was unsatisfactory and they had to give up the tenancy in about 1917. Their next abode was The Hollies in Solihull; it is uncertain whether this was a smallholding or a pub. Finally, my grandparents returned to Montgomery as tenants of the small Cottage Inn.

Frank attended three different schools between 1911 and 1914 as the family moved repeatedly and he had to leave school at 14. At 15 or 16 he volunteered to join the Royal Flying Corps, perhaps to escape the family's downward spiral, but failed the medical – unsurprisingly as he was under-age. He then found work at the United Counties Bank in Birmingham, which was being taken over by Barclays. Him getting this job is surprising in view of his limited education but was doubtless facilitated by the absence of men in the forces. He studied commercial subjects at night school and developed a successful career in banking, of which more later. My Watkin grandparents had a belief in their social status out of proportion to their financial position, combining this with a disdain for education.

THE NICHOLLS FAMILY

My mother's family was completely different. Her father, James Nicholls, was a carpenter from Herefordshire who arrived in Stroud in 1902 with his tool chest (which I now own). He promptly married Frances Artus, who had been the assistant village schoolmistress in Rodborough, a suburb of Stroud, trained by way of apprenticeship. According to the census, her family had worked on the railway. Why did James move to Stroud? He must already have met Frances, but how? They lived throughout their marriage in a terraced cottage in Lightpill, Rodborough. James worked as a self-employed carpenter, with a workshop beside the nearby canal, and made exquisitely inlaid wooden boxes in his spare time. A long cottage garden was filled with flowers in front and fruit and vegetables at the back.

My Nicholls grandparents had three daughters: Norah, Frances and Mary (Mollie), my mother, born in 1900. Mollie's father had hoped for a boy and used to call her Tom, encouraging tomboyish behaviour in her teens. All three girls had scholarships to the Stroud High School for Girls. Its founding headmistress from 1904 was Miss DM Beale, niece of Dorothea Beale who was the second headmistress of Cheltenham Ladies' College and a colleague of Frances Mary Buss, the first headmistress of North London Collegiate School (mentioned in chapter 9).

Norah went on to Bristol University and read French and English, with a view to teaching. Instead, she married Harry Cook. He worked as a foreman in a plastics factory making telephone receivers while Norah ran a small village shop attached to their cottage in Rodborough and established a youth group at the church. My mother, like Norah, went to Bristol to train as a teacher. It is remarkable that, in the second decade of the 20th century, two of the three daughters of a carpenter went to university.

HOW MY PARENTS MET

My mother's first job was in an elementary school in Erdington, Birmingham, roughly where Spaghetti Junction is now. When teachers were absent classes were doubled up. Then, with responsibility for 90 children, her instructions from the dragon of a headmistress were to keep order and not worry about teaching them anything. She lived in lodgings with Cecil and Letty (née Watkin) Coleman. Cecil's family were prosperous pawnbrokers, but he had a chequered career. My father often visited, and a prolonged courtship developed.

My father worked in the head office of the bank in Birmingham, except for an interlude (at the age of 22) when he was sent to manage the branch at Solihull, where there had been irregularities. He returned to headquarters six months later, having sorted out the problems. This was to be his only time as a branch manager.

My mother described a visit to meet her future in-laws, in about 1925. They travelled to Montgomery by train and walked the mile and a half to the Cottage Inn where my grandfather was by then the tenant landlord. I have no details of how the visit went or of its duration. Within a year Thomas Watkin was bankrupt, with debts to tradespeople in Montgomery. My father felt embarrassed about this throughout his life and it may have contributed to his financial caution.

Thomas Watkin died in 1929 and was buried next to his parents in the churchyard at Montgomery. Granny Watkin and Frank then joined forces. At about that time my father was transferred to Barclays head office in Lombard Street, London, as an assistant inspector, working with Mr FC Parsons, the senior inspector for the large London area which extended to Norfolk and the Channel Isles.

My mother moved to teach at a junior school in Ealing, living in digs nearby, while my father and Granny Watkin lived in south London. It was a long while before my parents married. I gathered that employees wishing to marry needed the bank's permission, unlikely to be granted to a humble assistant inspector. My mother was impatient at this delay.

SHREWSBURY

They were married in Rodborough church in May 1934, both aged 33. It was not a white wedding and was attended only by close family. The wedding breakfast was at The Bear Hotel, Rodborough, with a main course of salmon, then regarded as a luxury.

My father had just been promoted to the grade of inspector, as second in command in the Shrewsbury district. That district covered Shropshire, Cheshire, North and Mid Wales, Liverpool and Manchester. Many of the visits to branches involved staying away through the week.

They rented a semi-detached house in Heathgates, on the outskirts of Shrewsbury. It had been built by a builder for his own occupation about six years previously and had a garage (not so common in 1933), with a large greenhouse extending behind it. There was gas lighting, replaced by electricity a few years later.

Granny Watkin came to join them, bringing her maid with her; she had apparently always had a maid, despite her straitened circumstances. The maid did not last long, being replaced by a daily woman, Mrs Williams. Milmy (as I called her) was of gypsy origin and proved to be a wonderfully loyal helper.

She did the washing and housework and when I arrived provided childcare. I remained in Christmas card contact for many years.

There was a gardener by the name of Neat, who grew vegetables and looked after the tomatoes in the greenhouse. My father had his first car, a Singer Nine, with a vertical back end. My mother had driving lessons and acquired a licence, before the driving test was introduced, but never drove subsequently. They both played golf (badly). Granny Watkin died in 1938, not much mourned by my mother who had found her difficult.

I was born on 10th July 1935 at The Limes nursing home in Shrewsbury. My mother and I frequently visited Stroud, by train, to stay with Granny Nicholls, while my father was away inspecting the more distant branches of the bank. I can just remember visiting in 1939, two years after my grandfather James had died. I was impressed by Granny cooking on a coal range in the living room/kitchen and by the fact that the front room, containing a piano, was only for special occasions. We were not a 'special occasion'.

Early in 1938 my father was appointed to a new post as assistant to the local director for Yorkshire, to amalgamate the Yorkshire part of the Union Bank of Manchester, which had been taken over by Barclays. He commuted weekly by car from Shrewsbury, while looking for a house to rent, a process which took many months.

2

MENSTON IN WHARFEDALE

My parents rented a newly built house in Burley Lane, Menston, about a mile's walk from the station, with a frequent service to Barclays district offices in Bradford and Leeds.

Soon after we arrived, while having tea in the small kitchen, I pulled a kettle of boiling water off the gas stove and scalded my left forearm, which took about six weeks to heal. The GP managed this, without a visit to hospital. Soon afterwards an extending mahogany dining table was delivered, and all meals were then eaten in the dining room.

In the summer of 1939, we set out for a holiday in a bungalow at Hunmanby, on the Yorkshire coast. After about a mile the brakes failed, and we had to walk home. A garage in the village repaired the car so we could leave the next day. The only detail I have about that holiday is that I fell over in shallow water and just lay there, face down, until rescued by a Mrs Dixon who had been taken with us to help look after me.

Another memorable event was an illness described as 'meningitis', for which I was given a new drug, M&B 693 (a sulphonamide, precursor of antibiotics), with rapid recovery at home.

STARTING SCHOOL

In September I started at Littleburn School, about a mile away in Burley-in-Wharfedale, owned by Miss Brooks and Miss Little. Miss Brooks took the younger class, teaching us to read and do simple sums. The senior class, run by Miss Little, followed the liberal PNEU (Parents' National Education Union) ethos, which encouraged us to produce verbal material, which was written down for us by numerous student teachers. While encouraging fluency, this may have contributed to my later poor handwriting and difficulty with spelling. There was a playing field, where we ran about freely, keeping clear of the two tethered goats, and occasionally played rounders, but no football.

Most of the neighbouring youngsters went to Littleburn, though they separated out later, some to the private sector, some to Ilkley Grammar School. I rapidly made friends with the vicar's two children, and a couple of others who lived nearby. We roamed into the small farm across the lane and around the woods and fields.

In 1942 I was given my first bicycle; it had an 18-inch frame and was too big for a seven-year-old beginner, so I found riding it difficult, practising with my father's hand on the back of the saddle. Cycles were also purchased for my parents, but my mother never took to it. My father scarcely used his, but it had a second life years later at St Edward's and Cambridge.

THE WAR

My father was not called up for war service. He was 39 and was designated by the bank as an essential worker. Instead, he enrolled in the ARP (Air Raid Precautions). It was decided that we should have an air raid shelter. Ernest, a long-stay patient from the psychiatric hospital in Menston (later notorious as High Royds) was employed to dig a large hole, into which pre-cast concrete slabs were to be inserted. However, when my mother went to inspect the hole, she said that she couldn't go out there at night, so Ernest was employed to fill it in again! As an alternative the larder was fortified with sandbags on the outside walls and sand and corrugated iron on the flat roof. We spent only a few sessions in there and thereafter ignored the warning sirens. One bomb was dropped in open country about five miles away; we were lucky.

Granny Nicholls was taken ill in the autumn of 1940. My mother and I travelled by train to Stroud to visit her in the cottage hospital. She had suffered a heart attack and looked very frail, fancying only 'a little soup'. We returned home, and she died about a week later. In view of the problems of travel in wartime we did not attend her funeral, everything being taken care of by Auntie Norah.

RATIONING

With the war came food rationing. Sugar, jam, butter, margarine, cooking fat, cheese, bacon and tea ranged from two to eight ounces per head per week. Meat was limited by cost: at one shilling and four pence (6p) per head which would buy a smaller quantity of roasting meat or a larger weight of a cheaper cut. Offal was not rationed, nor were rabbits, so both featured in our diet. There might be one or two eggs each per week, so eggless recipes for cakes were sought out; later dried egg became available. Bread was not rationed until after the war. Vegetables and fruit were unrestricted but there were usually no oranges or bananas. Milk continued to be delivered daily from the farm nearby.

Sugar rationing was particularly limiting, at eight ounces per head. My mother devised various strategies to deal with the shortfall: golden syrup was used to sweeten puddings and porridge was accompanied by sweetened condensed milk. The jam ration could be exchanged, weight-for-weight, for sugar; three pounds of sugar made five pounds of jam yielding a surplus of two pounds of sugar. Despite rationing, we always had a cooked breakfast, even if it was just a little bacon with a stuffed tomato or scrambled eggs made with dried egg. Clothes rationing started in 1941 and soap was rationed in February 1942, followed in July by sweets and chocolate at two ounces per week.

We were all encouraged to 'Dig for Victory'. I took this seriously, writing to the Ministry of Agriculture for advice about the rotation of crops and the use of fertilisers. They duly sent the pamphlets, but I wonder what they thought of my seven-year-old's handwriting.

A more up-to-date Singer Ten with a sloping back and a boot had replaced the old Singer Nine. Petrol was rationed from the start of hostilities, enough for about 200 miles per month; then in 1942 none was available for non-essential users, so the car was laid up. My father already travelled to the office by train, walking the mile to Menston station. My mother and I made shopping trips by bus to Bradford where Brown Muff's department store was our main destination. As a treat, we sometimes took in the Bradford Museum en route. Occasionally we all went to the smaller towns of Ilkley or Otley on a Saturday afternoon.

WARTIME HOLIDAYS

Auntie Lettie and her Coleman family visited from Blackpool, where they were running a small hotel. I found them loud, and Uncle Cecil had what would now be called designer stubble, which prickled when he kissed me.

We stayed with them in Blackpool once. Resorts on the east and south coasts were closed to visitors during the war and all the large hotels in Blackpool had been taken over for evacuated government offices, so their establishment was doing very well. It had to operate in Lettie's name as Cecil was an undischarged bankrupt. They boasted of their wealth and sported diamond rings.

We had two more family holidays while in Menston, one in the Lake District, by car while a petrol ration was still available, and one travelling by train, via Carnforth, to Arnside. I have some miscellaneous memories of the latter: there were quick sands in the bay, and there was a Pele Tower at Silverdale.

MOVING TO NORTH WALES

By 1943, my father had completed the task of amalgamating the Yorkshire part of the Union Bank of Manchester with Barclays Yorkshire district. He was offered a district inspector's post based in Leicester but didn't fancy this and managed to get it exchanged for the North Wales job, returning to the team where he had previously been an inspector. He remained in that job until he retired 17 years later.

During the several months that it took to find accommodation he travelled home to Menston at weekends by car, despite petrol being restricted to essential users. It was difficult to find a house but finally, with the help of the local Barclays manager, an unfurnished flat was found in Rhyl. A solicitor neighbour (and fellow member of the ARP) suggested buying the rented house in Menston as sitting tenants and then selling it with vacant possession, a procedure which produced a profit of about £1,500, a hefty sum in those days, which was to fund the building of a house in 1947/8.

3

RHYL

We moved into the flat early in the summer of 1943. It was intended to be a temporary expedient while we looked for a house, but we were there for five years. It occupied the ground floor of one of a pair of fine Edwardian semis on the seafront, near its eastern end. Sand dunes separated it from the promenade by about 50 yards, with the beach beyond. The west wind carried clouds of fine sand along the front, penetrating the flat, and may have initiated my mother's asthma.

The front room, with a view out to sea, was used as the lounge and contained the dining table, used only for entertaining. Behind this was my parents' bedroom, then four steps led down to a room which served as my bedroom, and the everyday dining room, a bathroom and a primitive kitchen. Only towards the end of our stay did we acquire our first fridge, which was placed in the lounge, there being no room for it in the kitchen.

My sister Margaret was born on 7th November 1943 in a small maternity home in Prestatyn, under the supervision of our GP. She shared my parents' bedroom until we moved to Wrexham in 1948. Margaret had a mass of curly blonde hair; she was pushed around in a Dunkley perambulator and much admired by the neighbours. She did not go to nursery school (few did in those days), and her only playmate was a child from the top flat. Meanwhile I had started as a day-boy at St Chad's, a prep school in Prestatyn.

LIFE IN RHYL

A walk of about a mile (and we did walk) took us to the top of High Street. On the right, the sand dunes gave way to municipal gardens, crown bowling greens, a large outdoor swimming pool (sea water, unheated) and the pier. On the landward side of the road was the Royal Alexandra Hospital, then mainly used for injured servicemen, who lounged on the sand dunes in their blue invalids' uniforms. Heading further west there were more gardens, Punch and Judy and a free open-air theatre. Beyond this was a large fun fair and then the small harbour at the mouth of the River Clwyd. Over the next year increasing numbers of American troops were present in the build-up to D-Day and tanks became a common sight.

At intervals along the prom, there were ice-cream kiosks, boarded up; only after the war ended did I realise that these were camouflaged pillboxes. However, I did understand that the 10-foot-high poles planted in the beach were to prevent enemy aircraft from landing. I had a large map of Europe on the wall in the hall and I plotted the bombing raids on Germany and followed the advance of the Allies after D-Day.

There were occasional visits to the cinema (I remember seeing Olivier's *Henry V* with my father), though fewer than were reported by my school contemporaries, who could describe the plots of many films in the dormitory after lights out.

ST CHAD'S

My parents wanted me to be educated in the private sector, reflecting my father's limited schooling and his perception that the top jobs in the bank went to public schoolboys. Soon after we arrived in Rhyl, my mother – with me in tow – set about selecting a prep school. There were three possibilities: Epworth, just south of the town, but she didn't like the headmaster; another school in Rhyl, which took an extended age range and finally, St Chad's, Prestatyn. We met the head, Mr Payne, white haired, balding and wearing plus-fours, and liked him. He had bought the school in 1925 and promptly built new premises at Meliden, west of the town.

I started at St Chad's in September 1943 as one of only five day-boys among about 60 boarders, mostly from Merseyside. Aged eight I travelled unaccompanied the five miles there and back by bus at a cost of three old pence (1p) each way. I started in the fourth form, taught by the wife of the vicar of Gwaenysgor who walked over Meliden hill each day. Mr Payne had his own logical system for numbering the classes, with the first for the most senior down to the fourth. If there were two boys with the same surname, they were numbered rather than the classical major and minor. When Margaret was born, I boarded for the second half of my first term and enjoyed it.

After one term I was promoted to the third form. The boarders did prep in the evenings, but I took the work home. I usually got good marks and was accused of getting help at home though I was careful to decline any assistance offered by my mother. The next September I went up to the second form and a year later, aged 10, to the first form, where I remained for two years, as was not unusual.

The curriculum was aimed at getting boys through the common entrance examination for public schools. This comprised the same question papers nationally, but the papers were marked by the school to which the candidate was applying. The subjects were English language, maths (arithmetic, algebra and geometry), French, Latin, history and geography.

There was no science, and art was taught for only one term, by a young woman who then disappeared from the scene. Mr Payne taught maths very effectively. He also covered geography, entirely in terms of the physical features. I could name all the rivers, capes, bays etc. in Britain and the major ones throughout the world, but there was no mention of economic or social aspects. He taught the Old Testament story, from memory, in a very lively manner. He was a believer, serving as churchwarden, but did not discuss the New Testament or theology.

Due to the war, teachers were difficult to find, resulting in a rapid turnover. Almost all were male and some quite incompetent. English lessons suffered most: at one stage, the curate from the parish church was pressed into service, but he had no control at all. Others were more successful. Mr Jackman had been born on board a square-rigged sailing ship and had travelled all over the world. He taught history and coached the first XI at cricket, bowling 'round arm', a style long out of date. Major Bower arrived after the war to teach Latin. He was an effective teacher and a fierce disciplinarian. Bob Junker, an old boy, returned from the Navy having won a Distinguished Service Cross. He threw himself into the life of the school while teaching French, entirely written with no attempt to get us to speak it. There was concern at home regarding my English and my mother helped to rectify this by encouraging books; I remember us reading *The Wind in the Willows* and *Uncle Tom's Cabin* together.

The school comprised one long corridor with wings at either end. Along one side were the classrooms, which also served as our living space, and Mr Payne's study. The dining room, a library and a changing room were on the other side. Above these were the dormitories, a sick room, bathrooms and toilets. There was no central heating, we were warmed by coal fires in all the classrooms, managed by Mr Payne's former batman.

Games were important for prestige, but I had no skills. I don't think I had previously kicked a football and certainly had never played cricket. There was no instruction, so those who lacked experience gravitated to the 'lower' game. This was soccer in the two winter terms and cricket in the summer. Matches were played against the half dozen other prep schools along the coast of North Wales. I never played in more than the third team, but in view of my academic status I was regularly included with the first team's visits as linesman or scorer.

There was an outdoor swimming pool, built into the side of a hill by Mr Payne himself. I made no progress at swimming in the first summer term but succeeded during the holidays with private lessons in sea water at Rhyl baths. In our free time, we could roam the extensive school grounds and climb the many large trees. If the ground was frozen, a walk replaced games. Once, crossing a railway bridge, some of the boys tried to drop stones down the funnel of a passing steam train. One smashed a window in the driver's cab, and he suffered an eye injury, but none of the boys was prosecuted; fortunately, I was not involved. Incidentally, there was no corporal punishment at the school, which must have been unusual at that time.

There was an evening Christmas party and one year, aged 10, I missed the last bus home and elected to walk the five miles. This took about an hour and a half, by which time I had been declared missing. In each of my last two years, plays were performed on an improvised stage in the gym, before an audience of parents. I was the duke in the trial scene from *The Merchant of Venice* and in my final year I was Pickwick in scenes from *Pickwick Papers*.

For my last year I was a boarder (and thoroughly enjoyed the companionship) in preparation for going away to public school. I would be only 12 years old by then, which is younger than usual, but there would be no boys remaining at my level so it was decided that I should move on. On Sunday mornings we all walked, in a crocodile, to the parish church where we formed about 40 per cent of the congregation. Once a week we had a film show in the gym; the 35mm projector was silent and unreliable. In the summer term, we started the day by plunging naked into the outdoor pool. With many opportunities to see the others in the nude, the boys classified themselves into 'roundheads' and 'cavaliers'; there were approximately equal numbers, so no stigma attached to either group.

In my last summer term, we were helped to measure the height of the nearby Meliden Hill and Dyserth Mountain, using Mr Payne's theodolite. Solving the various triangles gave a height for the mountain differing by only a few feet from that of the Ordnance Survey.

Barclays Bank offered scholarships for the children of staff, based on the results of common entrance papers, taken in February and marked centrally for this purpose. The scheme included a limited list of public schools, and my parents selected The Wrekin, conveniently placed in Shropshire. I had extra coaching in Latin in preparation for the examination. After the exam I was unexpectedly called up for interview at the bank's head office in London. I remember being asked which author I liked and replying 'Arthur Ransome'. The outcome was an offer of a place at St Edward's, Oxford, a school not on the list for the scheme. This scholarship was given to the best candidate nationally.

My parents were delighted and gave me my first watch, which continued in service until there were electronic watches. Cheekily, Mr Payne wrote to St Edward's asking whether I could also enter their scholarship examination in May. The answer was 'Yes'. I sat their papers at St Chad's and was then called for interview. A frail, white-haired master (Mr Tilly) set me some geometrical problems and a few equations, which I solved to his satisfaction. Meanwhile my father was asked where he had been to school and, having left at 14, could only reply 'Wolverhampton'. I was given an exhibition of £30 per annum and adding this to the generous payment of £150 from Barclays left only £10 of the annual fees of £190 – less than the cost of keeping me at home!

I left St Chad's in July 1947 apprehensive about my move to St Edward's, but looking forward to starting at a school which offered rowing as an escape from cricket.

As enthusiasm for boarding prep schools diminished, all six along the coast of North Wales closed; St Chad's survived the longest.

HOLIDAYS

As my school was five miles away, I had little opportunity to meet boys in Rhyl. I did however strike up a close friendship with Stuart Shelley, whom I met on the beach. We played endless games romping around in the sand dunes and constructing fortifications on the beach to resist the incoming tide. His father was a violinist and leader of the Liverpool Philharmonic Orchestra. He also taught his son, whose declared aim was to become a famous composer. Stuart went on to become leader of the Welsh National Youth Orchestra, adopting the professional name of Julian Shelley, his father's first name.

While living in Rhyl we didn't have a family summer holiday, on the grounds that we were already at the seaside. Certainly, I got a lot of enjoyment from the beach, swimming there and at the baths. I became interested in boats, fuelled by reading the Arthur Ransome books and looking at the small craft aground on the sand in the harbour and decided that one day I would go to sea, superseding my previous idea of farming.

HOUSE BUILDING

Once the war was over, the search began for a house to purchase but none seemed satisfactory. My father was keen to build, but plots with planning permission were difficult to find, even though the location was flexible between Shrewsbury, Wrexham and Chester. Government policy was to concentrate on council houses, discouraging approvals for private building. After some false starts a site was discovered near Wrexham at a price of £750. The land was owned by the chairman of the planning committee, which may have facilitated planning approval.

In view of the restriction to 1000 square feet of floor area, the plans needed to provide for a later extension. My father was impressed by a house built for a colleague; he borrowed the plans and I copied them over the weekend. An architect was then employed to modify these and supervise the project. Finding a builder was difficult because all major firms were busy with public contracts and the government cost limit of £1,300 (excluding land) was not economic. Nevertheless, a builder agreed the contract and work started in the autumn of 1947. In the following spring, work was suspended until a further payment of £300 was agreed. I enjoyed weekend visits to watch progress and decided to become an architect rather than join the Navy.

In August 1948, the house was ready for us to move in.

4

ST EDWARD'S – THE EARLY YEARS

I started my first term at St Edward's in September 1947 aged 12 years and two months, the youngest boy there. I was delivered by my parents, but for all subsequent journeys I travelled alone by train, with a change at Banbury.

The new boys arrived a day early and I was allocated to Macnamara's House (Mac's), one of an intake there of about a dozen; all the others were at least a year older. It was, of course, a single sex school – girls were not accepted until 1982. Each new boy was attached to a slightly more senior pupil as their 'teacher', the objective being to pass the new boys' test in school rules and nomenclature: you must not have your hands in your pockets when the chapel bells are ringing; you must run in the rain; the bearded violin teacher is known as Weetabix and many more.

I lived in the junior dayroom where we each had a desk with a lift-up lid and a compartment in open shelves. Our clothes were in our cabin trunks, kept under our beds, and we had lockable wooden tuck boxes in the basement. The dayroom housed about 30 boys, with the president and the six next most senior having 'horse boxes' – five-foot-high cubbyholes with a seat, a desk surface and some shelves above it. We did our prep in the dayroom, with a prefect to ensure quiet, for half an hour before morning chapel and about an hour and a half in the evening. Later, one moved on to the middle and then the senior dayroom, each with 12–15 boys. There were eight to ten house prefects occupying two studies. The head of house was also a school prefect.

Every new boy had to sing a song, standing on the table in the dayroom. I'd been dreading this, not knowing what to sing. When my turn came, I nervously performed the first verse of the Welsh national anthem. It was doubtless out of tune, but no one else knew how it should sound and the ordeal passed uneventfully.

Of the seven houses, only Mac's and Field House had accommodation for a married housemaster; other house masters had to be bachelors, as were very many of the staff. Shortly after I left, married quarters were created for all the housemasters.

ROUTINE

Having passed the new boys' test, we were subject to fagging for the house prefects. We each had a weekly quota of fags to perform, the quota diminishing with increasing seniority. The fagging tasks ranged from running errands to some regular jobs, such as shoe cleaning and desk tidying.

We slept in dormitories of six to 20, with one or two prefects in charge. The dormitories were named after Church of England bishops. Each morning we were supposed to take a cold shower. This ensured that we got up as soon as the bell rang, to be out of the communal washroom before the prefects got there. Weekday dress was grey trousers with turn-ups, a tweed sports jacket, black shoes and a black tie, in memory of Queen Victoria. On Sundays, we wore regulation dark blue serge suits.

Prep and then the morning chapel service were followed by breakfast for the whole school in the dining hall. This started with porridge, made as a thick tepid paste, undercooked and quite inedible. The alternative was to have one's own packet of cereal. However, the porridge was not wasted; it went to feed the school's pigs, which provided an occasional feast of roast pork.

CHAPEL

St Edward's was founded in 1863 by a clergyman to produce more clergy, so the chapel had been one of the first buildings and attendance was compulsory. There was a 15-minute service before breakfast on weekdays and another before supper in the evening. On Sundays, there was choral eucharist at 11am and evensong, with a sermon. Everyone was expected to take confirmation classes at the age of about 14, followed by the annual confirmation service with the bishop officiating. For some this religious activity led to a lifetime of faith but for others, including me, it was counterproductive.

PREPARATION FOR SCHOOL CERTIFICATE

I was placed in Upper Shell B, a curious terminology for the classes between the fourth and fifth forms. Most new boys started in the fourth form, but exhibitioners and scholars went straight into the Upper Shells or even the fifth form. Upper Shell A was for those who had some Greek, while in Upper Shell B we had introductory lessons in Greek taken by the chaplain, who was a hopeless disciplinarian, so we gained nothing apart from the alphabet. Maths was setted and I was naturally in the top set, taken by Mr Tilly, who had interviewed me. He was an excellent teacher, at least for those who liked maths. Latin consisted entirely of preparing a passage from *Caesar's Gallic Wars* and then translating it around the class. I hated this and hoped each time that I would not be called upon to speak.

The fifth form was preparation for School Certificate, replaced by O-levels in 1951, which later gave way to GCSEs. No certificate was awarded if fewer than six subjects were passed, including English language and elementary maths. There were five fifth forms: (a) to (e), in descending order of ability, with their objectives adjusted accordingly. I was in V(a) doing English language, English literature (*Twelfth Night* and the prologue to *The Canterbury Tales*), Latin, French, history (Britain 1715–1914 and the USA from Independence to the end of the Civil War) and biology. Maths and additional maths were setted (Mr Tilly again). I chose 'Physics-with-chemistry' (as an alternative to Greek or German). French lessons consisted of reading *Around the World in 80 Days* around the class. The science subjects were very well taught and I loved history with 'Guts' Whitrow. Thus, about the time of my 14th birthday, I passed the school certificate with five distinctions, three credits and a pass in French, 'with oral proficiency'.

SIXTH FORM

Aged 14, I chose to go into the science sixth, which was in two streams: one doing chemistry, physics and maths; the other with biology in place of maths. I opted for the biology stream, though I was sad to drop maths. Initially Mr Tilly agreed to take me and another enthusiast for single maths as an additional A level, but he died suddenly early in the second term. The head of maths would not take on two biologists, so this idea had to be abandoned. I had also considered going into the history sixth, but I couldn't see where this might lead as a career.

Joe Church, who had been a pilot during the war, arrived to teach physics brilliantly. Jack 'Crasher' White (who had won the Manx Grand Prix in 1938) taught biology inspiringly. A-level chemistry was boring, seeming to consist of the methods of industrial extraction of the various metals from their ores and endless titrations; almost no organic chemistry was included. Once in the sixth form, though unusually still in the junior dayroom, I was delighted to be exempt from fagging.

SPORT

As in all boys' public schools, St Edward's allocated a lot of time to sport, partly as a means of occupying us and keeping us out of trouble. In the Michaelmas term we all played rugger, for a 45-minute spell between 2.00 and 4pm and then returned for two periods of lessons before evening chapel. Being still a 'junior' while in the lower sixth, I was pulled into the 'elite' squad and, for half a term, I was moderately successful as hooker and played in several away matches; often we would be taken for a beer on the homeward journey, though all aged under 15. The team's results were not good and my skills outside the scrum were poor, so halfway through the term I was dropped. Mac's did, however, win the junior inter-house knockout competition at the end of term.

In the Lent term we again played rugger, and then the last three weeks were for athletics. The main feature of the latter was 'standards'. Each boy had to perform in each of seven events, ranging from the 100yds to the long jump and hurdles. If he reached the required standard for his age group, he scored a point for his house. The cup was awarded to the house with the highest average score per person, about 5.7. I was small for the under-15 age group and managed only four in my first year but achieved the full seven thereafter.

In the summer term, the timetable was switched around so that we worked for the first part of the afternoon and then had sport from 4pm. I opted for rowing rather than cricket. We walked to the boathouse at Godstow, by way of the canal towpath, then crossed the railway to Port Meadow, a total distance of about two miles. Those in a school or senior house crew cycled, as could those with medical reasons (e.g., hay fever). My rowing for the first two years consisted of sculling in a clinker-built 'whiff'. There was no instruction.

THE COMBINED CADET FORCE

One afternoon per week, sport was replaced by the Combined Cadet Force (CCF), participation in which was compulsory. We drilled, armed with the short Lea-Enfield rifle. Most parades were in mufti, but occasionally we wore battledress ('fug') with brass to polish and webbing which had to pass inspection. Each term there was a Field Day when we were bussed to a training ground where two companies fought the other two. The ostensible purpose of all of this was to prepare us, if it came to it, to defend the realm, but I suspect the real aim was to ensure that when we came to do national service, we would promptly be selected for officer training.

After two or three years we were examined for Certificate A, parts I and II and were then eligible to become lance corporals in the large army section or to move into the smaller Royal Naval or RAF sections. I opted for the Royal Naval Section and passed further tests to reach the rank of petty officer.

HEALTH AND DIET

Towards the end of my second term, I developed half a dozen spots, becoming part of a five-person epidemic of chickenpox. This necessitated isolation in the school sanatorium under the care of its Irish matron. We were not allowed home at the end of term but had to live out the prescribed three weeks of quarantine in the 'san'. Matron was not pleased at having to stay on to supervise us and described our condition as 'this filthy disease'.

Most of us kept our own breakfast cereal and jam on the table. We stored other goodies in wooden tuck boxes in the basement. I used to receive a parcel from home about every three weeks, containing a packet of cornflakes and a Victoria sandwich cake.

THE OUTSIDE WORLD

We were not allowed out of the school grounds without written leave, for which a good reason was required; mine was to purchase photographic materials, for which I had to go into the centre of Oxford. When in the city we had to wear a straw boater or 'basher', which made us conspicuous; surprisingly, it never led to ridicule from the locals.

There was a half-term weekend during which parents could take us out for much of the day, but we had to return for chapel and overnight. My parents with my younger sister Margaret, like several others, stayed at the Linton Lodge private (unlicensed) hotel where we enjoyed decent food. The more affluent families used The Randolph or even The Bear at Woodstock. Parents were invited to some school events but for much of the weekend we visited local sights, such as Blenheim Palace. These biannual visits must have been a financial burden for my parents but were never begrudged.

Entertainment during term time comprised a school play (in which scientists did not seem to be involved) and a couple of films. I particularly remember *The Lady Vanishes*.

PUNISHMENT

Order and discipline were maintained at various levels. The president of the junior dayroom could punish misdemeanours by ordering 25 press-ups. House prefects could order '100 lines' for minor offences such as not running in the rain. The lines consisted of writing out pages from the tables of irregular verbs in *Kennedy's Latin Primer*, so I suppose the punishment was thought to have educational value. The head of house could administer up to six strokes of the cane for serious offences, I once received this, but I cannot remember what for. Housemasters and the warden (headmaster) could also use the cane, but I do not recall this happening.

I had the impression that the regime had become much less brutal in the few years since the younger members of staff returned from the war and in the case of Mac's with Roger Northcote-Green taking over as housemaster just before I arrived. I was lucky to be allocated to Mac's – some of the other houses had a less liberal atmosphere. My later years at St Edward's are described in chapter six.

5
WREXHAM

Work on our new house, the planning of which was described in chapter three, started in 1947, but was subject to many delays. The builder often ran out of cement and my father would then obtain a bag or two from somewhere in West Wales. The specification exceeded the timber allocation and again supplementary supplies were obtained on the grey market; the parquet floors were said to be made from off-cuts. The coke boiler and the bathroom tiles were sourced from mid-Wales. The final cost of building was £1,600, excluding land (£750) and items obtained by my father. The profit from the purchase and resale of our rented house in Menston covered two-thirds of the total.

We moved in at the start of the school summer holidays in 1948. The NHS, which was to play such a large part in my life, was established just four weeks earlier. I recall going to see our GP in Rhyl a few months before this, paying his fee of five shillings (25p) and receiving a bottle of medicine, dispensed in his house, as treatment for a sore throat.

EARLY DAYS IN WREXHAM
The new house was a huge improvement on the flat. A landscape gardener was employed to lay out the grounds of about a third of an acre. There were shrubs, a splendid rockery, fruit trees and a vegetable plot. The garden became my mother's pride and joy, while my father managed the lawn and compost heap.

Rhosnessney village had become a suburb of Wrexham. It had a pub, The Gate Hangs High[1], and a resident village policeman on a bicycle. There was a temporary church of corrugated iron but no shop. Jeffreys Road, where we lived, was named after the notorious 17[th]century 'Bloody' Judge Jeffreys, who had owned Acton Hall, set in parkland on the opposite side of the lane. The Hall had been the headquarters of Western Command during the war and was left in an extremely poor state. It was demolished in about 1950 but the parkland was retained by the council, providing a fine view from the house and pleasant walks around the lake.

LIFE IN RHOSNESSNEY

Margaret, aged five in November, started at the Convent School in Wrexham in the autumn term after the move. When aged 11, she also won a Barclays Bank award, to cover the bulk of the fees for Huyton College in Liverpool (it closed in 1993). Having a sister who was eight years younger put me in an odd position. Was I her brother or a third parent?

My mother was an excellent cook, within the range to which she was accustomed. Rationing continued and my father, on his visits to West Wales, continued to source extra butter and dozens of eggs, which were preserved in water glass (sodium silicate solution). Fruit and vegetables were plentiful, from the garden and from 'Old Price', who did a twice-weekly round selling from his horse-drawn cart. Mr Price was an ex-miner whose legs had been crushed when working in Gresford Colliery, the site of a major disaster in 1934 in which 266 men died. He walked quite stiffly but managed a full day on his round and did gardening jobs as well.

In 1952, when the building restrictions ended, the planned extension was built. A dining room was added downstairs, with a fourth bedroom above it. My mother, who was troubled by insomnia, moved into the new bedroom. We at last acquired a telephone when a 'line' became available.

SEASIDE HOLIDAYS

Once we were established in Rhosnessney, an annual seaside holiday was considered appropriate and my father's banking contacts were a useful source of landladies. The first time, in 1949, we stayed in a bungalow at Morfa

---

1   This gate hangs high and hinders none
     Refresh and pay and travel on

Bychan, near Porthmadog with easy access to Black Rock Beach. This was the last time my father entered the sea; my mother had long since given up bathing. Neither of them could swim.

Thereafter we stayed in Rhosneigr in Anglesey. The arrangement there was that the landlady cooked whatever food we bought, a very satisfactory arrangement. For a few years we were looked after by Mrs Owen, a delightful lady of about 80. She had once been on a coach trip to Red Wharf Bay but had never been out of Anglesey. On hearing that my parents had lived in Birmingham, she mentioned another of her guests, a Mr Smith who came from there: 'Perhaps you know him?' When Mrs Owen decided to give up taking visitors she arranged for Miss Prytherch, across the road, to take us on. She came from a long line of lifeboat-men, whose group photographs adorned the hall; she had no surviving relatives and the lifeboat station had been closed.

ISOLATION

During my teenage years I was quite socially isolated at home. There were no children of my age along Jeffreys Road and having moved from Rhyl and being away at school I didn't have any local school friends. I read, gardened, cycled around the nearby countryside and went on shopping errands on my new Raleigh bicycle. When shopping in Wrexham I would prop it up on one pedal at the kerbside and leave it; it was never damaged or stolen.

Aged 13 I acquired my father's Zeiss-Ikon camera, with an f4.5 lens and bellows, in 3¼ x 2¼ inch format giving eight exposures on 120 roll-film. He had bought it when living in Shrewsbury but never got to grips with its functions. Jack James, our neighbour, showed me how to develop, contact print and enlarge. Then a year later I was given a 'Gnome' enlarger, setting up my darkroom in the downstairs toilet. The enlarger travelled to St Edward's with me each term for use in the darkroom there. It was still in use in 2009.

SAILING AT WHITEMERE

I had learned to sail at St Edward's. Later in 1954 after going to university, I identified the Shropshire Sailing Club at Whitemere, near Ellesmere. I persuaded my parents to buy me a second-hand Firefly sailing dinghy, one of the two classes sailed there. Whitemere was only about 65 acres in area, but still gave enjoyable racing. On Sundays in the Easter and summer holidays I drove the dozen miles, using the family car, taking Margaret as my crew. This provided welcome social contact, including some young people of my own age. There was an open meeting for Fireflies and another for GP14s, each with an associated social event at a hotel in Ellesmere.

What I lacked was a road trailer. Over the winter I advertised and found a cheap, home-made dinghy trailer in Reading. I obtained confirmation that British Rail would transport it to Wrexham for a modest fee and settled the deal. However, when the owner took it to the station, he was told that it would need an extra carriage, at considerable expense. Not to be defeated, I wrote to the chairman of British Rail, and he ruled that they must honour the original agreement!

From 1954 through to 1958 we took *Mystic* with us to Rhosneigr each August. Margaret and I sailed her around the inshore islets and across the bays; and my parents even came on some voyages. In 1959 we sold *Mystic*, for the same sum as she had cost, to a couple from East Yorkshire. When on holiday in 1969, we came across her at Hornsea Mere, still in good order.

6

ST EDWARD'S – THE LATER YEARS

After a term as president of the junior dayroom I moved on to the smaller middle dayroom, which contained an unruly element. That group lifted floorboards under one of the horseboxes to access the void below. They were not the first to do this, for down there they found copies of 1930s newspapers. These same boys were keen smokers, their favourite place being behind the boiler house. Smoking was a beatable offence, on the grounds that it was bad for boys and might stunt their growth, though it was all right for the masters, many of whom smoked in class.

Going up to the senior dayroom, I found a wind-up gramophone (for 78rpm records, each lasting two to three minutes) and a selection of manuals on sex, obtained in plain covers by mail order. A-levels replaced Higher School Certificate in 1951 and I passed in my three subjects of physics, chemistry and biology, my 16th birthday occurring during the exams. No grades were given but the school had access to the marks (which were good) and I had won the sixth-form prizes in all these subjects, so I felt that I was doing well.

During our middle years, the housemasters discussed our futures with us and our parents. I had been through a long series of career ideas. In Menston I wanted to be a farmer, in Rhyl I fancied going to sea and still thought the Royal Navy a good choice for national service. When the Wrexham house was being built, I became an architect and did a useful extra course in mechanical drawing one evening per week. As I moved into the science sixth,

I focused on the possibilities based on biology and these seemed to amount to farming, which needed capital, or medicine. Thus, by a very roundabout route, I was to embark on the medical course, which turned out to be a most agreeable choice. This late decision contrasted with many who had wished to be a doctor from much earlier in their childhood. But I was still only 16 when I took A-levels, with two more years at school.

APPLYING TO CAMBRIDGE
Having decided on a medical career, my options seemed to be Oxford or Cambridge. Oxford required a credit in French at School Certificate, which I did not have. Both needed Latin, which I had, so Cambridge became my target, with the additional advantage of being a change from Oxford. The careers master suggested Christ's College, as the school had placed students there recently. It was thought that I might win an open award, so I was to take the Cambridge Colleges' scholarship examination in Decamber 1951, in my seventh term in the sixth form.

As I'd found chemistry boring, I decided to offer physics, zoology and botany as my three subjects. In retrospect this was an unwise decision as I had no understanding of the scope of the latter two. I was left to my own devices to work for the exam. As president of the senior dayroom during that term I couldn't get any work done there, due to the noise and requests for help with prep, so I used the latter argument to get permission to spend prep time in the school library.

The day before I was due to travel to Cambridge I was struck in my right flank while playing rugby. I experienced a lot of pain in the loin and made only my second visit to the school doctor, who dismissed my complaint as a 'twisted hip'. On arrival I was bowled over by the fairy tale appearance of Christ's College, with its painted coat of arms lit up over the gate. In my room that evening I had right renal colic and profusely blood-stained urine; I made my first diagnosis, of a right kidney injury. I did not seek medical advice and never went back to tell the school doctor of his error.

The senior tutor, Dr CLG Pratt, asked about my interests and, having just read Fred Hoyle, I mentioned astronomy. Asked why I wanted to read medicine I could only say vaguely that I wanted to do something useful. In the physics paper we had to design an economical can for tomato soup, not the sort of question I was expecting.

Dr Pratt's letter, at Christmas, explained that I had just reached minor scholarship standard in physics but was below the exhibition level in zoology and botany. Nevertheless, I was offered a place for the medical course in October 1953, which I gladly accepted.

HOUSE PREFECT

Returning for the Lent term I was promoted to house prefect; one of eight sharing two studies, though there was little studying there. I thought I had to try to obtain either an open award by resitting the colleges examination in December 1952 or a state scholarship when I resat A-levels in 1952 and 1953, but no scholarship was achieved. The provision for boys remaining after A-levels was poor. This was a missed opportunity; it would have been better to spend the two years doing A levels in another subject, either maths or history.

Additionally, there was the complication of Part IV of the Cambridge First MB. Most students had exemption from the other three parts from their A-level results, but the organic chemistry of Part IV was not covered. The custom was to take this from school, but little teaching was provided. I failed Part IV three times – it was the only exam I ever failed until I took the MChir (Master of Surgery) in 1964. I therefore had to do an organic chemistry course in my first term at Cambridge, with consequences described in the next chapter.

WATER-BORNE SPORTS

Having rowed in the winning four in the inter-house competition, I was selected for trial with the school crews in the Lent term of 1952. This involved a sliding seat rather than the fixed seats of the house fours. I rowed bow in the 'colts' (under 17) eight, competing unsuccessfully in the Public Schools' Regatta at Pangbourne Nautical College in the summer. In my final year, I rowed at three in the third eight, again racing at Pangbourne.

In 1952 the school purchased one sliding-seated four for each house, a great improvement. There were also inter-house bumping races in fours, modelled on the events at Oxford and Cambridge. Each house entered a crew in each of the four divisions. At the end of bumps in 1952, Mac's I and II had reached the first and fourth places in division I, but we slipped down again in 1953.

In my third year Mr Jack Tait founded a sailing club. He owned a 12-foot Firefly dinghy that he sailed on the river from the school boathouse at Godstow. The school then purchased six 10-foot-six Cadet dinghies. Having a long-standing ambition to sail, originating from the Arthur Ransome stories, I promptly joined the club. However, I couldn't get on with the Cadet, a boat with only a small gap in the decking and little room under the boom. Later I had access to a much roomier 14-foot Royal Naval Sailing Association (RNSA) dinghy and taught myself to sail, a skill which later had important benefits.

FORMER NAVAL PERSON

After passing Certificate A part II, I joined the Royal Naval section of the CCF, commanded by Lieutenant Manning (director of music) assisted by Sub-Lieutenant Tait. We practised knots and learnt Morse code and semaphore. On fug parades we wore sailors' No 1 dress.

Promotion was by examination, and I progressed to able seaman, leading seaman and petty officer. On field days we paraded at the boathouse, with a plan to rig a breeches buoy, to carry a man from ship to ship, but this never happened; I had a suspicion that the officers didn't know how to do it. At lunch time, the officers repaired to The Trout nearby, while we walked about a mile to the pub at Wytham. In 1951 in the summer holiday, we had a two-week visit to the destroyer *Agincourt* at Portsmouth. Unfortunately, it proved to be in dry dock, but we made interesting visits to various naval establishments.

The great benefit of the naval section was the RNSA sailing dinghy which needed some attention. I took charge of re-varnishing it in 1952 and thereafter was allowed to sail it independently on Sunday afternoons.

When King George VI died in 1952, the succession had to be proclaimed in all cities, ideally with a guard of honour but no troops were available in Oxford. Several platoons of the CCF were mobilised to meet this need, led by the senior service with one petty officer in front and another (me) behind. After the proclamation had been read the contingent moved off and was ordered to right wheel; unfortunately, one file of the naval section wheeled left, resulting in a most undignified end to the ceremony.

For the coronation of Queen Elizabeth II on 2nd June 1953, members of the CCF were offered the privilege of helping to line the route of the procession, but I declined and took the alternative of a weekend at home. Our first television (black and white) was purchased for this event. Thus ended my six years at St Edward's. I'd had a wonderful time socially as a prefect but academically these had been two wasted years, establishing a poor approach to study, which lasted into my years at Cambridge.

MEDICAL STUDENT

7

CAMBRIDGE

I started my first term at Christ's in October 1953. My room in the recently built 'W' block was spacious, with a gas fire and ring, two easy chairs, a coffee table, bookcase and table with two upright chairs. At the end of the corridor there were communal lavatories, wash basins and baths (no shower). The room itself compared very favourably with student rooms half a century later but modern students would expect an en suite. Those in the older rooms had to walk across the courtyard to the bathrooms but had wash basins in their rooms.

All meals, except Sunday lunch, were provided in the splendid 16th century hall and we paid a termly fee for these, with a deduction if one signed out, which was permitted for two evenings per week. We had a cooked breakfast and returned from lectures and practicals for lunch. Dinner was preceded by a long grace in Latin. There was often a huge roast, carved in full view by one of the senior servants (as they were then called) and distributed among the seated students by other (male) servants. Our rooms were cleaned daily by 'bedmakers', who were mostly female.

Christ's was then a single-sex college; women were not accepted until 1978. It was a delightful surprise to find that Bill Burgass, who had left Mac's two years earlier, was living in a room on the ground floor of 'W'. He was in his second year, reading chemistry as preparation for working in the family dyeing business in Nottingham. He used to host impromptu dinner parties in his room, all cooked over the single gas ring. Basil Middleton (who had been in Mac's with me) was at Trinity Hall, starting the medical course and we joined forces for the practical classes.

THE PRE-CLINICAL COURSE

Some 250 students entered the pre-clinical medical course each year, the number of females being in single figures. About 10 were from Christ's. We took Part I of the Natural Sciences Tripos in anatomy and physiology, structured as a two-year course. Concurrently, we did two half-subjects, in pathology and either organic chemistry or biochemistry, each lasting a year. The director of studies advised biochemistry, but as I'd failed to gain exemption from Part IV of the otherwise defunct First MB, I had to start by taking a one-term course in organic chemistry to pass this.

To proceed to the clinical course, it was necessary to achieve a 2:2 in anatomy and physiology, or take the separate 'Qualifying Examination', but all three years could be devoted to this. That is what most medical students chose to do. Alternatively, if one could reach this standard in two years one could go on to a Part II in one of the subjects already mentioned or in psychology or anthropology. Students in subjects other than medicine usually did a Part II.

The physiology course was excellent with three lectures per week, covering the systems of the body very clearly, but not always indicating how these interact. Each lecture was followed by a two-hour practical; in my opinion too much time was devoted to practicals. The core of the anatomy course was dissection of the whole human body in the dissecting room, guided by *Cunningham's Manual* for each of the five 'parts', doing one part per term.

Basil and I started with the upper limb, making slow progress with the cutaneous nerves. Little advice was available, but our progress was checked by vivas at prescribed stages, conducted mostly by 'demonstrators'. Only much later did I realise that these were recently qualified doctors preparing for the primary FRCS exam. The anatomy lectures were excellent but related only to embryology, comparative anatomy and neuroanatomy. For topographical anatomy we had to rely on our dissection, *Gray's Anatomy* and the half-skeleton we each purchased. There really should have been lectures on regional anatomy and guidance towards a more suitable regionally orientated textbook, as I realised seven years later, when doing the Primary FRCS course at the Royal College of Surgeons.

I duly passed the Part IV exam in organic chemistry, but starting a term late meant I never really got to grips with biochemistry. In the second year, biochemistry was replaced by pathology, taught very effectively and integrating tissue pathology, bacteriology and immunology. Many of the lectures were given by Professor 'Daddy' Dean, so called because of his age (77); he'd been appointed to the chair before there was a retirement age. I enjoyed learning about the mechanism of diseases.

Medical students were expected to return for one 'long vac term' of about six weeks at the end of their first year. The college was occupied by various groups of overseas students. Basil and I dissected the thorax and attended a course (and did an exam) in pharmacology. There was much less pressure than in the other terms.

The university courses were supported by a weekly supervision in each subject, arranged by the college. Dr Pratt's one-to-one physiology supervisions in the first year were rigorous, with discussion of a weekly essay. Supervisions in anatomy and biochemistry were held en masse for all the Christ's students and were useless, though the anatomist concerned went on to be a professor. The physiology supervisions in the second year were adequate. My experience did not confirm the much-vaunted Oxbridge advantage of personal tutorials!

I took the Part I exam at the end of my second year, being placed in the third (and largest) class. I suspect I failed biochemistry, pulling my overall performance down. I was given exemption from the qualifying exams in anatomy and physiology, so must have achieved a 2:2 in those subjects.

Commoners (non-scholars) were resident in college for only one year, the remainder being spent in digs in the town. These varied in quality and cost. I settled for rooms in a terraced house about half a mile away. The landlady worked as a bedmaker in the college, while her husband was disabled by cardiac problems. It was a miserable household, but cheap. I had the front downstairs sitting room, with a gas fire and ring, and a tiny, unheated bedroom. For washing, there was a porcelain basin and a large jug of cold water, supplemented in the morning by a small jug of hot water. I walked across Christ's Pieces into the college for breakfast as well as my other meals, and to use the baths. Another student occupied the upstairs front bedsitter. He was reading music but left abruptly during his third year; I scarcely knew him, but the senior tutor suggested that I might have made more effort to help him adapt to university life.

SOCIAL LIFE

Encouraged by Bill Burgass, I joined the college boat club. I was a welcome recruit because I had rowed at school, whereas most were novices, so in that term I rowed bow in the college first crew. I cycled to the boathouse using the machine purchased for my father in 1942, leaving my Raleigh safely at home. It was difficult to attend daily training outings when some of my afternoons were scheduled for practical classes. In the Lent term of 1954, I found a solution – rowing at seven in the third eight which trained only three times per week. This crew included several who were worth places in a higher boat, but couldn't spare more time, so it was a false third boat. It went well, and we made four bumps in the Lent Races, so gaining our 'oars', emblazoned with the College crest. I could not carry the whole oar home on the train, so I cut it in half; I still have the blade end, inscribed with the names of the crew and the boats that we bumped. I rowed only intermittently over the next two years and was never again in a winning crew. Nevertheless, my boat club contacts provided important friendships in Christ's (particularly with Tony Eastwood, an engineer) and some fabulous bibulous dinners.

Socially the situation was asymmetrical. Most students had done two years of national service, some of them in the Korean War; one of these had lost a leg and won an MC. They had much more experience of the world than the medics, who had deferred service and come straight from school. Pubs were popular in the evenings, but I rationed my visits for reasons of economy; of course, the pubs then closed at 11pm.

Anyone who had a place at university received a county grant. This paid my university and college tuition fees and provided a means-tested allowance of £13 6s 8d (£13.33) per term for living expenses. My father supplemented this, but I can't remember the amount. The students who had done national service had usually saved some money. My finances were tight – I withdrew cash from the bank £3 at a time and the college bill for meals (£25 per term) was always in arrears. I had the occasional meal out and on one occasion Basil and I had insufficient money to pay the bill. We offered to wash up, but they let us off! I organised two annual lunches for St Edward's alumni, to which the warden and a few masters came as guests. Some of my contemporaries had girlfriends, but they were in short supply in Cambridge, and it did not seem worth the attempt. Friends wanted me to go with them to the College May Ball in my last year, but I had no one to take as a partner.

Sailing was under the auspices of the grandly named Cambridge University Cruising Club. Basil and I joined but found the clubhouse in the town unfriendly. A small fleet of Fireflies was kept on the River Ouse at St Ives, and we sailed one of these a few times on the short stretch of the river between the bridges. There was an intercollegiate sailing competition, but Christ's had never entered. With Tony Eastwood and others, I founded a college club. Our team of three crews lost in the first round of the 'cuppers' but we enjoyed a splendid dinner.

Many of my peers worked in the long vacation, picking peas or fruit to supplement their grants. I took over the patch of ground outside our garden, between the new front wall and the old field hedge, and ran this as a market garden, selling the produce – new potatoes, broad beans and carrots – to 'Old Price' for sale on his round.

THIRD YEAR

I chose to do my Part II course in pathology which was most enjoyable. We were a small group of about a dozen – only one other was from Christ's. There were many opportunities for discussion with the lecturers. The course comprised advanced teaching across all the disciplines of pathology. Practicals included reviewing a selection of that week's histology slides from Addenbrooke's Hospital, growing sundry pathogenic bacteria and raising anti-paratyphoid serum in rabbits. On Wednesday mornings, we went to the Molteno Institute, endowed by an Argentinian sheep farmer for Research in Parasitology; I didn't take this topic very seriously and can only remember that the natural reservoir for Chagas disease is the armadillo. I spent a lot of time in the departmental library and had hopes of a better result in the exam. However, I had a disastrous viva on lice and ticks, which I had not bargained for, and again got a third.

Cambridge did not then have a clinical course. Most students went on to a London teaching hospital while a few, with local connections, chose a provincial school. I applied to St Thomas's, but was rejected at interview. Some applicants (not me) were asked if they rode to hounds! By then, many London teaching hospitals were full, but I was accepted for the Westminster, together with Colin Prentice from the pathology course and Anthony Bryceson and Michael Wilson from Christ's. I should have tried to negotiate a joint arrangement for accommodation in London but did not think of this.

The author in 1956

Each year I had attended Henley Royal Regatta in support of my friends in the Christ's first eight, usually eliminated in the first round. In 1956, I took this opportunity to arrange my 21st birthday dinner at the uniquely named Beetle & Wedge Boathouse at Moulsford-on-Thames, a few miles up-river. It was a very enjoyable occasion. I think my father would have liked the event to happen near home to meet my friends but doubt whether many would have made the journey.

I'd had enjoyed Cambridge, apart from financial limitations, but I was ready to move on.

8

WESTMINSTER HOSPITAL MEDICAL SCHOOL

I arrived in London for the clinical course at the beginning of October 1956. My father had sought the help of one of his former assistant inspectors, who had arranged digs for me in Coulsdon, south London. This was a comfortable house with one other long-term lodger, but it was too far out. Recognising that I'd been hard up at Cambridge, my parents had increased my allowance; I suspect they had to cash in an insurance policy to cover this. Though I still had to be careful, I was no longer struggling to make ends meet.

Westminster was the smallest of the London clinical schools, housed in the newest buildings, which in 1939 had replaced the old hospital opposite Westminster Abbey. There were two blocks situated in Horseferry Road, quite close to the Palace of Westminster: a hospital of 427 beds was separated from the medical school and the nurses' home by St John's Gardens, a former cemetery. They were connected by a subterranean passage.

The student entry each year was about 45, just under half from Cambridge, a few from Oxford and the remainder via the pre-clinical course at King's College in The Strand. Because the latter course was of only 18 months duration the two groups were six months out of phase, resulting in separate clinical attachments in the first year and to some extent after that. Fifteen per cent were female – a marked contrast to 60 per cent in the 21st

century. Our small sub-group of 22 Cambridge students (all male) made for a very friendly atmosphere. The clinical teaching was entirely in the hands of the NHS staff. There were no academics apart from professors of pathology and chemical pathology and their lecturers. In this the Westminster lagged behind other London medical schools and was even further behind those in the provinces.

The introductory course comprised an excellent series of lectures on the basics of medicine, given by the consultant staff. We had Ernie Lloyd, a white-haired Welsh chest physician, who lyrically described the esoteric 'whispering pectoriloquy'. Sir Adolphe Abrahams (brother of the Olympic athlete) declared: 'You may make a patient of your mistress but not a mistress of your patient.' There were sessions on the wards for senior registrars to teach us physical signs. Other half days were spent in the quiet casualty department, which provided a first opportunity to chat up the nurses.

Additionally, we were involved in the preparations for the annual pantomime, a production prestigious enough for a review in *The Times*. As I had no recent experience as a performer, I gravitated to the stage management team. This involved making the scenery and building the stage. The large Meyerstein lecture theatre was converted for the one-week run. A scaffolding company loaned steel poles, brackets and floorboards and we built a raised stage, a proscenium arch (covered with flat panels) and gantries from which to fly the backdrops. There can be few surgeons who are experienced in the erection of scaffolding.

Students wrote the script, with some songs contributed by the staff, and a trio of female students provided the wardrobe. *Hiawhatnot* was great fun and welded us together as a group. The last night was followed by the Pantomime Ball held in the nurses' common room, with the fire doors through to the medical library opened for sitting out between dances. I was nervous about my lack of dance skills and had no partner, so I didn't attend. A few days later a lovely student nurse, called Jo, agreed to go out with me; we had a meal in Soho and then saw the original production of *Under Milk Wood*. This was my first real date! We met several times after Christmas. I was very keen, but she made it clear, very kindly, that she wanted to keep her options open and by March the relationship had fizzled out.

A ROOF OVER MY HEAD

I soon realised that my digs in Coulsdon were too far from the medical school and gave notice in December, so when I returned after Christmas I had nowhere to live. For the first few nights I stayed at a cheap hotel near Paddington Station. The other option would have been the hostel run for Westminster students in Pimlico and known as 'The Doss House' but this had a bad reputation. Then Tony Bryceson and Michael Wilson (from Christ's), realising my predicament, generously offered the floor in the flat in Belgrave Road that they shared with a friend from St Thomas's. A few weeks later another student, who had been sharing a flat in Warwick Square with Brian Martin and John Roberts, moved out and they offered me his place. It was a poorly adapted basement, with no natural light in the kitchen.

A better basement in Charlwood Street, Pimlico, became available and we moved there in the summer of 1957. The house was owned by a widow from Leeds, who used the ground floor as a pied-à-terre, while three Westminster nurses lived on the top floor. We had a well-furnished front sitting room, where John slept, a twin bedroom for Brian and me, a bathroom and a large kitchen, leading to a back yard. The passageway through to the kitchen, where the stairs had been, was large enough to accommodate a dining table. The rent (shared) was £6 per week. We often cooked supper together; a favourite meal was spaghetti bolognese, made with a tin of minced beef and a quarter of a pound of mushroom stalks from the corner shop nearby. For a while, a Rugby school friend of John's, labouring on the Victoria Line, camped in the front room, sometimes joined by his girlfriend. We stayed there until Brian, and I qualified; John had to resit and moved in with Michael Wilson for their final six months.

ON THE WARDS

In 1957 we did four 12-week 'firms', two medical and two surgical. There was scope to influence the formation of student groups and the sequence of these attachments by negotiation with Miss Bottomley, the assistant secretary of the medical school, who did all the work. (The medical school secretary did *The Times* crossword.) Tony, Michael, Brian, John and I, together with Colin Prentice, who had done Part II in pathology with me, formed a group and started on the surgical firm of Sir Clement Price Thomas (who had removed part of King George VI's lung) and Messrs d'Abreu and Drew.

We clerked the patients and presented them on ward rounds. Each morning we were responsible for taking the routine blood samples – phlebotomists had not been invented and it was not a nursing duty. We went to outpatients and the operating theatre as observers. Sir Clement suggested that we attend his bronchoscopy list. He lined up the rigid metal tube with a view of the cancer and invited the first student to admire it, but before the student could orientate himself Sir Clement became impatient and knocked his head aside with his own head. We went only once.

There followed the medical firm of Dr Meadows (a neurologist) and Dr Tonkin (a gastroenterologist). Next was the Gordon Hospital, at that time almost equal to St Mark's for coloproctology, where we encountered Mr Ronald Raven, a tremendous surgical showman. He told us to 'Never refuse the call my boy', saying that his house had a lavatory on each of its seven floors to facilitate this! More straightforward teaching came from Mr Lawrence Abel, who had the largest pair of surgical scissors named after him. One anaesthetist seemed heavy handed: 'Give her another gram of Pentothal.'

The last of these four firms, and the best, was at St Stephen's[2] on the Fulham Road. We were bussed there each day after the morning lecture. Dr Philip Harvey, socialist and early anti-smoking campaigner, was an excellent teacher. One day he was delighted to bring Dr Sheila Sherlock as a visitor. She looked us up and down, asked one question, dissatisfied with the answer, said: 'You're all damned ignorant', and stalked off. Dr Sherlock became Professor of Medicine at the Royal Free and a world renowned hepatologist. I have since thought that she resembled Mrs Thatcher. Then there was Dr Philip Ellman, a rheumatologist, who was delighted when we imitated his ornate and emphatically delivered definitions.

Various consultants gave series of lectures, without any obvious overall plan to cover the syllabus. It appeared that any consultant could give lectures on the topics of his choice. Sir Clement gave half a dozen talks demonstrating that surgery was the answer to lung cancer. Professor Maclagan (a chemical pathologist) discussed liver function tests exhaustively. Others such as Dr Bayliss (future Sir Richard, physician to the Queen) gave excellent lectures across the whole subject of medicine. We backed this up with the standard textbooks: *Bailey & Love* for surgery and *Davidson* for medicine. We also attended Professor Pulvertaft's most informative post-mortems. The dress code for all these activities was suit, collar and tie, the women wearing skirts not trousers.

It had been customary for students on each firm to treat their chiefs

---

2   St Stephen's was redeveloped as the Chelsea and Westminster Hospital in 1993.

to dinner, and our little group maintained this tradition for our first few attachments. Before one such dinner we were invited to drinks at Frank d'Abreu's luxurious flat overlooking Regent's Park; his wife was a cousin of Elizabeth the Queen Mother.

The pantomime in 1957 was loosely based on *Old King Cole*, with a script by Tony Bryceson and others. I was stage manager, Brian was musical director and John ran the box office. The plot somehow incorporated Madrid, a gondola in Venice and a four-poster bed which had to collapse at the critical moment. The latter was to my design and worked perfectly every night. I noticed Elisabeth, one of the three-person wardrobe team, happily watching the audience through a chink in the proscenium and wondered idly whose girlfriend she might be. I only discovered the answer the following summer. *Old King Cole* played to a full house of 400 on every one of the six evenings.

SPECIALTIES

Over the next year, the 12-week blocks covered paediatrics, odd combinations of various specialties (e.g., orthopaedics with psychiatry), pathology, and then gynaecology and obstetrics, timed to prepare us for Part I Cambridge finals in December 1958. Obstetrics involved our first real hands-on work as we were expected personally to deliver at least 20 babies while living in hospital; I think my total was over 40. The first part was at the Westminster, including a few deliveries 'on the district' with a midwife at the patient's home.

After this initiation period we went in pairs (I was with Colin Prentice) to St Stephen's and then to St Teresa's in Wimbledon. While at St Stephen's we had a patient who had unexpectedly gone into labour in the house of a Chelsea GP, causing him some embarrassment. Her baby was delivered uneventfully. He was most grateful and invited us to lunch in his elegant Georgian home. Memorably, as we finished the first course he rapped on the floor and a trolley rose with the dessert.

Nuns ran St Teresa's, with an occasional visit from a consultant who was reputed to have NHS sessions at 16 hospitals. We lodged in a small annexe where the presence of female visitors was closely monitored.

BACK ON THE WATER

London teaching hospitals were keen on sport, particularly rugger. My flatmates were fanatical golfers. I was persuaded to join the boat club, rowing at seven in the eight that took part in the London University Head of the River

Race. This was a timed pursuit over the Boat Race course, but in the reverse direction, from Mortlake to Putney. Hundreds of crews took part, hoping to move up the order compared with the previous year's result. I only rowed for a couple of terms. I was more interested in the sailing club. Westminster had a Firefly dinghy kept on the Welsh Harp (now Brent Reservoir), competing in a weekly inter-hospital race during the winter.

In the summer, we were based at the United Hospitals Sailing Club at Burnham-on-Crouch in Essex, racing on Saturdays throughout the summer. The dilapidated clubhouse, where we stayed on Saturday nights, had bunkrooms and basic meals. The club had just exchanged old Uffa Fox one-design dinghies for a fleet of 12 Square Metre Sharpies. These had been the two-man Olympic class in 1956 and were recommended by the Commodore, Sir Heneage Ogilvie of Guy's Hospital, as 'a damn fine boat'. They gave an exciting sail but proved not to be ideal; being heavy they were kept on moorings, and so collected weed. To accommodate as many members as possible they were raced with a crew of three.

In 1958, I was secretary of the Westminster sailing club and organised a determined attack on the inter-hospital trophies. At Burnham we drew lots for boats, but each medical school had its own sails. Often small items of gear, such as a burgee, were missing so I always took spares with us. We were fortunate to have a gifted helmsman in John Blackburn, and I made sure that there was always an experienced third member of the crew, while other teams were more casual. Sailing these dinghies hard, three up, put an excessive strain on masts and stays, so breakages were common. However, this did not matter to us, as in the event of a major incident, such as dismasting, we were entitled to a re-sail. That year Westminster won all three of the trophies for racing at Burnham *and* the series on the Welsh Harp. We held a celebratory dinner at which I had to make my first after-dinner speech.

That summer, Mr Miles Foxen, the younger of the two ENT surgeons, invited John and me to help sail his boat. He had bought a small centreboard cruiser, converted from a Morecambe Bay prawner. *Rover* was broad in the beam, sloop rigged, with an unreliable inboard engine. She was moored at Fambridge, up the estuary from Burnham and on Sundays we used to meet there to sail. Miles was inexperienced and valued our assistance. He generously allowed us to borrow *Rover* as a base for one of the Westminster regatta days. All 25 students from the Sharpies came on board for a picnic lunch; *Rover* was then so low in the water that she began to flood via the centreboard case, and we had to hastily offload the crowd. On another occasion, in 1959, I was allowed to borrow the boat for a weekend. Beating back up the estuary, against the ebbing tide, we were making little headway and the engine would not start. Tacking close to the shore, where the stream was less, we stuck on the mud and remained there overnight. Miles took all of this in good part.

FINAL EXAMINATIONS

In addition to the university MB, most students also took the examinations for the diplomas of the Conjoint Board as an insurance, but I felt that to prepare for the four parts of this would be a distraction, as did Colin. The others thought we were over-confident! The results for the Cambridge finals the previous year had been poor, so the medical school provided an excellent series of revision tutorials in medicine and surgery.

Simultaneously we were manoeuvring for our first pre-registration jobs. Originally, I had no clear idea about a career in medicine other than that of a GP. I had never been a patient in hospital and did not know any hospital doctors. However, once at the Westminster I was attracted to hospital work, with its clinical 'firm' structure and residents' mess. In contrast there was then no vocational training for general practice. So, a hospital specialty it should be. I considered medicine and surgery and judged that the brightest of my colleagues would opt for medicine, so I chose surgery. Besides those considerations, I liked doing practical things.

I may also have been influenced by an episode which had occurred while still at Cambridge. We were on the way home to Wrexham, from the pantomime in Liverpool. As we drove up Marford Hill from the Cheshire plain, we came upon a motorcyclist who had sustained a compound fracture of the femur. He was pumping blood from a severed femoral artery. I removed my tie and improvised a tourniquet, following him into the hospital. I explained that I was a junior medical student and was invited to watch the amputation in the theatre. Had this injury happened in the 21st century, he would have been taken to a trauma centre where arterial reconstruction would at least have been considered, aiming to save the limb.

Because the Oxbridge and the King's students qualified three months apart, the house officer posts were allocated between them. Cambridge students had two of the three general medical posts, but only one general surgical job, with Messrs Lee and Drew, for which I was competing with several others. I had a reasonable, but not outstanding, academic record, having won the prize for midwifery and come second in those in medicine and surgery. All the candidates for this job attended Mr Lee's outpatient clinic for revision and to make themselves known to him.

I duly passed my finals, and when the committee met to allocate the jobs, I think I had a stroke of luck. The meeting should have been chaired by the senior dermatologist, who didn't know who I was, but he was indisposed. My sailing companion Miles Foxen deputised, and I got the one general surgical job. A small group of us immediately went off for a week's sailing in Devon and Cornwall (described in chapter nine), returning on the evening before my pre-registration year began.

9

ELISABETH

In June 1958 I organised a two-week cruise for the Westminster Hospital Sailing Club, a new venture. The previous summer, Tony Bryceson had arranged for me to join the crew of *Dayspring*, a converted ketch-rigged Rye trawler built in 1905, for a most enjoyable cruise to Holland. Most of the students were there for the travel, but as I was interested in sailing, I was taught a lot. The boat's owner, Captain Walter Brown RN, was retiring from the Navy and planning to do charter work. He agreed to take my party on a two-week voyage to Brittany at a very reasonable rate.

I had expected that several students with experience of offshore sailing would be interested but, in the event, only three males signed up. Two others had opportunities to crew elsewhere free of charge (though the cost for my voyage was very modest) and two were committed to charter from other sources. However, quite unexpectedly two girls from the King's College entry six months behind us asked if they could join in. A few days later, they came back with their friend Elisabeth Appleby, who also signed up. I had noticed her around the Westminster and when she was working on the wardrobe for the pantomime but had scarcely spoken to her as we were in different years. She lived at home in Edgware and so was not around at weekends. Tony Eastwood, an engineer friend from Christ's, also joined.

Most of the crew arrived on board *Dayspring* at Portsmouth on the Friday while John Blackburn and Tony Eastwood weren't due until the Sunday.

Captain Brown was surprised to find that half the arrivals were female, but he took it in good part. On Saturday, we sailed out into the Solent to try out the recently fitted square rig. Once everyone was aboard, we set sail for Brittany, arriving the following morning off the Rade de Morlaix, and then motored up the estuary and through the lock to the marina. After spending a couple of nights in Morlaix, we made our way via Brest to the south coast, to visit Concarneau and Bénodet.

Elisabeth was in my watch, and we often went exploring on shore together. On a headland near Bénodet we kissed! On the return journey, we experienced a gale off Ushant, during which the mizzen shroud attachment was damaged while executing a gybe. We all huddled together in the saloon while riding out the storm. The damage necessitated a two-night stay for repairs in St Peter Port, Guernsey. Elisabeth and I set off to explore the island. I was very taken by her, but a mixture of nerves and naivety made me suggest that we should slow down a bit. I did not put this well and she was upset. Nevertheless, on the train back to London, we agreed to go out together.

FAMILY HISTORY

Elisabeth's grandparents had emigrated from Poland, settling in London. Her father, Jack, was a self-employed manufacturers' agent in the rag trade. He had strong socialist principles, honed in debates at the polytechnic. Her mother, Bertha, despite a childhood marred by a wicked stepmother, had won a scholarship to the grammar school and then trained as a teacher, continuing after her marriage, contrary to the regulations. Elisabeth, born in 1937, was their only child. In 1946 they emigrated to South Africa, travelling by sea on the Union Castle Line. The plan was to set up a distribution network for a manufacturer of fancy goods.

For a year they moved around South Africa and Southern Rhodesia (now Zimbabwe). During this time Elisabeth was educated by her mother, against a backdrop of visits to sights such as Victoria Falls, viewed from an aircraft whose door was held shut with string. At the end of this period, Jack and Bertha decided they did not want Elisabeth to grow up with black servants at her beck and call and they returned to England via the Suez Canal. It must have been quite an experience for a nine-year-old! Elisabeth went back to Edgware Primary School and despite having missed a year won a scholarship to North London Collegiate School (NLCS) under the direct grant system. This prototype girls' day public school was founded by Frances Mary Buss in 1850:

Miss Buss and Miss Beale
Cupid's darts do not feel
How different from us
Miss Beale and Miss Buss

Miss Beale, a school contemporary of Miss Buss, was the first headmistress of Cheltenham Ladies' College; her niece was headmistress of my mother's school in Stroud.

When Elisabeth decided to study medicine, the school advised her to apply to the Royal Free, a predominantly female medical school. Elisabeth had other ideas and won a scholarship to the Westminster, doing the pre-clinical course at King's College in The Strand and moving on to the Westminster in April 1957. She commuted from Edgware, which was far from convenient once she reached the clinical part of the course. The obvious solution was to move into a flat with other female students, but her Jewish parents vetoed the idea 'lest she should meet someone'.

ENGAGEMENT

Over the months following our return from Brittany we spent a lot of time together. Fortuitously we were both doing the three-month pathology course, which was scheduled earlier in the clinical years for the King's College students than for the Cambridge ones. We shared economical meals out, went to the theatre, walked in the parks and once rowed on the river at Richmond. At the sailing club's two-day regatta at Burnham, when we were coming off the beach, I capsized a Sharpie with Elisabeth and a friend on board. Fortunately, this did not dampen our relationship.

In December Elisabeth persuaded me to take her to the Pantomime Ball, the major social event of the year at the Westminster. Afterwards, it seemed a suitable time to pop the question, but I phrased it cautiously, concerned about her Jewish parents' opposition:

'Elisabeth, some day when it is possible will you marry me?'
'Yes David, of course I'll marry you.'

We agreed that we should not marry until after our pre-registration jobs. With over two years to wait and sensing that her parents would disapprove, we decided that our engagement should be kept secret from everyone except her friend Hazel, a student at St George's. We spent the remaining few days before Christmas celebrating, before I went home to Wrexham, where I did not mention my good fortune, wanting to introduce Elisabeth first. For her to come and stay at Wrexham, without her parents' knowledge, required the subterfuge that she was going to stay with Hazel's family in Bournemouth. We managed to arrange this visit in the spring of 1959; by chance, my father was away on an inspection in the Isle of Man that weekend. My mother was polite but did not approve.

A PROLONGED ENGAGEMENT

In the summer of 1959, I arranged another sailing holiday, for the week just after my finals. I chartered *Erla*, a five-berth sloop, from Blue Water Charters at Salcombe in Devon. My experience with Captain Brown was sufficient to convince them of my competence; no paper qualification was required. We hoped to get to the Isles of Scilly.

Elisabeth and I were accompanied by Tony Eastwood, his then fiancée and John Blackburn. The latter had to join us a day late and we planned to pick him up from Penzance station. This proved hopelessly optimistic. There was just a light breeze and we had only got as far as Fowey. Elisabeth and I waited on the station platform until his train arrived, then ran along hoping to find him. Fortunately, we managed to get his attention and he disembarked. Back on board, we had a relaxing trip but only reached the Helford River.

That summer, four of Elisabeth's female medical school contemporaries went on a charter flight to Mallorca. On the return journey, the Dakota (left over from the Second World War) crashed in the Pyrenees and all were killed. This was a great sadness for the medical school and Elisabeth could so easily have been among them. We later decided not to fly until our children had grown up.

During my house surgeon post at the Westminster, we scarcely saw each other, so overwhelmed was I by the job. I was on duty continuously for the six months, with one weekend off in the middle. This was hard for Elisabeth, who I believe thought I was drifting away. We did go to the ball and afterwards I produced an engagement ring that I had sneaked out to buy at a jeweller near Victoria Station. She was delighted to receive it but couldn't wear it in public because we were not ready to inform her parents.

My house physician job at Kingston upon Thames was much better, with half the evenings and weekends off duty, so we had a more normal life. Meanwhile, Elisabeth completed her finals. The Westminster would accept a woman in only one pre-reg. post, in radiotherapy. To their surprise, she turned it down and instead opted for a proper medical post with Dr Philip Harvey at St Stephen's, Fulham, starting in May 1960.

We had a further two-week cruise in *Erla* in July 1960, this time with John Blackburn, his future wife Maureen (Mo) Winter and Nigel Lever, who had been on *Dayspring*. Nigel had to join a day late, so we decided to spend the first day cruising around the Salcombe estuary. We turned into a side branch to anchor for lunch and despite soundings ran aground on the mud, on a falling tide. Attempts to motor off in reverse failed and *Erla* lay there, heeled over, through the rest of the day. We were on the top of a mud bank, with a deep channel nearer ahead than astern. We placed the anchor well ahead in the main channel and dug a trench towards it. At high tide, about midnight, hauling on the anchor chain and pushing with the engine, we slid *Erla* over the bank and into deep water, to our great relief.

The next day, with the full crew, we set off across the English Channel, arriving at Tréguier in Brittany the following morning. We called at the Rade de Morlaix and Roscoff and went on to l'Abervrach, further along the north coast, and it was then time to return. We knew a gale was forecast and this duly arrived when we were in mid-Channel; we rode it out under bare poles (without sails). When it subsided, we made sail, setting the course only by dead-reckoning – GPS was far in the future. Later we saw our objective, the Eddystone Lighthouse, straight ahead. A peaceful day anchored in Cawsand Bay was followed by a night in the Yealm Estuary and then we returned to Salcombe.

GETTING MARRIED

During the autumn, we grasped the nettle of introducing me to Elisabeth's parents. The first time she took me home to Edgware the atmosphere was extremely tense: Jack Appleby argued that it was not to be, while Bertha froze. Gradually, over several meetings they came to realise that we were serious. When we told my parents of our engagement, they were unenthusiastic. My father realised we should drink a toast, but only sherry and port were available. Subsequently Margaret confirmed that they were unhappy about it.

By the spring of 1961, while I was a senior house officer (SHO) in casualty and orthopaedics at Kingston, we were still worried about our parents' disapproval. Finally, Elisabeth suggested that we should 'just do it' and fix a date for the wedding for soon after she finished her second pre-registration job in May. We chose Friday 14th July and set about making the arrangements, within the limited fund that we had saved from our salaries. Elisabeth's parents clearly would not be paying for it and indeed Jack Appleby would not even attend, though Bertha did. Four weeks before the wedding we had no future jobs and hence no means of deciding where to look for accommodation. With hindsight, it was an extraordinarily rash situation to get into.

Fortunately, just in time, I was appointed to the SHO rotation in Bristol. Elisabeth had arranged to travel down and meet me after the interview. We got to an estate agent's office shortly before they closed for lunch and viewed and took the one furnished flat that was on offer. We then hired a car and drove to Barnstaple, where Hazel was working, and slept on the floor of the doctors' mess. The next day we called at Stroud to introduce Elisabeth to Auntie Norah, Uncle Harry, Doreen, and her husband Desmond (the latter two came to the wedding). Driving back to Edgware that evening, we ran out of petrol and had to sleep in the car until a garage reopened in the morning.

The only legal venues for marriage were churches and register offices. Chelsea Register Office was popular with celebrities and Elisabeth, when resident at St Stephen's Hospital, was within its catchment, so it seemed the best option. Only our immediate family plus Tony Eastwood, as best man, and Hazel Read, as matron of honour, were at the civil ceremony. That evening, we had a wedding dinner at a restaurant at 55 Park Lane with about 30 guests and the usual speeches. It was a very happy occasion, with everyone signing the label on a jeroboam of Champagne which we still have, converted into a table lamp.

Our honeymoon was in the Isles of Scilly, chosen partly because we had failed to reach there on two sailing holidays and partly because a car was not necessary. The plan was to travel overnight by sleeper to Penzance, but by the time I applied all the berths were booked, so we had to doze in an ordinary compartment (main-line trains at that time had compartments, seating six, connected by a corridor). We stayed at Tregarthen's Hotel on St Mary's in the one-room annex, which had an en suite bathroom, unusual then. On many days, we took boat trips to the other islands and the sun shone all the time! It was a lovely fortnight. Then we made the train journey to Bristol to start our lives together.

SURGICAL TRAINING

10

WORKING IN LONDON

We had no induction for house jobs but fortunately the Lee and Drew firm had a most helpful ward sister, Jean Rose, not the traditional dragon. I followed Eddie Ashby (see also chapter 31) as house surgeon (HS), but there was no provision for handover.

One of my first tasks was to send an urgent blood sample for electrolytes. I requested every physiological ion I could think of (calcium, magnesium etc), and was promptly put in my place by the chemical pathologist who brusquely explained that they normally did only sodium, potassium, chloride and urea. Those were the 'bad old days' of house jobs in teaching hospitals. We were on duty 24 hours a day for six months with one weekend off in the middle. The days were long: we had to attend all ward rounds and be present in theatre for all six operating lists. With the daytime hours occupied in this way, much of my routine work – clerking admissions – had to be done in the evenings.

Mr Stanley Lee did a mix of general surgery, with a slant towards head and neck cancer, though Sir Stanford Cade (who led another firm) did the major operations in this area. Mr Lee was also involved in adrenalectomy for advanced breast cancer. This procedure was done through bilateral incisions in the loins, with limited access making it difficult to deal with any problem; on one occasion a patient bled to death on the operating table. Stanley Lee was nevertheless a kind man.

Mr Charles Drew was a cardiothoracic surgeon, having taken on the mantle of Sir Clement Price Thomas. He had devised a novel method for open-heart surgery. Other surgeons were bypassing the heart and lungs for the duration of the operation with a pump-oxygenator to replace heart and lung function. However, the early versions had a high mortality, partly due to destruction of red blood cells in the oxygenator. Drew's 'profound hypothermia' pumped the blood around the body as a refrigerant, cooling to about 12°C, while using the patient's own lungs for oxygenation. The surgeon then had about 60 minutes to operate on the still heart before the body warmed up significantly. The pump was then restarted to bring the temperature back up to normal. With this technique, it was possible to carry out the simpler reconstructions, mainly for 'a hole in the heart'. The first few operations were done during Eddie Ashby's tenure and about 20 more were completed while I was the HS.

One of my duties was to book the theatre lists. Miss Minter, the theatre superintendent (who had been scrubbed up when King George VI had his lung resection), insisted that the list be submitted by 5pm on the previous evening. Mr Lee invariably changed the order of the list during the subsequent Monday morning ward round, and I then had to face the wrath of Miss Minter. After several weeks, I solved the problem by submitting various versions of the list at intervals throughout one Sunday, until at last she accepted that revisions were inevitable.

One night in three, we were on take for emergency admissions but there were few of these because the central London hospitals had only small local catchment populations. Out of hours the pre-registration house officers (PRHOs) were the only resident medical staff, but as each of us was on duty for only his own firm, the night-time workload for inpatients was light, covering about 30 patients, so I mostly had a full night's sleep. Many of the procedures that would now be done as day cases, for example patients having hernia repairs, stayed in for 10 days, often helping with the teas.

There were no senior house officers (SHOs) and the registrar and the senior registrar (SR) lived at home, sometimes on the other side of London. We tried not to trouble them, resulting in occasional errors: I once misdiagnosed a perforated ulcer (needing an emergency operation) as a kidney stone. Another time I set about aspirating a large pleural effusion, in a patient who'd had a lung removed, and the needle broke off in his back. I phoned Charles Drew and his response: 'He moved, didn't he?' was interesting medico-legally.

Before working with Lee and Drew, I had never inserted an intravenous cannula – a more difficult task then than now. We had reusable steel 'Guest' cannulas. The stylets and cannulas were separated for sterilisation in a dish of surgical spirit. The nurses then laid up a 'drip trolley' and often produced a cannula and a stylet that were mis-matched for length, a recipe for failure. We also struggled to catheterise the male bladder, trying in desperation all sorts of catheters: rubber or gum elastic, straight, coudé (elbowed) and bi-coudé. When I had been with the firm for about three months the SR, knowing I was interested in becoming a surgeon, suggested that I could do the next appendicectomy. So few were the emergency admissions that two months elapsed before I got this opportunity and there wasn't another before I left the firm.

LIVING IN AT THE WESTMINSTER

The PRHOs slept in tiny bedrooms in the medical school, with just enough room for a bed and a washbasin. We ate in the 'mess', with the resident medical officer (RMO) presiding, separate from the canteen used by consultants and students. Dinner was at 7pm and we were expected to be on time. We were served by a male waiter in a black waistcoat and bow tie and the food was good. If one was not busy there was the possibility of drinking in the bar afterwards. Women were not allowed in there and had to ask at the door if they wanted to communicate with a man! Overwhelmed by the job, I neglected Elisabeth badly during those six months.

Our pay was £420 per annum, but after deduction for board and lodging we were left with £240 – less than a dustman would have earned. My salary for the six months paid off my overdraft, with about £40 left to buy Elisabeth's engagement ring.

We were not usually given a second PRHO post in the Westminster group, but it was suggested that I would be likely to get the job with the paediatric cardiologist at Westminster Children's Hospital. However, I'd already had several child patients with congenital heart disease admitted for heart surgery and felt that my one medical post should be in general medicine. Michael Butler (SR to Lee and Drew), who had rotated in from Kingston Hospital, suggested I apply for a job there. Doubtless due in part to his influence, I was appointed.

HOUSE PHYSICIAN AT KINGSTON

The post of house physician (HP) to Dr Bevan Hollings at Kingston upon

Thames was quite different from my experience at the Westminster. There were two HPs on a rota, so I had half the nights and weekends free. The firm consisted of a consultant, a registrar and me. I was the only one who was resident; I used to report to the registrar in the late evening, but he rarely needed to come in. Dr Hollings had worked with Paul Wood, a leading cardiologist, and did gastroscopies with the semi-rigid Hermon-Taylor instrument and selected patients for the fortnightly Saturday morning clinics with the visiting neurologist. In short, he covered all the medical subspecialties apart from diabetes, the preserve of his senior colleague. We had two Nightingale wards, men downstairs and women upstairs. There was no lift, so patients were carried up on a chair; fewer were obese then.

There were some memorable patients: a young woman dying in status asthmaticus (in later years she would have been ventilated on ICU); and a man severely short of breath due to chronic lung disease, for whom I called Dr Hollings in at night (the registrar was on leave). Most interesting was an air hostess with severe pain in the shoulder. She developed a paraplegia overnight and then had difficulty in breathing during the morning ward round. She recovered after a neurosurgeon drained an abscess in the cervical spine secondary to a back-street abortion. It was a most enjoyable and enlightening six months.

PRIMARY FRCS

After completing the 'pre-reg' year we were liable for deferred national service. This would comprise working as a medical officer in one of the armed forces. However, I had received two pieces of advice regarding my choice of a surgical career: 'Don't do it, the prospects for progression are too poor;' and 'If you must do it, get the primary FRCS exam out of the way as quickly as you can'. The pass rate for the latter was said to be 10 per cent, and the best way to tackle it was to do a four-month full-time course at the Royal College of Surgeons (RCS). This qualified for a further six-month deferment, to January 1961, when entry to national service was expected to end. I duly signed up for the course, starting in October. Deferment of national service was subject to approval by a government official. Of the nine Westminster graduates who applied, one was rejected. He was the one who we all knew was planning to do the course solely to avoid conscription. Somehow the authorities also knew this.

I went home to Wrexham to start work for the primary during the intervening two months. I was worried about the cost of living during the course and as a contribution towards this signed on for unemployment benefit. I had barely got home when the labour exchange phoned to say that they had found me a job – HS at Chester Royal Infirmary. I didn't want a job, just the benefit money, so I enquired about the hours of work. The man from the labour exchange had no idea, but (knowing there were only two house surgeons) I suggested that this would amount to about 104 hours per week and declined the offer. Shortly afterwards I learned that my appeal against loss of benefit had been allowed, recognising that the hours were unreasonable. They did not try to find me another job.

The course started in early October. There were eight of us from the Westminster, would-be surgeons and anaesthetists, including Brian Martin, my former flatmate, who was planning to do ophthalmology. Brian had taken the option of living in the Nuffield Building next to the College, but I could not afford this. Elisabeth found me a two-roomed ground-floor flat in Pimlico, recently vacated by her medical registrar. The owner, a single mother who lived in the basement, was planning to furnish it once she had saved enough money. Meanwhile I got it for a pittance, together with babysitting once a week when she was out giving an evening lecture. Initially I set up a camp bed in the back room, and later the owner replaced it with a divan. There was no other furniture; a tiny scullery served as a washroom and a makeshift kitchen.

There were lectures in the mornings, covering topographical anatomy in detail, physiology, with emphasis on the integration of the systems of the body, and pathology. There were also afternoon practical classes, but by the time I applied these were full. In retrospect this time was better spent studying in the library at the Westminster. I usually had dinner in the medical school cafeteria and worked on until about 11pm. On the other evenings Elisabeth and I either went out or ate at St Stephen's, where the food in the mess was considered the best in any of the London hospitals. The teaching on the course was of an excellent standard and was exactly directed at the primary exam, which the College ran.

The exam was in January. At lunchtime, the word went around that one of the examiners in physiology was asking: 'What is the neutral pH of plasma?', which no one could answer correctly. I hurried to the library to discover that chemists define neutral pH, at laboratory temperature, as 7.0. At body temperature, with more ionic dissociation, it is 7.38. My luck came in when I met the same examiner, with the same question. I made a preamble about the higher temperature and hence a higher figure and then made a 'guess' of about 7.38. He looked pleased. At the end of the day's examining, a porter appeared on the steps to call out the names of the minority of successful candidates; I had passed the primary FRCS at the first attempt, as had one of my Westminster colleagues.

ORTHOPAEDICS

Before sitting this exam, I needed to arrange my next job, but with no guarantee that I'd pass the primary I was not a strong candidate. While a house physician I had discovered that Kingston had six-month SHO posts that combined inpatient orthopaedics with duties in casualty: the latter met a requirement for the final Fellowship of the Royal College of Surgeons (FRCS). Dr Hollings had said that he would be happy to support me for one of these posts.

A vacancy with Mr Douglas Freebody at Kingston was advertised and I was appointed and started on 1st February. The shifts in casualty were covered by four of us. The daytime duties on weekdays were taken by the casualty registrar and SHO. They were joined by the two orthopaedic SHOs to be on duty one night and weekend in four; additionally, we were second on call one-in-four. If the doctor in casualty saw a fracture needing an emergency operation, then he or she followed the patient to theatre and the second on call went to casualty. This system provided us with valuable continuity of experience.

Douglas Freebody's particular interest was lumbosacral spinal fusion, for which he had devised an anterior approach through the abdomen. Postoperatively the patient had to lie in a plaster 'boat' from neck to ankles for about 10 days. This was made as a cast, preoperatively, with the patient lying face down. Experience of this operation was helpful when applying for my next post.

Fractures of the neck of the femur were operated upon as emergencies, during the night. A senior hospital medical officer was responsible for most of the emergency operating, apart from reduction and plastering of fractures which we did independently. He was a very experienced and competent operator, aged about 45, who had repeatedly failed to pass the FRCS and was still trying. He taught us to 'pin' or 'pin and plate' these upper femoral fractures. On one occasion while doing this my theatre trousers fell down. None of the female staff felt it was appropriate to fix these for me, so they sent for a male orderly to do so. I also set up traction on the ward and attended the orthopaedic clinic, doing minor procedures there. This was a happy job.

WHAT NEXT?

The conventional career path was to seek junior surgical posts at one's own teaching hospital, but I had noticed the limited operative experience offered to the registrars at the Westminster. I still have copies of the discharge summaries from my time as an HS. Analysis of these shows an average length of stay of 15 days, with seven patients staying for more than 60 days. Only about 20 per cent of the 237 admissions were emergencies, whereas in many hospitals these amounted to 50 per cent. The registrar did no elective operations more complex than hernias and varicose veins, apart from two small thyroid procedures.

These issues aside, we did not think London was a good place to bring up a family and so wanted to look elsewhere. In the spring of 1961, there was a party at the Westminster to celebrate Charles Drew's 100th heart operation under profound hypothermia. Among those present was Eddie Ashby, my predecessor as HS, who was doing a casualty and general surgery SHO rotation at the Bristol Royal Infirmary (BRI). He told me about an even better rotation due to be advertised there, comprising three four-month placements, including the professorial unit.

I duly applied for this and was interviewed on a Saturday morning, four weeks before our wedding. All three posts in the rotation were being filled, so there was a large shortlist including two South Africans who had been doing orthopaedics at Kingston before me. About 10 consultants were seated along one side of a table, with the candidate opposite. I found this quite intimidating and cannot remember any of the questions.

To my surprise I got the job. One of the other successful applicants proved to be the son of the senior anaesthetist and the other had been working at the nearby Homeopathic Hospital, so I was the only outsider. We had arranged that Elisabeth would come down by train and meet me to learn the result. We called in at an estate agent and acquired the tenancy of a furnished flat in Clifton. A job and a flat were settled just in time, as mentioned in chapter nine.

I had booked two weeks' holiday for our marriage on 14th July and our honeymoon. Mr Freebody kindly agreed to release me so I could go straight on to start work in Bristol on 1st August. This left me three weeks short of the six months' casualty experience required before sitting the FRCS exam, and I had to make that up later.

11

SENIOR HOUSE OFFICER IN BRISTOL

Following our honeymoon, we arrived in the flat in Bristol three days before my new job began. Four weeks earlier we'd hired a Morris Minor and delivered most of our scanty belongings from Kingston and Edgware. We then ordered a king-sized bed to replace the narrower one.

The flat was the ground floor of a Victorian house in Beaconsfield Road, Clifton. It comprised a spacious living room, with a bay window, one bedroom, a bathroom and a tiny, poorly equipped kitchen. The predominant colour was brown. We tried to liven this up with some floral Sanderson fabric, made into curtains by Elisabeth and still in use until 2015, cut down, on the half landing in Leicester. We also made deep red shades for a table lamp and a standard lamp. By this stage, having paid for the wedding and the honeymoon we had about £100 left!

I walked over the hill to the Bristol Royal Infirmary (BRI) to start work as an SHO on 1st August 1961. Not knowing where to go, I approached the porter's lodge: 'We have a letter for you sir.' How efficient, I thought and opened it. A single sheet of paper made it clear that if I were caught stealing the hospital's linen I would be instantly dismissed. Somehow, I found my way to the ward and met the senior registrar (SR), Johnny John, who was to be my principal mentor over the next year. He was an excellent surgeon, who had been a much-decorated bomber pilot in the Second World War. My first four months were with Mr Robert (Bobby) Cooke and Mr J

Ashton Miller. Robert Cooke was a stern taskmaster who seemed to delight in posing difficult questions for me on ward rounds. His great interest was thyroid surgery, which he performed beautifully. One day we had a visiting surgical club:

> Visitor: 'Mr Cooke, do you think it is ever necessary to divide the strap muscles?' (To improve access.)
> Cooke: 'I suppose if you are just starting thyroid surgery, it *may* be necessary.'
> Visitor: 'I'm not talking about just starting; I'm talking about six hundred.'
> Cooke: 'And I'm talking about six *thousand*.'

I did a rough calculation: at his customary four or five per week, it was only a slight exaggeration. Although he had never assisted me in any stage of thyroidectomy, I had absorbed his technique and followed it successfully throughout my career.

Ashton Miller was quite different, a gentle academic and the first specialist urologist in Bristol. During his cystoscopy lists he supervised me performing all the examinations and helped me to do all parts of a retropubic prostatectomy. He and his colleague John Mitchell (who promoted the revolutionary idea of conservative treatment for urethral rupture) suggested a clinical research project, but I made little headway. One of my jobs in outpatients was to dilate numerous urethral strictures under local anaesthetic, mostly in veterans of the First World War. There was a weekly X-ray conference, a rarity at that time. One urological patient, then in his 90s, had been the first specialist physician in the south-west; he described how in the late 19th century he travelled to consultations throughout the region on horseback.

Johnny John patiently took me through the repair of inguinal hernias and operations for varicose veins, about half a dozen of each. We were 'on take' for emergencies one evening per week and one weekend in four. The BRI had to accept six emergency patients and could then shut up shop and leave the other two hospitals to cope. My instructions were to complete our quota early, ensuring a peaceful night. The sanction reinforcing this was that appendicectomies coming to theatre before midnight would be mine, supervised by the SR, but any cases after midnight he would do himself. When on take I lived in, but this amounted to only one night in four, with three consecutive nights on the infrequent weekends. This was my best rota so far.

ORTHOPAEDICS AGAIN

The next four months were in orthopaedics, mostly fractures, as there was an orthopaedic unit out in the countryside for elective work. Clinically I was in my element, experience gained at Kingston enabling me to manage the common fractures independently. During a wintry spell, I reduced 16 Colles' (wrist) fractures in one day.

One of the consultants, Mr Eyre Brooke, planned to start anterior spinal fusion and took me out to the country branch to participate in this, presumably because of my experience with Douglas Freebody. Towards the end of my year in Bristol he suggested that if I would like to move into orthopaedics as a career, he could promise speedy progress to registrar. I declined this kind offer, saying that I wanted to continue in general surgery. He was miffed.

Besides me, there was only one PRHO to share the rota in orthopaedics, so I was resident for half the nights, including a spell from Friday morning to Tuesday evening covering the weekend. This was hard for Elisabeth, who had yet to find work or make friends in Bristol. One solution would have been to stay with her parents in London over the weekend, but we could not afford the rail fare. On some nights, she came and slept in my room. This was against the rules, so she had to creep out before the domestic staff arrived. We were not the only couple.

THE PROFESSORIAL UNIT

My final four months were with Professor Milnes Walker and his senior lecturer. Fortuitously, Johnny John had moved to a lecturer's post on the unit, which was to my advantage. The professor's major interest was porta-caval shunting for portal hypertension, but he did a range of general surgery with skill and unshakeable confidence. I remember a patient booked for an operation for rectal cancer:

SR: 'Shouldn't we have a biopsy first?'
Prof: 'I know a cancer when I see one.'

It proved to be tuberculosis, treatable medically, but the patient was left with a permanent colostomy. Omission of a biopsy would now be judged a serious error but was then not uncommon. A few years later, St Marks (a London hospital for colorectal surgery) bravely published a collection of 14 instances of inappropriate abdomino-perineal excision.

On Tuesdays, the SHO on the unit was seconded to assist the cardiothoracic surgeon, Mr Ronald Belsey. Based at Frenchay Hospital, he was just starting to do a weekly open-heart operation at the BRI, using Charles Drew's profound hypothermia; he had come to the Westminster to watch this during my HS post. I think he was glad to have the company of someone, however junior, who had assisted at it previously. An innovation in managing these patients was to monitor the central venous pressure (CVP) as suggested by Dr McGowan the chemical pathologist. We improvised the equipment, passing a ureteric catheter via the long saphenous vein in the groin and connecting this to a water-filled manometer. This may have been the first use of CVP monitoring, at least in the UK.

One morning, when checking the previous day's cardiac patient, I was summoned to theatre where Professor Milnes Walker was offering to help me do a cholecystectomy (gallbladder removal). He was a man of few words and just muttered throughout the operation: 'Keep close... Very close... Close... Keep... Very close...' This was in fact excellent advice for a safe cholecystectomy! Johnny John also took me to a few operating lists at the Children's Hospital, doing babies' hernias and circumcisions.

Surgically, Bristol was a revelation. Vagotomy for duodenal ulcer and transurethral resection of the prostate had not arrived at the Westminster but were commonplace at the BRI. I surmised that my junior experience in profound hypothermia and anterior spinal fusion had helped to get me the job. There was also the curious belief among the SRs that I had won the Hallett Prize in the primary FRCS. This was not the case; I wondered whether I had been discussed by the examiners as a possible winner and this had filtered back inaccurately to Bristol.

My clinical duties in Bristol were not heavy, leaving time to study for the final FRCS exam. Several times each week there was a tutorial for the SHOs at 5pm, covering most of general surgery. The professorial unit had a small library where I devoured the recent issues of the *Annals of the RCS*, which at that time contained many review articles. I also set myself three little projects to research the history of operations for hernia, duodenal ulcer and the prostate, reading the original articles in the university library.

Thus, I was becoming well prepared for the final FRCS exam in November. Though I had done only a little operating, this had been well supervised.

FAMILY MATTERS

Elisabeth had hoped to find a job in Bristol, but all the medical SHO rotations had gone to the locals. She did short spells as a locum medical house officer and in casualty. Five weeks as SHO, in charge of a small maternity hospital passed off safely, enlivened by undiagnosed twins. We bought our first piece of furniture, a little oval mahogany coffee table, for £12 12s 6d (£12.63); we re-polished it in the 1980s and it is still in use. Both sets of parents came to stay in Bristol. We had decided that we would like to have three children and by January we knew that the first was on the way.

We explored Bristol on foot and made the odd trip, by train, to Bath, but money was tight. One Sunday one of the younger orthopaedic surgeons invited us to tea. His wife mentioned that she was replacing her old soft-topped Morris Minor. I enquired about the price, and she sold it to us for £160, which I had to borrow from the bank. NOJ 867 was the early 950cc version with a divided windscreen, not the Morris 1000. It enabled me to drive to the BRI and us to make trips out to the coast at Clevedon and Weston-super-Mare and to the Cheddar Gorge. In May we celebrated our new car-owning status by driving, via Wrexham, to Skye.

A couple of months after I started work, my sister Margaret arrived in Bristol to start the dental course. We thought she was settling in well, but after a few months she gave up the course, finding the male banter in the dissecting room more than she could stand. She went home to Wrexham and the next year started a teachers' training course at Margaret McMillan College. Afterwards I felt that I should have done more to support her.

THE NEXT MOVE?

The question was what next? I was still undifferentiated with respect to the choice of surgical specialty. I was offered a fast track in orthopaedics but while I enjoyed fractures, I thought they would prove boring. Elective orthopaedics in adults had limited scope, lacking effective procedures for severe arthritis; joint replacement had not yet started. I had good contacts in cardio-thoracic surgery but most of the operations carried serious risks and I preferred a mix of stressful and more routine work. General surgery promised variety and the greatest diagnostic challenges, particularly when dealing with abdominal emergencies. Hence, I chose general surgery.

I thought I needed more SHO experience in general surgery, so I applied for a six-month post at Southmead Hospital in Bristol. At interview, the panel said they didn't know why I was applying and that I should be seeking a registrar post. Two good registrar jobs were advertised in the same week in the *BMJ*, in Leicester and Norwich and I applied for both.

When I was interviewed in Leicester, it became apparent that I had far less experience than the other two candidates. I was asked if I was perfectly fit and, by the chairman, whether: 'If appointed, would it be your intention to bring your wife to Leicester?' Despite my inexperience, I got the job, to start on September 1st. I suspect that Robert Cooke had phoned recommending me to his friend Ernest Frizelle, who was on the interview panel.

On our next free weekend Elisabeth and I travelled to Leicester to find somewhere to live. After viewing some dismal flats to rent in the city, we were offered a nice furnished house in Rothley, about six miles to the north, and took it. We then went on to stay overnight with Bill and Sue Burgass in Nottinghamshire. I would have been unemployed during August but managed to negotiate a three-week locum in casualty at the BRI, so completing the six months' requirement in that specialty for the FRCS.

Our baby was due towards the end of August and Andrew arrived on the 24th. In those days, mothers stayed in hospital for about 10 days after giving birth and I needed to start on time at the Leicester Royal Infirmary on 1st September, so I packed up our belongings, crammed as many of them as possible into the Morris Minor and sent the larger items by van. I arranged for Elisabeth and Andrew to follow in a taxi, not an ideal start for our new chapter but under the circumstances it was the only option.

Six weeks after I started work in Leicester, I was invited to interview for the Norwich job. The pace of life is clearly slower in East Anglia.

12

REGISTRAR IN LEICESTER

After arriving on my own at our rented house in Rothley, I reported to the front desk at the Leicester Royal Infirmary (LRI) on Saturday 1st September 1962 and one of the registrars came down to see me. The conversation went as follows:

> Registrar: 'I'm awfully glad to see you. We've been one short for a month and you're on for the weekend.'
> DW: 'There is an SR covering me?'
> Registrar: 'No, he's off with glandular fever.'
> DW: 'Who is the consultant on call?'
> Registrar: 'It's Mr Barrett's take but he retired a month ago and hasn't yet been replaced.'

There I was, a very inexperienced registrar, responsible for surgical emergencies in Leicester for the weekend without any senior cover. Mercifully, nothing more difficult than an appendicectomy was required or my career as a surgeon might have come to an abrupt halt.

Over the next week I established who among the consultants would be prepared to advise if I were in difficulty. Some were not helpful. Having been to see a patient on the medical ward with bleeding from a gastric ulcer I sought advice. I was asked if I was an 'ace gastrectomist'. When I replied that

I had never done that operation, I was advised to 'Drip ice-cold water, with adrenaline, into his stomach' – a useless treatment. Fortunately, the patient did not bleed again and so did not need an operation.

Elisabeth and Andrew duly arrived by taxi at our new home later in the week, but I was on duty at the LRI. It must have been difficult for her, coping with her first baby when her husband was absent one night and one weekend in three, resident on take at the LRI. At least our new home was comfortable with a nice garden, overlooking fields at the back, and Rothley had some food shops and a GP. However, I needed the car to get to work so Elisabeth was stuck in the village.

SEE ONE, DO ONE, TEACH ONE
The registrars rotated, at eight-monthly intervals, around the three consultant firms. I worked in the following order with:

- Mr Donald McGavin and Mr Ken Wood (replacing Mr Barrett about a month after I arrived).
- Mr John Leslie and Mr John Bolton-Carter (who shared the neonatal surgery and did sessions at Hinckley & District Hospital).
- Mr Ernest Frizelle (the senior surgeon).

My first, and independent, operating list included some varicose veins; I tore the junction between the long saphenous and femoral veins and had to call for the arterial instruments. With the help of a very calm theatre sister, I repaired the damage. Some of the consultants were generous in giving me operations to do, though only very occasionally assisting me. I would have welcomed more input from them, but the established system was 'see one, do one, teach one'. There were no specialist urologists, and each consultant had a day-case cystoscopy list. Mr Barrett's list fell to me, and it was extremely fortunate that I had been taught cystoscopy so well by Ashton Miller in Bristol.

After I'd been there for a few weeks, James Hadfield, the SR, returned to work. He really ran the whole show: any operations that the consultants did not wish to do were offered to him and he had two independent lists for these. He was on call to support the registrar every night and weekend and was very willing to turn up and supervise us, except for the most challenging cases, which he did himself. I did many operations with James instructing me. He was a volatile character. One of the three registrars was usually out of favour and remained so until another upset him, for example by operating on a patient, as instructed by his consultant, without offering it to James. He was a surgical enthusiast who would roam the medical wards looking for patients to operate on! Under his leadership, the general surgical waiting lists were virtually cleared.

The number of emergency admissions and operations, including abdominal, chest and head injuries was large, and I rapidly gained a lot of experience, well supervised by James. We never refused an emergency admission. If all the beds were full, we called a porter to set up an extra bed in the middle of the ward. Sometimes by the morning there were four or even six extra beds. These patients had no privacy, but even the normal beds had no curtain rails. To examine a patient, portable screens were moved into place; they often fell over at a critical moment. A consultant was never called in for an emergency unless the patient was a doctor or his or her spouse.

The 'bleep' system had not yet arrived. The switchboard could contact a junior doctor using the 'lights'. Each ward and department had a vertical row of four different coloured lights on the wall. We each had our own combination of lights; the possible combinations were sufficient to cover the small number of resident doctors.

FELLOW OF THE ROYAL COLLEGE OF SURGEONS

In November 1962, I sat the final FRCS exam. There were many tales of the idiosyncrasies of the examiners: Professor d'Abreu (brother of Frank at the Westminster) would smilingly encourage a candidate as he dug himself into a deep hole and then write 'fail'. Another was 'Mr Daintree Johnson fails everyone'. I met the latter in the surgical pathology viva, and he went out of his way to help me. Years later I met him and mentioned his reputation; he said he was frequently criticised by his fellow examiners for being too lenient. In the clinical I was examined by Bill Capper from the BRI, who opened by saying: 'I think we've met before.' To my great relief I passed and emerged as an FRCS.

The next day, at Ken Wood's outpatient clinic, I said nothing. I think he assumed I must have failed. By the coffee interval he could contain his curiosity no longer and said brusquely, 'How did it go?' Later, John Bolton-Carter, to whose firm I next rotated, pointed out that he had gone straight on after the FRCS to sit the Cambridge Master of Surgery exam (MChir) and suggested that I should do the same. At that time Cambridge was the only university to offer an MChir by examination and without a thesis. I followed this advice, sitting the exam in January 1964, but did not pass on that occasion. It was unusual for anyone to pass as a registrar.

GENERAL SURGICAL OPERATIONS

The range of general surgery at the LRI was very wide. All five surgeons did urology, gastrointestinal malignancies and breast cancer and three of them did a few arterial operations, femoropopliteal bypass grafts for calf claudication, using a synthetic graft. Ken Wood did occasional operations for abdominal aortic aneurysm. There was no neurosurgical service for emergencies, so for patients with head injuries, suspected (on clinical grounds) of having intracranial bleeding, we made diagnostic burr holes in the skull, using a brace and bit. If we found a haematoma, we turned a skull flap for access to try to stop the bleeding. This was primitive surgery compared with later in the 20th century and was very rarely beneficial.

Another primitive activity was resuscitation. A patient whose heart stopped unexpectedly while in hospital would have their chest opened for internal cardiac massage, by whichever doctor was present. This nearly always proved ineffective and the surgical registrar on call would then be summoned to close the wound. I remember having to do this on the floor of the waiting area in the diabetic clinic with only a mobile screen between me and the queue of patients. This procedure was replaced by closed chest cardiopulmonary resuscitation, a much more civilised process.

Babies with myelomeningocele (a defect in the spine which exposed the spinal cord) had the skin closed as an emergency by the registrars, but I have no idea of their subsequent neurological function. James Hadfield promoted innovative definitive procedures for perforated peptic ulcers and large bowel obstruction. These policies gave me my first publication, on vagotomy for perforated duodenal ulcer, while in one memorable weekend I did three anterior resections of the rectum, for intestinal obstruction.

On routine operating lists I assisted the consultant or in his absence was often taken through the operation by James Hadfield. On only a very few occasions did a consultant supervise me doing an operation; I did one total gastrectomy for cancer while the consultant relaxed in the coffee room. For rectal cancer, the operation was usually a synchronous combined abdomino-perineal resection, with the registrar deputed to do the 'lower' end. With some consultants this was less a 'combined' operation and more a competition to see who could complete his part first.

When I was with Ernest Frizelle, he decided that we should take it in turns to do each part of the synchronous combined abdomino-perineal excision of the rectum (for rectal cancer). The first time he did the lower end, the patient suffered a cardiac arrest during the dissection, due to the large amount of blood on the floor, which had not been replaced by transfusion. When Friz had last done the perineal part, many years before, it was customary to press on without any attempt at controlling the bleeding, relying on the anaesthetist to replace the volume lost. However, with the routine use of diathermy for haemostasis, those large blood losses were avoided, so the anaesthetist was not prepared for, nor aware of, the massive loss. Fortunately, this patient responded to internal cardiac massage plus transfusion, and recovered fully.

HOSPITAL ANACHRONISMS

Outpatient sessions were in an old building with a large central waiting area. The original philosophy was indicated by past ENT outpatient sheets, found in the case notes: 'Leicester Royal Infirmary, Ear, Nose and Throat Department. Outpatients Tues and Thurs 1.45, doors closed 2pm'. Many of the referrals to general surgery, ostensibly posing a clinical question, were really aimed at getting an X-ray investigation. 'Open access' radiology for GPs had not yet become available and when it was introduced there was much opposition from consultants.

The Leicester hospitals were seriously underfunded, at about 70 per cent of the national average for the population served. An example of the necessary economies was the decision by the head pharmacist to purchase a bulk supply of reusable red rubber intravenous giving-sets, 'at a very advantageous price'. I had been surprised to find these still in use; in Kingston and Bristol they already had disposable plastic ones. The red rubber sets were associated with a high incidence of inflammation of the vein, due to the impossibility of cleaning them. We all realised they were a menace but were told that the plastic ones would not be provided until all the rubber ones had been used up. They had a fragile glass drip chamber and by dropping and clumsily treading on them they were all disposed of in record time. Another surprise for me was to find urinary catheters draining into open-necked jars, despite a trial in Bristol having shown that a closed drainage system much reduced the rate of infection. The A&E department was one of the busiest in England, so the waiting room became crowded. Rather than employing more staff to speed things up, the management decided to double the size of the waiting area.

INTENSIVE CARE

A few months after I arrived, a six-bedded general intensive care unit (ICU) was created by conversion of a small ward. The first such unit had been opened at Whiston Hospital in Liverpool in 1962 and the LRI's was only the second general ICU in Britain, though there were others used specifically for cardiac- or neurosurgery. It was a far-sighted development, but was not supported by active consultant involvement, The anaesthetists did not initially participate in running the ICU, so it fell to James Hadfield and the surgical registrars to run it, including managing the ventilators. We made good use of it for severe head or chest injuries and for patients seriously ill due to postoperative complications. James was also an early adopter of intravenous nutrition. We had one case of tetanus, successfully treated by artificial ventilation for 10 days, who then unfortunately died of a pulmonary embolus.

GETTING PUBLISHED

Publications were necessary for promotion, but I had none, so James Hadfield suggested two projects. The first was a review of patients with perforated duodenal ulcers treated by vagotomy and pyloroplasty (for lasting cure of the ulcer), compared with those treated conventionally by simple suture of the perforation. These two policies had been followed by different surgical firms at the LRI and so the groups were comparable. No one had reported such a comparison in Britain. We showed that, after vagotomy, there was no increase in postoperative mortality and the long-term results were superior. The paper was published in the *British Medical Journal* in July 1964[3]. Of more immediate benefit for me was the opportunity to read it as a paper at the East Midlands Surgical Society in Sheffield in April of that year.

The second project related to patients with multiple rib fractures and a fractured sternum, resulting in paradoxical movement of the anterior three-quarters of the chest wall, causing respiratory failure. This injury was usually the result of impaction against the steering wheel, before seat belts were in

---

3   Hadfield JIH, Watkin DFL. Vagotomy in the treatment of perforated duodenal ulcer. *Br Med J* 1964; 2: 12-17

common use. Ten patients had been successfully treated by external fixation of the sternal fracture, with or without added traction and the series was published in *The Lancet*.[4]

Both these methods of treatment have since become irrelevant: duodenal ulcers are cured medically. Seat belts have virtually eliminated that type of chest injury and those that do occur are treated by artificial ventilation; that would have been feasible in 1963 but we didn't consider it,

TIME OUT

Lunch was available in 'Alice's' on the ground floor. There was a U-shaped table for junior staff and two tables for consultants and this meeting place enabled many items of business to be dealt with. The occasional mess dinners were popular and rowdy; one medical registrar's party trick was to eat the flowers. Housemen (nearly all were male) and most SHOs were fully resident, occupying rooms on the main hospital corridor. When resident on take, we registrars slept in another of these rooms, furnished with only an iron bedstead.

The very few female residents lived in the nurses' home, out of bounds to males. I once intervened in support of a married house officer, whose husband was not allowed to visit her there, but I was told that if she didn't like this she should resign. There was nothing more that I could do. She persevered to complete her six months.

At Christmas, it was customary for the juniors to put on a show for the entertainment of the nurses and patients. I have no talents as a variety performer and avoided participating. One of my co-registrars did a brilliant series of mimes on activities such as putting up a drip. Afterwards, Dr Jamie, a retired physician, used his speech of thanks to castigate the juniors for refusing to run the show on Christmas Day, 'Putting their families before the welfare of patients and nurses'. The show did not happen again.

When I was off duty, we enjoyed life in Rothley. For shopping with a pram, Loughborough was more manageable than Leicester's larger centre. Both sets of parents came to stay in our second bedroom. When Andrew was a year old, we parked him in Edgware with Elisabeth's parents and spent a week in a tiny, engineless two-berth sailing boat on the Norfolk Broads.

We began to purchase a few items of furniture – a settee, a single pedestal

---

4   Hadfield JIH, Watkin DFL. Device for the stabilisation of anterior chest wall injuries. *Lancet* 1965; 1: 634

dining table and some basic dining chairs. On 2nd June 1964 Sally was born, a few weeks early, in the old Bond Street maternity hospital – a converted terrace of small houses. The Morris Minor became increasingly crotchety, and I replaced the cylinder head gasket myself. I often had to crank the engine with the starting handle. Finally, we replaced it with a second-hand Morris 1000 shooting brake, which more easily accommodated Andrew, Sally in her carrycot and the pram base.

PROGRESSION TO SENIOR REGISTRAR

The normal tenure of the registrar post was two years, so by 1964 I had to think about the next job. James Hadfield moved on to a lecturer's post in Oxford in March and the consultants expressed some surprise that I did not apply for the vacancy. I explained that I thought it important to vary my experience of hospitals, without mentioning that I did not wish to be on call constantly. Nevertheless, I was asked to cover the duties for the six-week interregnum, and one of the SHOs was promoted to fill my place. This passed off satisfactorily but reinforced my decision not to take a post that was continuously on duty. Though I was acting up as SR I was told there was no possibility of being paid accordingly.

I enquired about a lecturer's post in Birmingham and was courteously shown around by Professor d'Abreu (brother of the Westminster surgeon) but was not shortlisted. I fancied an SR post in Norwich, rotating to the Middlesex Hospital, but heard no more about it. I was interviewed for a post in Nottingham, rotating to the Sheffield teaching hospitals, as did all three SR posts in the region, but was not successful.

Then there was an SR vacancy to start in Derby. As was customary, I went to 'look around', but really to make myself known to the consultants. I was very politely received apart from by Mr Ainslie Anderson, who challenged my paper on vagotomy for perforated duodenal ulcers, saying: 'They should all have a gastrectomy!' He later became a great friend. There were two surgical firms at the Derbyshire Royal Infirmary (DRI). The recently retired senior surgeon, in a firm with Mr George Harrison and Mr Anderson, had monopolised the SR, while Mr Joe Wilson and Mr Gordon Hollands made do with the registrar. The latter firm felt that as they were senior to Mr Harrison, they should now have the SR. I was advised by consultants in Leicester to decline the job unless rotation between the firms was guaranteed.

At interview, the Sheffield representatives were feeding favourable questions to me about my experience of trauma (a lot of it at the LRI); and neurosurgery (I had arranged to attend some operating lists in the neurosurgical unit in Derby). I am sure reading my vagotomy paper in Sheffield must have helped my case. Asked if I had any questions, I enquired whether the post would rotate between the two firms in Derby. Messrs Wilson and Hollands looked uncomfortable but had to say that it would. To my delight, I got the job. Later, I learned that the candidate with the strongest application had been blackballed.

Flushed with this success, we decided to buy a house in Derby. We agreed the purchase of a small, unfurnished three-bedroomed detached, near the Territorial Army barracks, funded by a 100 per cent endowment mortgage negotiated through the Medical Insurance Agency. Just before we were due to complete, we were gazumped (a new phenomenon) by a better offer. The average duration of stay for an SR in one of the three out-of-Sheffield hospitals was 16 months, so it did not seem worth trying to buy another house. Our only option was to fall back on the flat provided for SRs in the grounds of the other hospital, Derby City.

Leicester gave me a great grounding in general surgery. I gained experience in most of the operative procedures and learned a lot about diagnosis in the emergency admissions. I was introduced to intensive care and gained my first two publications. It was all extremely hard work, with many sleepless nights on duty. Several times when driving home the following evening I fell asleep at the traffic lights at the turn for Rothley and was woken by the motorist behind me.

13

SENIOR REGISTRAR IN DERBY

W e moved into the furnished flat in Derby at the end of October 1964. It was the first floor of the former residence of the medical superintendent of the City Hospital[5]. Bertie Matthews, the medical SR, and his wife occupied the ground floor. Each flat had a large living room, two bedrooms and a poorly equipped kitchen. We brought in our limited furniture, stacking the displaced sofa, dining table and bed in the second bedroom, which also accommodated Andrew and Sally, and replaced some of the kitchen equipment. Our new home was 10 minutes' drive from the Derbyshire Royal Infirmary (DRI) and, for the first time, I was not required to live in when on take.

There was a large lawned rear garden, but while we were on the upper floor this was of limited use for our small children. Later, Bertie became a consultant and was replaced by Geoff Cohen (a year ahead of me at the Westminster) and his wife Margaret, who was training in diagnostic radiology in Sheffield. They had no children, so we took the opportunity to move to the ground floor.

Like many cities, Derby had entered the NHS with two general hospitals.

---

5   Derby City Hospital was originally established by the local authority. In the 1990s it was rebuilt and expanded as the Royal Derby Hospital to replace the Derbyshire Royal Infirmary, which then closed.

The DRI, previously a voluntary hospital, had more facilities and was the more prestigious place to work. The City Hospital was originally run by the local authority. The DRI was very different from the Leicester Royal Infirmary (LRI). The physicians were in the ascendant, whereas in Leicester the surgeons ruled. As evidence of the quality of the staff, two consultants – a paediatrician and a neurologist – went on to professorial posts elsewhere. The DRI had one of the two regional neurosurgical departments and a world-famous hand surgery unit.

The general surgeons had exclusive use of new twin operating theatres, the second used by the SR (or the registrar) of the firm. I had five half-day sessions in theatre, providing invaluable experience, entirely unsupervised, with just occasional advice from the consultant in the adjacent theatre. As always, the theatre nurses were friendly and helpful. My first list included a radical mastectomy, by that time a less popular procedure, most breast cancers being treated by the less extensive simple mastectomy plus radiotherapy. Nevertheless, it was assumed that I could do this operation and fortunately I had done one or two for John Bolton Carter in Leicester.

SEPTICAEMIA

Four days into the post, I developed a severe flu-like illness and had to take to my bed. A raging temperature prompted us to seek advice from our neighbour Bertie, who promptly admitted me to the City Hospital for assessment. All the investigations for this pyrexia of unknown origin proved negative but my symptoms persisted, and my weight dropped to seven-and-a-half stone. The antibiotics used did not help and finally my consultant decided to try a new antibiotic, cloxacillin, with dramatic improvement. The presumption was that I'd had staphylococcal septicaemia, picked up in the ICU in Leicester.

I spent about three weeks at home regaining my strength and weight before returning to work. I felt bad about needing so much time off work so soon after starting the job, but everyone was extremely understanding. The bonus was time at home with the family and I was also able to do some revision for the Cambridge MChir exam in January. This time I was one of the three successful candidates.

TESTING TIMES WITH THE SENIOR CONSULTANTS

I started with the two senior surgeons, who at my interview had had to accept that I would rotate between the firms. I had interesting experiences in their outpatient clinics. As at the LRI, consultations took place at a long table. The consultant sat towards one end of the long side, and I sat towards the other end. A patient sat at each end while we took the history or explained the results of investigations or the proposed treatment. The only privacy was for examination in one of the cubicles.

When I was working for one of these consultants, the outpatients were randomly allocated to him or me. If he didn't know what to do, he would order a Mantoux test (a skin test for tuberculosis, not a common condition in general surgical patients) at a strength of one in 10,000. The patient returned with the result a week later and was equally likely to see him or me. If allocated to the consultant, he would repeat the test at one in 1000 and subsequently one in 100, by which time there was only a one-in-eight chance that the patient would still be with him. When the patient reached me, I was expected to deal with the problem. This was most educational, reminding me to avoid the short-term expedient of ordering an irrelevant test.

I did not attend the other consultant's outpatient clinic, but he would often give me the pile of case notes with instructions to write to the GPs about patients that I had not seen. In contrast, in the following year in George Harrison's outpatients, his secretary sat in a cubbyhole nearby with her typewriter. At intervals she would remove the tapes from our dictating machines and type the letters to the GPs. At the end of the session, we had coffee and discussed cases of interest. Then the secretary appeared with all the letters for signature, and they were posted on the same day. I never managed to emulate this efficient system.

Some patients on the second consultant's waiting list were marked: 'Not to be sent for until I say so'. After we'd cleared the rest of the list, I asked whether he had yet decided about these patients. It then became apparent that he intended to leave them on the list indefinitely. As they had conditions for which no surgical solution was apparent, it would have been better to explain to them that an operation would not be of benefit. However, I encountered some patients who derived status and enjoyed sympathy from being on the waiting list.

I was given a free rein in the second operating theatre, doing a wide range of gastrointestinal operations, hernias, varicose veins and operations for breast cancer. Occasionally, I was called to the parallel theatre when the senior surgeon felt out of his depth! He was aware of his limitations and retired early a few years later. His colleague was a very capable operator but frequently arrived up to two hours late. As I was already committed in the other theatre, I was not available to fill in for him, as would have happened in many other hospitals. The DRI had a private ward, and his private patients were included in the routine theatre lists, always taking first place. The other consultants rarely made use of this facility, instead using a private hospital run by nuns. Apart from the Royal Hospital in Sheffield, none of the other hospitals where I trained had private beds.

Two of the general surgeons had a major interest in urology but used contrasting techniques for transurethral prostatectomy, a procedure not available at the LRI. The senior one used the resectoscope, as they did in Bristol, cutting away little slivers of prostate with a diathermy loop. His younger colleague favoured an older instrument, the cold punch: a sharp cylinder slid down inside a closely fitting sheath to remove the fragments of the prostate. Supporters of the cold punch waxed lyrical that: 'It cuts cleanly and neither chars nor burns'. Neither was keen to devolve this endoscopic work, so I had more than my share of open operations on the prostate.

BREAST CANCER

During this time, I encountered two striking malfunctions in the treatment of breast cancer. I saw one patient (with an incidental condition) who'd had a forequarter amputation in the 1930s, which left her without a right upper limb and shoulder. I was curious about the reason for this and went through her notes carefully. In 1937 she had had a mastectomy based on a clinical diagnosis of cancer, but histology did not confirm this. Nevertheless, she was referred for radiotherapy, which was given in what was later realised to be an excessive dose. This resulted in necrosis of the bones around the shoulder and damage to the nerves supplying the limb; it became useless and painful, hence the amputation. There was no record of any admission of error in this catalogue of errors and the patient remained grateful!

Frozen section to determine whether a breast lump was a cancer was first described in 1905 but did not come into widespread use until the 1940s. When cancer was suspected the lump was removed, frozen and sectioned, enabling it to be examined under the microscope while the patient remained asleep. If cancer was confirmed, the surgeon then went on to perform a mastectomy. This was disturbing for the patient, who did not know whether they would wake up lacking one breast or not. Nevertheless, it was an improvement on the previous practice of mastectomy based on only a clinical diagnosis. There were no preoperative diagnostic tests for breast cancer until the 1970s.

I had a near disaster with this policy. I removed the breast lump and when I cut it across, it had the typical consistency of a cancer. Surprisingly, the written report from the lab was: 'No carcinoma'. I took off my gloves and walked downstairs to confront the pathologist, who said: 'Of course it was a cancer'. He was a fast worker and would dictate the report to his secretary, reach out and sign it while looking down the microscope at the next slide. He had said 'Adenocarcinoma' and she had misheard it as 'No carcinoma'. Never sign a document without reading it!

ASH CASH

For patients dying in hospital who were to be cremated, a form had to be signed by an independent doctor, to confirm that there were no suspicious circumstances. The fee payable for this service was colloquially referred to as 'ash cash'. In most hospitals, the financial beneficiaries were the SRs and registrars. However, in the DRI the sole consultant radiotherapist would attend post-mortems, clutching the case notes and cremation form for any patient he had seen, to ensure that no one else had a chance to sign it.

MOVING ON TO THE OTHER FIRM

The most enjoyable period of my time in Derby was the second year, which I spent with George Harrison, Ainslie Anderson and the newly appointed Peter Goodall. They encouraged me to do complex operations including resections for oesophageal cancer or for parotid tumours (where it is necessary to carefully preserve the facial nerve which runs through the gland), fortunately without any major complications. I had little direct supervision, but George would talk me through a new procedure while sitting in the coffee room. Ainslie and Peter were challenging in their comments, which I enjoyed. They took me with them to clinical meetings at the Royal Society of Medicine and the Royal College of Surgeons and encouraged me to attend a course on health service management at the King's Fund. George also did some vascular surgery, but that specialty was in its infancy. I remember mentioning the recently introduced operation of carotid endarterectomy; he said he was 'waiting for the ideal case'. I heard that reason for not adopting a new procedure on other occasions.

I collected series of cases of intestinal pseudo-obstruction[6] and ischaemic

---

6   Watkin DFL. Spinal ileus. *Br J Surg* 1970:57: 142-8

colitis, both recently described diagnoses. I also ran a controlled trial of post-prostatectomy irrigation with epsilon-aminocaproic acid, which blocks the action of naturally occurring anticoagulant urokinase. I had expected to show a reduction in blood loss in the treatment group, but blood loss in the control group was unusually low (perhaps due to the diluting effect of dummy irrigation), resulting in an insignificant result, which I never published.

EMERGENCY SURGERY IN ADULTS AND CHILDREN

The emergency 'take' was shared with the City Hospital, with GP referrals going to the two hospitals on alternate days. As in Leicester, the DRI was always open for cases presenting in casualty. There were also internal referrals from other specialties, particularly general medicine. Thus, there was still emergency work on the 'City' days. I was on call from home for emergencies at the DRI in alternate weeks, also covering the Derbyshire Children's Hospital, which was then on a separate site in North Street[7]. The other weeks were the responsibility of the registrar (working on the other firm), while the City Hospital had its own junior rota. It was a busy but manageable workload and the weeks off take were wonderful.

I built up considerable experience in abdominal trauma and upper gastrointestinal bleeding. I even did one operation for a ruptured abdominal aortic aneurysm. I completed the procedure, but the patient died a few hours later – there were very few survivors until a decade later. When covering the Children's Hospital, I dealt with appendicitis, intussusception and infantile pyloric stenosis. The latter was under local anaesthesia, with a nurse comforting the month-old baby with a finger dipped in a mixture of honey and brandy. A paediatrician greeted me one morning: 'I see you've set another one on the primrose path to the eternal bonfire.' After some delay I realised this was a joking reference to the alcohol.

I was attracted to paediatric surgery and applied to spend the next year as a locum SR in the Sheffield Children's Hospital, with a view to getting a general surgical consultant post with this as my special interest. The senior surgeon there seemed keen to take me on, but the regional training committee rejected my request for a year out. I believe the senior surgeon at the Sheffield Royal Infirmary was expecting that I would replace his current SR when he

---

7   In 1996 the Derbyshire Children's Hospital moved from North Street to the rebuilt Royal Derby Hospital.

got a consultant post, and therefore blocked my secondment. Entering my third year as an SR I reverted to the senior firm.

INTENSIVE CARE

While I was at the DRI a three-bedded intensive care unit was opened, nominally under the care of a trio of consultants: an anaesthetist, a physician and Ainslie Anderson, with an anaesthetic SHO to provide daytime care. Building on my previous experience at the LRI, I became interested in this, particularly in the management of circulatory shock. This involved monitoring treatment by measuring the central venous pressure (CVP, the filling pressure for the heart), as pioneered in Bristol, but now with commercially made catheters.

The DRI had purchased a 'Volumetron' to measure the patient's blood volume using an indicator dilution technique, but this information proved irrelevant to management. Patients with 'septic shock' would have a normal blood volume but a low blood pressure, due to dilatation of the blood vessels. CVP monitoring was much more useful than the Volumetron, which became redundant. The DRI had also invested in a device to cool the lining of the stomach, with the aim of permanently reducing acid secretion and so curing duodenal ulcers. However, Les Blumgart, then a research registrar in Sheffield, had demonstrated that it was both ineffective and dangerous, so it too languished in a cupboard.

LIFE IN DERBY

Apart from the limitations of the flat, our work-life balance in Derby was better because I could sleep at home when on duty, and every other week I was not even on call. I usually needed the car to get to the DRI and make calls at the Children's Hospital, so Elisabeth had to walk up the hill to Littleover to go to the shops, with Andrew in tow and Sally in the pushchair. One day I came out of the DRI after a long shift, got into our grey Morris 1000 shooting brake, started the engine and reached for my seat belt, but it wasn't there. I then realised that I was in the wrong car, but the key had worked. Only our seatbelts, which were voluntary at that time, saved me from accidental theft! Seatbelts did not become a legal requirement until 1983. Another time, returning home at 3am, I was stopped by the police. They obviously thought anyone driving such an old car at that time of night was up to no good.

In the summer of 1965, we had our first seaside holiday, in Pembrokeshire, staying in an upstairs flat. The owner (who had lived downstairs) had died after we made the booking, so the house felt spooky. On most days, we took the children to the beach at Saundersfoot in the morning in beautiful weather. Andrew had a plastic boat that he pulled along on a string, even on dry land. Sally, who was not yet mobile, sat on a stone for lengthy periods with her feet in a rockpool. In the afternoon, when they were suitably tired, we went sightseeing.

The next spring, Andrew came rushing in from the garden shouting: 'Sally's talking!' and she was, starting with complete sentences at the age of about 21 months. Before that she had not uttered a single word. Winston Churchill is said to have started speaking in the same way.

In September 1966 Clare was born, in the City Hospital, and Ainslie Anderson arrived in the maternity ward with champagne. Each of the five consultants invited us home for a meal during our time in Derby.

ELISABETH'S NEW SPECIALTY
Our GP invited Elisabeth to do sessions in his practice, which provided useful supplementary income. However, she found the work frustrating because no one would give her any help or advice. The only feedback she received was: 'You're doing well.' We were still hard up, with serious debate before Elisabeth bought a new winter coat – the first since we had married.

At about this time Elisabeth was struck with the idea of doing radiology when my job moved to Sheffield. She was inspired by Margaret Cohen, the wife of the senior medical registrar, who was training in Sheffield. Radiology had the advantage of being under-populated and, at that time, it involved little emergency work. In 1965 Rosemary Rue, the recently appointed senior medical officer in the Oxford region, had started the Married Women's Training Scheme to enable women doctors with children to train part-time in a hospital specialty. Funding was provided centrally, so there was no cost for the training hospital. Elisabeth wrote to the senior radiologist in Sheffield, Dr Thomas Lodge (later Sir Thomas), explaining that since house jobs she'd had three children and wished to train in radiology, once we moved to Sheffield.

The leaders of radiology in Sheffield were reluctant; they argued that as a woman she would not be able to cope with the necessary physics. However, after repeated applications, they agreed to take her on as an SHO, though she would only be paid for two clinical sessions per week until she had completed the first part of the Diploma in Medical Radio Diagnosis (DMRD). We gratefully accepted this offer; we reckoned it would pay off in the long term.

MOVING TO SHEFFIELD

I was conscious of the lack of research in my CV and hoped to correct this during my time in Sheffield. However, although we had expected to move after about 16 months, our stay in Derby had continued for two-and-a-half years. There were four SR posts in Sheffield and rotation in from the three district general hospitals (DGHs) depended on those SRs getting consultant posts, which they were slow to do. Meanwhile, we decided to pre-empt the move by buying a house in Sheffield. We purchased a nice modern semi-detached in the Edwardian suburb of Nether Edge for the sum of £5,750. We thought we were getting a 100 per cent mortgage but the building society's valuer gave a figure of £5,500, so we had to find £250 from our scanty reserves.

Having gained possession in the spring of 1967, we made weekend trips to carry out various minor works in preparation for the expected move. These visits, travelling up the Derwent Valley through Matlock, took us past a gasworks. Andrew, being of a practical bent, soon understood the mechanism of gasholders. One day, Sally (aged three) was keen to join the conversation:

Sally: 'Those gasholders are full.'
Andrew: 'What are they full of, Sally?'
Sally: 'Things.'

Our middle child would never be an engineer, but she was most adept with words.

I began to agitate about moving to Sheffield, via George Harrison and Donald McGavin from Leicester, who was a member of the Regional Hospital Board. The regional training committee responded by ruling that my predecessor in Derby should return there. Naturally, he was cross about this. Fortunately, before the decision could be implemented, another SR in Sheffield got a consultant job, so I was able to move into his post on 1st August. We had been in Derby for two years and nine months. As this was a reciprocating post, our removal expenses, including solicitor's fees, were reimbursed. At that time expenses were not paid for any other hospital moves, at junior level or on consultant appointment.

Derby had provided the best clinical experience in my whole training. The staff were very friendly, the duty rota was civilised, and I was completely non-resident for the first time, but we were still glad to be moving on at last.

14
SHEFFIELD

Before starting as senior registrar at the Royal Hospital[8], I took annual leave, enabling us to move into our house at 80 Osborne Road, Nether Edge in mid-July. A roll of cheap mottled-blue carpet had just been delivered, and my first task was to fit that in our bedroom and cover the areas between (but for economy not under) the children's beds in the large second bedroom. Later, Elisabeth assembled the offcuts to fit the third bedroom.

Then we had a fortnight's holiday at Brancaster in Norfolk, renting Saltingsgarth, a large house right on the edge of the salt marsh; there was even a table tennis table which we used every evening after putting the children to bed. We had beautiful weather for the whole 14 days and Andrew and Sally revelled in the beach and the sea, Clare less so, as at 10 months she was not yet mobile.

Returning home, we set off to Wrexham for Margaret's wedding to Stuart Moorhouse at All Saints Church, Gresford. Andrew and Sally were page and bridesmaid, dressed in turquoise outfits made by Elisabeth, while Clare slept in her carrycot in the car. We then went on to the reception at the Wynnstay Hotel. Driving home over the moors at dusk Sally spotted 'two real elephants' (sheep).

---

8   The Royal Hospital was closed, and the work transferred to the Royal Hallamshire Hospital when this was completed in 1978.

Our house was built with three others on the steep site of a former quarry. As was common in Nether Edge, the garage was dug into the side of the hill in front of the house. There was a large living room, which accommodated our small dining table, the settee, a new easy chair and a modular range of bookcases that I'd made in Rothley and Derby. We used the small dining room at the back of the house as a playroom, with a wall storage unit that I had prefabricated in Derby. I also built a peninsula unit for eating in the kitchen. We purchased further items of furniture in auctions and from antique shops, including the clothes press (£14) and dressing table (£2) still in our bedroom today. Some of the cheaper items came from a junk store near Matlock, notably a huge roll of felt carpet underlay described as 'railway lost property'. The garden was steep, with a dozen steps up to the front door and three terraces at the back. It was wonderful to be in a house of our own at last.

STARTING IN RADIOLOGY

Elisabeth was due to begin training in radiology for six sessions a week in the autumn. Andrew was starting at Hunter's Bar Infant School in September, but we needed to arrange childcare for Sally (three) and Clare (one). An advertisement produced Judith, who had been a live-in nanny, but having recently married wished to be non-resident and part-time. She was aged 24, appeared to be ideal and proved to be so. Her husband drove her to our house before Elisabeth left for work and she stayed until one of us got home. The children loved her, and she became particularly fond of Clare. We remained in Christmas card contact.

We also had an application from an elderly woman living nearby. She had worked for many years as a sales representative for a large, old-style grocer's shop, travelling around Sheffield taking orders. When that business ceased, she worked as a nanny, first for the Northcote Greens (formerly my housemaster at St Edward's, and by then headmaster at nearby Worksop College) and later for a branch of the royal family. She was too elderly for our main job but proved useful as backup and for babysitting.

The first term of the radiology course included four sessions of lectures on physics each week. For Elisabeth, this left just two clinical sessions and she was paid only for these and at SHO level, so she earned less than Judith cost us. She and the other four or five beginners sat Part I of the Diploma in Medical Radio Diagnosis (DMRD) about six months later and, contrary to the original predictions, Elisabeth passed easily. She then moved on to six paid clinical sessions at the Northern General Hospital and into positive balance financially. Elisabeth found everyone in the department welcoming and helpful, though Dr Ronald Grainger, the senior radiologist, could be demanding. One of her duties was to assist him with arteriograms, which was stressful, although straightforward compared with the interventional procedures that she was to perform in later years. In due course, she passed the final DMRD, again at the first attempt, in contrast to some of her colleagues.

THE ROYAL HOSPITAL

My consultant John Rowling (JR) welcomed me warmly on 1st August 1967. He was a fellow Cambridge graduate and had been an SR in Leicester. Soon after we arrived, he and his wife invited us to their home for coffee, which seemed a very friendly gesture. However, we found that the real purpose of this visit was for Mrs Rowling to make it clear that I was never to bother her husband when he was at home. She then gave Elisabeth a large bowl of cacti. JR did a wide range of general surgery, including some vascular work. We had twin theatres, so I had my own lists, gastroenterology, hernias and varicose veins.

JR had unusual ideas about the treatment of breast cancer, doing an *extended* radical mastectomy (fortunately he accepted that I would not do these) and giving 'Coley's fluid' as adjuvant therapy. The latter was a historical mixture of pus and other liquids, designed to stimulate the immune response – a principle later accepted, though not using that stimulus. He found it difficult to get good biopsies of 'lumpy' breasts, arguing that the tissue slipped out of the way of a biopsy needle. His solution was to introduce the needle very rapidly. He achieved this by mounting the biopsy needle on a pistol bullet (he was a skilled metal worker) and shooting the breasts of dead bodies in the mortuary! Unfortunately, he did not appreciate that a high-velocity missile liquefies the tissues, so the biopsies were useless.

My boss also had unorthodox ideas about vascular surgery. He excised the blocked segment of an artery, rather than simply using a bypass graft. For aortic aneurysms, he reintroduced the old treatment of 'wiring'. He argued that feeding wire into the aneurysm by hand did not insert enough to reinforce its wall with clot. To rectify this, he modified a fisherman's reel to put in many metres of wire. I performed several of these procedures electively, but we never used the method for a ruptured aneurysm. The postoperative X-rays showed loops of wire reaching to the aortic arch and the neck, but this didn't seem to do any harm. There was no chance opportunity to examine the aorta at autopsy to establish whether the wire successfully reinforced the arterial wall with a layer of thrombus. I have no follow-up data to show whether this procedure reduced the risk of rupture.

He sometimes took me with him when visiting patients on the private floor. I remember meeting a past chairman of the Football League who was recovering from a prostatectomy (NHS patients would have gone to the specialist urology unit). JR's instructions were interesting: 'You should drink no coffee and not too much tea.' His outpatient clinic was organised for him to see the new referrals, with the students, and make a confident diagnosis. The patients returned to see me, with the results of their investigations, which often failed to substantiate the diagnosis. I then had to try to sort out what were often obscure problems. Only rarely did I give any feedback, so JR's confidence was not questioned.

Our emergency work was shared with the Royal Infirmary and the Northern General Hospital, the latter taking the largest share. Although we were only on take for GP referrals one day in five, JR expected his own firm to deal with the patients that he admitted from domiciliary visits on any day. The firm included a registrar on the multispecialty 'peri-FRCS' rotation who might or might not have spent a previous six months in general surgery. The registrar was on duty on alternate nights, with me supervising him. On the other nights, I was first on call. It was not a heavy workload, but it did restrict other activities. A mobile phone would have helped! The anaesthetist running the intensive care unit would not accept any suggestions about our firm's patients, despite my experience in Leicester and Derby.

At that time, many general practitioners were dissatisfied with their workload. The Department of Health (DoH) responded by instructing hospitals to encourage their junior staff to do sessions in general practice. Consequently, many registrars were not seen in the hospital until 10am and might also leave early in the afternoon! I felt that I had enough to do surgically and did not join in. Subsequently changes were made in general practice, including the introduction of vocational training. Had the latter been available sooner, Elisabeth might have trained as a GP, though I doubt this would have suited her as well as radiology.

Four medical students were attached to the firm so, for the first time since Bristol, I was involved in student teaching and very much enjoyed this. I added informal tutorials to the ward teaching. JR taught on his twice-weekly ward rounds, but always spent most time on the first patient. I used to move the patients around to avoid repetition. One day he remarked: 'There's a man in Manchester with feet just like that.' Only later did I discover that he was referring to an Egyptian mummy (with a bunion) that had featured in the research for his MD thesis.

While at the Royal Hospital I tried to set up an investigation to compare the tension in several types of repair for inguinal hernia but could not achieve a satisfactory method of measurement. With one of the registrars, I did a study of the significance of jaundice in acute cholecystitis, which indicated that it was nearly always due to a stone in the bile duct[9]. The statement in *Bailey & Love* (the standard surgical textbook) that 'lesser degrees of jaundice are due to the inflamed gallbladder' disappeared from the next edition!

Nearing the end of my fourth year, I felt I should start applying for consultant posts. In 1968 there were approximately 40 applicants for each vacancy and SRs would tailor their applications to the subspecialty interest of each post. I was conscious that the paucity of publications weakened my case. Aged 32, my application for Northampton didn't result in me being shortlisted but I received a nice letter explaining that they wanted someone aged about 40 but hoped I would apply for the next vacancy three years hence. I looked at jobs in Peterborough and on the Wirral but did not apply. I applied for a post in Nottingham with a vascular interest, for which I had little experience; unsurprisingly I was not interviewed.

LECTURER IN SURGERY

Then I heard that David Johnston was leaving his lecturer's job at the Royal Infirmary for a senior post in Leeds. To replace him seemed an ideal way to rectify my deficiencies of youth and lack of research. Encouraged by Elisabeth, I went to see Professor Duthie (the professor of surgery) and asked if I could move into the vacancy. I supported my application with an original suggestion for a research project comparing plasma and red cell circulation times in haemorrhagic shock in dogs. A low molecular weight dextran solution (LMWD) was advertised to prevent 'sludging' of the red cells and this study would demonstrate the degree of sludging and indicate whether LMWD did correct this. Fortuitously, the senior lecturer was doing animal research on oxygen uptake in shock, so suitable facilities were already available.

---

9   Watkin DFL, Thomas GG. Jaundice in acute cholecystitis. *Br J Surg* 1971; 58:570-3

Prof Duthie had in mind for the lecturer to continue David Johnston's work on the completeness of vagotomy in the treatment of duodenal ulcers. Nevertheless, he was impressed by my proposed project and, after talking to JR, offered me the job to do both studies in parallel. It was suggested that, to avoid any criticism that I had not completed my training, I should start on 1st November 1968, when I had completed four years as an SR, because at that time the lecturer post was not 'recognised' for training. I was allocated a desk in a room shared with four other researchers. Later, when a physician/senior lecturer moved on to Dundee, I got my own tiny office.

Working in the professorial unit at the Royal Infirmary I had three roles: my two research projects, covering the registrar when on take (one-in-five) and providing the surgery course for dental students. In addition, I took the daily ward round on Wednesdays and assisted the senior lecturer with his research, which was good preparation for my shock project.

When either the professor or the senior lecturer was away, I took over their operating list and so kept my hand in. The registrars had only six months' prior experience in general surgery, so I often needed to supervise their emergency work and do the more complex operations. Only once did I need to call the professor, when we were unable to stop the bleeding in a patient with an abdominal injury. This was a rare instance of death on the operating table. The registrar had embarked on this operation on his own and only called me when he got into difficulty. I wondered whether he had exacerbated the damage in his efforts to gain control of the bleeding but did not say so.

The dental students did courses in medicine and surgery for two terms in their third year. Each week, there were two clinical sessions and one lecture on surgery. One of my predecessors had written a slim textbook: *Surgery for Dental Students*. With this as a guide I was left to design the course and set a written exam at the end. There were about 40 students and I had to recruit two other tutors for each clinical session. We concentrated on diseases affecting the head and neck, searching the surgical and radiotherapy wards for suitable patients. It is hard to know how much the students benefitted, but it was certainly a valuable experience for me.

I also continued to give tutorials for the medical students attached to the unit and was allocated one formal lecture to the full year group, on the spleen, a topic no one else was interested in. I started by saying that there are only two things you can do with the spleen: feel it (when enlarged) or take it out. I then went on to discuss the diseases in which it becomes palpable and the circumstances in which it should be removed. I was also the organiser for the final clinical examination in surgery, contacting suitable outpatients suggested by the consultants and scouring the hospital for others. My reward was to participate as an examiner.

RESEARCH

For the study comparing red cell and plasma circulation times I was joined by a graduate from the Medical Physics Department to deal with the radio-isotopes. Fortunately, I had access to a primitive Olivetti computer, about the size of a small desk, and I wrote a simple programme to analyse the curves of this radioactivity to derive the mean circulation times. Calculation would have been very laborious.

The initial results, for the lower limb, formed my first presentation to the Surgical Research Society (SRS)[10], being selected for the Patey Prize session. The SRS had strict rules: papers must be spoken, not read, and must not exceed the 10-minute slot or the speaker would be stopped. Questions could be fierce, especially from one or two senior professors. Giving my first paper at the SRS was daunting despite supervised rehearsals. With further data for the circulation in the kidney and bowel, the studies showed that red cell and plasma circulation times slowed proportionately in shock, with no evidence of 'sludging'. After this paper appeared in the *British Journal of Surgery* (BJS)[11], advertisements for LMWD for the prevention of sludging disappeared. However, this negative result was not considered a good basis for an MD thesis, so I was advised to concentrate on my other project.

The completeness of vagotomy in the treatment of duodenal ulcers was being monitored in the department with routine insulin tests of gastric acid secretion at ten days after vagotomy. A 'positive' result was thought to indicate a risk of further trouble from the ulcer. The accumulated tests also showed disparities in the effectiveness of individual surgeons. Patients presenting with symptoms of recurrence of the ulcer, months or years after the vagotomy operation, were also subjected to insulin tests. If these gave positive results indicating persisting vagal connection to the stomach, reoperation to complete

---

10   The SRS became the Society of Academic and Research Surgery (SARS) in 1992 but later reverted to SRS.

11   Watkin DFL, Hudson J. Erythrocyte and plasma circulation times in haemorrhagic shock. Br J Surg 1972; 59: 957-63

the vagotomy could be recommended. This evidence was considered to establish the value of early postoperative tests to indicate the risk of recurrence of the ulcer.

However, I surmised that the greater response in patients with a recurrent ulcer might be due to secretion recovering over time. I therefore tested a series of 40 patients at 10 days, two months, and six months post-operatively and indeed some patients showed a marked increase over this time, suggesting that these might be the ones at risk of recurrence. Additionally, 15 patients with recurrent DUs had test results both from postoperatively and when their symptoms recurred; several had negative early results but a substantial response later. (This research is described in more detail in chapter 27.) Together with an investigation into Burge's intraoperative electrical test for completeness of vagotomy, this was to be written up as an MD thesis. By the time I was appointed a consultant I had sufficient data, and I planned to complete the thesis after moving to Leicester, but this good intention gave way to other priorities.

FAMILY LIFE IN SHEFFIELD

We enjoyed Sheffield, which is a lovely hilly city, provided one averts the gaze from the run-down industrial east side. Our finances had improved. My salary as an SR had been increased to about £2,000 per annum and once Elisabeth passed the first part of the DMRD, she earned six-tenths of a registrar's pay.

Sally wanted a cat and Elisabeth obtained a kitten from a pathologist at the Northern General Hospital. Black with a white flash on her forehead, Starry was the first of our many animals. We made trips out into the Peak District at weekends and in 1968 had another holiday in Norfolk, staying in a modern bungalow, but unfortunately it rained for most of the fortnight.

We exchanged visits with Elisabeth's parents several times each year, facilitated by the recently extended M1. By the time we first arrived in Leicester the motorway already reached Lutterworth. When we moved to Derby it was extended to meet our needs and then just before we arrived in Sheffield it was extended again for us. The route to Wrexham involved a more awkward journey, with discussion as to the best route; my father always asked if we had used the route via Woore.

There were dinghy sailing clubs on two of the reservoirs north-west of Sheffield. Several colleagues on the junior staff of the hospitals were members of More Hall Sailing Club, while consultants tended to join the other club at Damflask. Before joining the former, I had to attend for a trial sail, in a Merlin Rocket, and was accepted. We then bought a second-hand GP14 dinghy and throughout the summer seasons I raced, with Andrew as crew and often the rest of the family watching. I was occasionally included in the team to race against other clubs in the area. This was a truly amateur club, like the Shropshire Sailing Club of my youth, with a wooden hut as a clubhouse and winter working parties to repair it. On one occasion, while the GP was at the jetty, I fell in the water and Clare screamed with concern. Another time, we collided with a Merlin that I had not seen, and which had the right of way, doing considerable damage to it, but none to the GP. The Merlin's owner was very understanding about it: I offered to take it for repairs in Nottingham and my insurance company (the grandly named Navigators & General) paid up.

Sally taught herself to read when she was three. We did not attempt to teach her; she just cracked the code by watching while being read to. By the time she started infant school at five she could read the newspaper, though often not understanding what it was about. Meanwhile, Andrew found reading difficult; he finally got there with the help of Enid Blyton, despite the educationalists' disapproval of her works. Elisabeth would read one chapter of *The Famous Five* and to find out what happened next, he had to read the following chapter.

Having bought the boat in 1969 we had little money left for a summer holiday, so Elisabeth booked a cheap caravan on a farm near Robin Hood's Bay for our first week. It was in poor condition and very cramped for five, but it is a lovely bit of coast. For the second week, we moved on to a house near Hornsea. As we came down the hill, the sea was straight in front of us. Clare (three) started a delighted chorus: 'We are going to crash into the sea, we are going to crash into the sea,' which became a cheery family anthem. Our stay was enlivened by finding a bat in the children's bedroom.

In the summer of 1970, we set out to tow the GP to Nefyn on the Llŷn Peninsula in North Wales where we had taken a cottage. After breaking the outward journey at Wrexham, the clutch on our Triumph Herald failed near Llangollen and we were towed to a nearby garage by the AA. My father came out and brought the GP back to Wrexham. Within a couple of days, the clutch had been replaced and we set forth again. We had a good holiday, sailing the GP several times around the bay. On the journey home, I dropped the family in Porthmadog for them to take the Ffestiniog Railway to its inland terminus. Driving up the steep hill to the station, the car proved to have insufficient power to pull the trailer. I had to chock the trailer precariously at the roadside while I drove the rest of the way to pick up the others, collecting it again on the way down. The Triumph Herald was clearly underpowered for towing.

MOVING ON

My research progressed satisfactorily so I was starting to have more papers published. It was suggested that I might follow an academic career and had there been a senior lecturer vacancy in Sheffield we would have been tempted, but there was no early prospect of one. Cardiff Medical School was looking for a senior lecturer to hold the fort after Professor Forest transferred to Edinburgh and his senior lecturer went to the chair in Liverpool. Prof Duthie suggested that I apply, but I declined. Les Blumgart, a Sheffield SR, was appointed. He subsequently became successively professor in Glasgow, the Hammersmith Hospital, Berne and the Sloan Kettering Cancer Centre in New York, in the evolving specialty of hepato-pancreatico-biliary surgery. Had I gone to Cardiff, I don't think I would have followed that path.

After much thought, I concluded that a professor of surgery is required to fill too many roles: clinical surgeon, director of research, teacher and university administrator, so once again I began to look for an NHS consultant post. Elisabeth and I had endless discussions about our requirements: a hospital large enough to provide a good service; scope for her to continue in radiology; good schools for the children; and ideally water so that I could sail.

I applied for a job in Norwich, advertised with an interest in neonatal surgery, to continue the work done by the general surgeon who was retiring. The shortlist comprised one SR from Great Ormond Street (who lacked training in adult surgery) and four, including the SR working in Norwich, who were adult surgeons like me. The local SR, who had been appointed when I applied in 1964, got the job. It was a difficult specification but if I had been allowed to spend a year at Sheffield Children's Hospital when I was in Derby, I would have been the perfect candidate. I also applied for Portsmouth, where a local SR was appointed, and Exeter, where the post went to a regional SR from Bristol; I was not shortlisted for either job.

Elisabeth and I would have loved to stay in Sheffield, but the next potential consultant surgeon vacancy was three years away. In those days, if a candidate delayed too long before applying for a consultant post there would be a suspicion that there was something wrong with him. Donald McGavin was due to retire but we were not keen on Leicester; Elisabeth did not want to go back there, and it was notoriously under-resourced. Then in November 1970, the Education Secretary, Margaret Thatcher, announced that the third of three new medical schools would be in Leicester. We judged that this would offer good opportunities and guarantee an improvement in funding, so we decided that I should apply.

This time I was the insider candidate, and it would have been a serious setback not to get the job. I 'looked around' the Leicester Royal Infirmary (LRI) and Hinckley Hospital, for which two sessions were allocated, and was welcomed by staff that I had known as a registrar. In my application, I emphasised how much I enjoyed teaching. As this was the first consultant appointment after the decision to establish a medical school, the committee was unusually strong. The chairman was Professor Sir Andrew Kay (Glasgow, formerly of Sheffield), who had chaired the meeting when I read my first paper in 1964. It included Professor Duthie as well as two Leicester surgeons. The only member I did not know was the external assessor from Newcastle. Also shortlisted were a future professor of vascular surgery in Nottingham and future consultants in York and Salisbury. Unsurprisingly – but to my great relief – I was appointed.

FINDING A HOUSE

We then had three months to find somewhere to live. We sold the Sheffield house, without using an agent, within 45 minutes of it appearing in the local paper, for £7,250, representing a profit of £1,500. Our search in Leicester was influenced by consideration of the educational options.

We had both been to independent schools, supported respectively by the Barclays Bank scholarship and the direct grant system. We would accept either the state or private sectors, but we did not wish our children to board. There was no private boys' school in Leicester, and we wished our three children to be treated equally. The Loughborough Endowed Schools were a possibility, but few Leicester children went there at that time, so they would lack local friends. Hence, we settled for the state secondaries.

The schools in Leicester City were in the throes of reorganisation into the comprehensive system, so we looked beyond the city boundary. The schools in the county had already completed that change. We decided to aim to be in the catchment area for Beauchamp College in Oadby, as it was the best secondary school. We limited our search to within a three-mile radius from the LRI. It was a difficult market for buyers as prices were rising rapidly, and houses were being snapped up quickly. We paid a weekly visit on Thursdays but failed to find anything that met our objectives: attractive, five bedrooms, good garden and affordable (£14,000 maximum). Our attempt to purchase a house, at an agreed price of £14,500, collapsed when they asked an exorbitant sum for the carpets.

Time was running out, so we decided to buy a temporary house with a view to moving within a couple of years and chose one on a Wimpey estate in Launde Road, Oadby for £9,950. It had four bedrooms so the children could have one each but share if we had grandparents visiting. The two reception rooms had been combined to produce a long room with two fireplaces and the original garage had been converted into a room, which we proposed to use as a playroom. There was a tandem two-car garage and a small garden. Completion was just before I was due to start work on 1st September 1971.

It would have been difficult to manage with one car as I needed to get to Hinckley, do domiciliary visits and start private practice, so I cashed in my university superannuation to finance a second-hand Triumph 1300 to add to the old Triumph Herald.

We gave a supper party at home for our Sheffield consultants and junior colleagues, thereby pre-empting any other leaving event. My fortnight of accumulated leave was spent on holiday in Norfolk, taking the GP14 to Brancaster and then leaving it at Launde Road on the way home. On the day of the move, we each drove one car to Leicester. I felt very well prepared for my future as a consultant general surgeon but had no inkling of the amount of change that I would experience nor the additional activities in which I would become involved.

Just before moving I attended the celebration of the 200th anniversary of the founding of the Leicester Royal Infirmary, to which past registrars were invited. Contemporaries asked where I was working, and I was proud to tell them that I would be starting there as a consultant in just a few weeks.

CONSULTANTS IN
LEICESTER

15

STARTING LIFE AS A
CONSULTANT SURGEON

I took up my appointment as a consultant in general surgery at the Leicester Royal Infirmary on 1st September 1971, on a part-time contract of nine 'notional half days'. At the LRI I had a weekly outpatient session assisted by a registrar, plus a monthly cancer follow-up clinic. We shared the same large consulting room as when I was a registrar, sitting towards either end of a long table, with tiny cubicles for examination. There were two half-day operating lists at the LRI plus a monthly list in the genitourinary (GU) theatre, in which I did a variety of simple day cases.

Tuesdays were spent at Hinckley Hospital with an outpatient clinic in the morning, seeing an average of 35 patients, half 'new' and half 'old'. In the afternoon I had an operating list, comprising hernias, varicose veins and an occasional cholecystectomy. The remainder of the week comprised ward rounds and correspondence and allowed two sessions for private practice. I enquired about joining the Association of Surgeons of Great Britain and Ireland (ASGBI) but was advised to wait; I didn't then get around to joining until 1986.

Soon after I arrived, I started a weekly radiology conference at the end of Friday afternoon. Initially this comprised Dr Derek James, consultant radiologist, and my registrar, who regularly fell asleep during discussion. When further young consultants were appointed, they and their teams joined in, until there was barely standing room in Dr James's spacious office. Afterwards we adjourned to a nearby pub. This meeting continued until it was replaced by more specialised gastrointestinal and vascular sessions in the 1990s.

I was a truly general surgeon, doing gastrointestinal, breast and a little vascular surgery. There was no urological service but one consultant at the LRI and one at Leicester General Hospital (LGH) had an interest in urology, so patients for whom a transurethral resection was strongly indicated could be referred to one of them. My most common operation was retropubic prostatectomy, for patients who had been admitted as an emergency with acute retention of urine.

I was fortunate to be allocated two of the younger consultant anaesthetists whom I had known and liked when I was a registrar. One continued with me until he retired. I lost the other when I changed my theatre sessions to accommodate the plans of surgical colleagues when we moved into phase II. He was miffed – I could have handled it better.

NEONATAL SURGERY

When I arrived, I was surprised to learn that, because of John Leslie's transfer to LGH, I would also be responsible for the neonatal surgery. Fortunately, I had done a little in my registrar and SR posts and I managed safely, with judicious referral of difficult cases. I undertook operations for neonatal small bowel obstruction, pyloromyotomy for infantile pyloric stenosis, operative reduction of intussusception and nephrectomies for Wilms' tumour. Oesophageal atresia was managed by a cardiothoracic surgeon from Groby Road Hospital, and I referred other complex cases, such as imperforate anus or Hirschsprung's disease, to Great Ormond Street (GOS) in London.

On one memorable evening, I was just completing a small bowel anastomosis for neonatal obstruction when the lights failed. The emergency generator cut in within a few seconds, as expected, but then blew up. No torch could be found and I closed the abdomen by candlelight. It was later discovered that there was no regular testing of the generator, which had not run for many years. Another time I operated on a 'Wilms tumour', diagnosed by palpation of the lump (ultrasound had not yet arrived), only to find that it was a large hydronephrosis, with a grossly dilated ureter. I brought the latter out as a temporary ureterostomy and referred the baby to GOS for reimplantation of the ureter into the bladder.

THE SCOPE OF GENERAL SURGERY IN 1971

The range of general surgery was wide, unchanged from when I was a registrar. We were responsible for the surgical treatment of severe head injuries, elevating depressed fractures of the skull and performing craniotomies for suspected intracranial haematomas. The latter decision was based only on clinical evidence of raised intracranial pressure. We made up to four diagnostic burr holes, using a brace and bit. Often only diffuse brain swelling was found, but if a collection of blood was revealed, then a skull flap was raised to enable the haematoma to be evacuated and the source of the bleeding to be controlled. If the bleeding was from the middle meningeal artery, textbooks suggested plugging the foramen spinosum in the base of the skull with a matchstick to compress the artery, but I never actually did this. The results of this amateur neurosurgery were unimpressive; I can remember only one dramatic return of consciousness. In the others the brain injury followed its natural course, and the patient either gradually recovered consciousness, often with residual disability, or deteriorated and died.

After a year or two, the visiting neurosurgeon from Derby described 'a new machine' that could give a picture of the brain and any haematoma within the skull. I could not understand his account of how this was possible and only later found an explanation of computed tomography (CT), which was limited at that time to examination of the head. Shortly afterwards, head CT scanners were installed in all hospitals with a busy A&E department. This removed our dependence on unreliable clinical evidence for the diagnosis of intracranial bleeding. It provided a basis for selective transfer to the neurosurgical unit in Derby and avoided subjecting many patients with cerebral oedema to inappropriate burr holes.

The general surgeons were responsible for the initial management of burns, supported by the sole plastic surgeon from LGH, who did the necessary skin grafts. He also came across to repair the occasional shotgun wound of the face. In effect he was on call all the time.

I inherited a few patients whose colonic cancers had been considered inoperable when in fact they were resectable, with worthwhile results. I was determined not to develop a long waiting list and to this end maximised the use of compression sclerotherapy for varicose veins (which had previously been deputed to SHOs) and injection, and later banding, for piles. I offered transfer to the Hinckley list to patients with suitable conditions and increased the range of day cases (though not yet adult hernias or varicose veins). Based on

Ainslie Anderson's practice in Derby I wanted to do children's circumcisions and herniotomies as day cases. The genitourinary (GU) theatre was not being utilised when there was a fifth Monday in the month. By negotiation with the sister in charge and the anaesthetists, but without reference to the management, I was able to take this over for a regular children's list.

I also provided small procedures in support of colleagues in other specialties – lymph node biopsies, central venous access for haematological cancers, and sural nerve biopsies for the neurologists.

SURGICAL STAFFING

There were five consultants in general surgery at the LRI. John Bolton Carter and Ken Wood formed one firm; George Sawyer (who had just returned from LGH, swapping with John Leslie, hence the vacancy for neonatal surgery) and Gordon Smart were paired as another firm, while I was the odd man out. Each of these three firms had a registrar (who usually had the FRCS) so I had one to myself. The downside was that to equalise the number of nights on call for the registrars I was on take for emergencies twice as often as my colleagues – two nights in five during the week and one weekend in five. I don't think the others regarded this as unfair, as there was then little consultant involvement in the emergency work.

The single senior registrar (SR) was required to support the registrar on take every night, as he was when I was a registrar, so he was on call constantly. I considered this quite unreasonable and unilaterally decided that I would cover my registrar, resulting in an appreciable number of night and weekend calls. I am not sure that this arrangement was entirely to the SR's liking as he had been able to claim the maximum number of hours of the 'extra duty payments', which had been introduced while I was in Sheffield, though as a university employee I had not been eligible.

In 1973 Peter Bell joined us as foundation professor of surgery, initially sharing a firm with me, before moving temporarily to new accommodation at LGH. He returned when phase II opened in 1978. Michael Johnstone, who had been a medical house officer at the LRI when I was a registrar, arrived in 1975 to share a registrar with me. He had had adult training in Oxford as well as paediatric training at GOS. As a result, my days on call came down to one-in-six and I was relieved of neonatal responsibilities.

My first registrar was clinically and operatively very competent, but he had some attributes that were considered unusual at the time: he was divorced, a vegetarian and a Buddhist. As a result, he was an isolated figure, who played little part in the social life of the junior staff. He was interested in the mechanisms of injury to car occupants, before this became fashionable, but failed to produce data for a publication. In my enthusiasm as a new consultant, I tried hard to get him appointed as an SR on the Sheffield scheme, losing some credibility in the process. He went to work as a surgeon in the Seychelles, whence Terence D'Offay (see chapter 27) had emigrated from Leicester General Hospital a generation earlier.

NEW CYSTOSCOPES

I was soon given the job of hon sec to the general surgeons' monthly meeting. My first task was to arbitrate in a dispute about new cystoscopes for the GU theatre. Each surgeon had his own favourite design of traditional instrument. These were lit by a tiny electric lamp at the tip, which frequently failed. Paul Hickinbotham, based at LGH but using the GU theatre at the LRI, had donated one new cystoscope with the revolutionary Hopkins lens system. This had lenses of air separated by quartz rods, giving a much brighter image, while light was transmitted down a glass-fibre bundle from a reliable external source.

These advances were not available for the favoured antique designs of cystoscope, and I managed to persuade all the surgeons to accept modern fibre-lit Hopkins lens instruments. Professor Harold Hopkins, at Reading University, also invented the zoom lens and the fibre-optic bundles used in flexible endoscopes, though these technologies were then developed abroad. He never received due public recognition in the UK, on account of his left-wing sympathies, but he was twice nominated for the Nobel Prize.

DOMICILIARY VISITS

Another feature of consultant life was the 'domiciliary visit'. These had been instituted early in the NHS to offer patients a consultant opinion in their own homes. Each visit attracted a fee and for consultants in specialties such as geriatrics these could provide substantial supplementary income. The intention was that the GP and the specialist should meet at the patient's home but, in my experience, it was difficult to find a mutually acceptable time, so I usually went alone, achieving a joint visit in less than 10 per cent of cases.

I collected data on domiciliary visits from 1972 to 1979, averaging 23 per year. Twenty-two per cent of patients were admitted as emergencies and a further seven per cent joined the waiting list. For a sizeable minority, I agreed a diagnosis of inoperable malignancy (often metastases in the liver), a decision then accepted by the patient and the family. In the 21st century it would have been necessary to prove this diagnosis by investigation. A few visits were prompted by the patient having declined the GP's advice regarding the need for emergency admission or an outpatient consultation; sometimes the patient agreed when I confirmed this, but not always. Over subsequent years there were fewer requests for these visits. I do not have data to quantify this, but for surgeons they had virtually ceased by the 1990s.

TRAINING FOR ICU NURSES

Soon after my arrival, I was asked by one of the assistant matrons to organise a new course in intensive care nursing. The Joint Board of Clinical Nursing Studies (JBCNS) was responsible nationally for the approval of a range of post-SRN training courses, of which this would be the first in Leicester. I would have expected an anaesthetist to do this job, but I suspect the consultant then in charge of the ICU had declined. Having been involved in the opening of units in Leicester in 1963 and in Derby in 1965 I thought I could do it.

With the cooperation of medical and nursing colleagues we produced a six-month programme of experience in the ICU with some attachments to other acute units in Leicester. Lectures were arranged in four week-long study blocks and six separate study days. The course ended with a written exam and a viva. A nurse tutor was appointed, the course was approved by the visitor from the JBCNS and launched with six participants. I gave a few of the lectures myself and recruited speakers for the rest. The LRI went on in 1975 to set up JBCNS courses in A&E and theatre nursing, for each of which I helped as an adviser.

OPERATING DEPARTMENT ASSISTANTS

Then in 1973, there was a national decision to re-grade theatre technicians as 'operating department assistants' (ODAs). The technicians, many of them former NCOs in the RAMC, had had no formal training in the NHS but had acquired the necessary skills on the job. They worked almost exclusively with the anaesthetists. Also, it was proving difficult to attract enough nurses to work in operating theatres, so the policy was to extend the scope of ODAs to include working as both 'runners' and scrubbed assistants.

The management of the LRI asked my anaesthetist colleague Dr Donald Turner and me (probably because of my work with the post-SRN courses) to consider the re-grading of the existing technicians, and to establish a City & Guilds training course for any who were considered to need this and for new entrants. We worked out a two-year programme of varied theatre experience around the Leicester hospitals, with full-time study blocks included.

The Regional Health Authority (RHA) agreed funding in 1975, but the first interviews to appoint a tutor did not yield a suitable candidate. Then the matron of the LRI suggested a very experienced staff nurse from one of the surgical wards. Kate Pittom was married and so, according to the rules at the LRI at that time, could not be a ward sister, but she was widely respected. After further advertisement she was duly appointed and ran the scheme very successfully for about 15 years until retirement.

In addition to one of the existing technicians, we attracted nine candidates by advertisement, including some from the Derby hospitals which had joined the scheme, bringing access to their neurosurgical unit. This new group of trainees was readily accepted by staff at the LRI and in the cardiothoracic unit at Groby Road Hospital. However, the nurses and some medical staff at LGH were initially resistant to their arrival; a visit to discuss the role of the trainees resulted in them being accepted.

In November 1977 I presented certificates to the first group of ODA trainees to qualify. This coincided with the opening of 12 new theatres at the LRI, ensuring that they all found jobs. They tended to specialise either in anaesthetic or surgical work, the latter including being the scrubbed assistant for major operations. I think it would have been difficult to staff the increased number of theatres without the output from this training scheme.

Some of these ODAs progressed to senior roles: one managed the cardiac theatres at Glenfield Hospital; another became responsible for all equipment and ordering of drugs for the suite of 16 theatres at the LRI. In the 1990s the management of the LRI theatres decided to merge the nursing and ODA staff, with the result that either could have charge of a theatre; my theatre was then run very satisfactorily for the remainder of my career by a senior ODA.

Colleagues from other cities often held negative views about ODAs being involved in surgical work. I suggested that they should visit the LRI and try to identify which of our theatre staff were nurses and which were ODAs, but no one took up the challenge. A grade of senior ODA (SODA) was introduced and later ODAs were redesignated as operating department practitioners (ODPs). In the 2000s, the training became a university degree course.

Thus, in my early years as a consultant I had a most varied case mix, including neonatal surgery and basic urology. Unexpectedly, I also found myself involved in setting up training schemes for other professions. This was before the opening of the medical school, which I had thought would be the main teaching challenge.

16

THE GABLES

Once we had settled into Launde Road, we began the search for a definitive house. Scanning the *Leicester Mercury* and scouring the estate agents yielded nothing that we fancied. Then, in September 1972, The Gables, 8 Knighton Rise, Oadby, was offered one Saturday morning. The dowager Mrs Bolton Carter, mother of my senior colleague John Bolton Carter, had moved there after her husband Felix (a former surgeon at the LRI) died, 'because she wanted a smaller house'. She had died earlier in the year.

We arranged to view it that afternoon and were received by a manservant, Thorpe, who had been Felix Bolton Carter's batman in the 1914–18 war. He was clearly not happy about the prospect of 'his' house being sold. Despite this unwelcoming reception, we were taken with the six-bedroomed Edwardian house, garden and situation and decided to try to purchase it. The house required rewiring, replumbing, a new central heating system and some minor building alterations.

Our solicitor recommended that we should use an estate agent for the negotiations; the agent also provided advice about the necessary works, which he suggested might cost about £5,000. A mortgage, backed by an endowment policy, was arranged with the Hinckley and Country Building Society, chosen because one of the directors had been a patient of mine. This provided 75 per cent of the valuation of £32,000, subject to retention of

£5,000 until the improvements had been completed. We made an opening bid of £24,000, instantly topped by another prospective purchaser. Over the next few days, the bidding went up in £200 steps. Then the selling agents decided that the matter should be settled at a private auction on a Saturday morning, when we happened to be visiting my parents in Wrexham. After a nail-biting few hours, we received a phone call from our agent to say that we had won, with a bid of £27,800, just short of our limit of £28,000. I was glad that we had employed a professional negotiator. Much later we learned that the other bidder at the auction was the incoming professor of anatomy. He bought a nice house in nearby Knighton Grange Road and bore us no ill will. One night I awoke worrying that we had overreached ourselves but was reassured by Elisabeth.

Our house in Launde Road was put on the market at £15,000, having cost us £10,000 16 months earlier. The only serious bidders were Arthur and Jane Moelwyn-Hughes, both of whose fathers were managers for Barclays in North Wales and well known to my father! The agent suggested that closed bids be invited. The Moelwyn-Hughes' offer was the only one, but it met our asking price. Jane was a theatre nurse and I arranged for her to see the matron of the Fielding Johnson Private Hospital, where she was given a job in the theatre.

MODERNISATION

There was a lot of work to be done. The servants' end of the house was delineated by green baize doors, which we removed. None of the rooms in that part of the house had windows overlooking the back garden and we wanted to insert one at the back of the kitchen. This required the demolition of a lean-to extension behind the original kitchen, comprising a kitchenette and a boiler house. The central heating used bulky fin radiators, convection driven through two-inch pipes, without a pump. It needed complete replacement, and all the plumbing had to be redone. Likewise, the house required rewiring; there were traces of three previous systems and pipes for the original gas lighting.

To brighten up the gloomy lounge hall we replaced the small window and door with a picture window overlooking the back garden. Part of bedroom three was sacrificed to create a second bathroom; we chose not to make this en suite to give greater flexibility in use. Of the 12 coal fires, we retained only the one in the sitting room, though we later regretted scrapping a fine wooden surround in the dining room. The servants' stairs were closed off to provide more space for kitchen units, although we could only afford to install half of these initially. My father had urged us to have undercover access to the garage and in preparation a doorway was made at that end of the hall. The cost of all these changes swallowed up our budget, so conversion of the single garage to double was deferred.

MOVING IN

John B-C very kindly allowed work to start before we completed purchase. We could not afford a bridging loan so in February 1973 we had to move in, before redecorating, for which we employed the cheapest decorator we could find. We camped in a few rooms while work proceeded in others. Meanwhile, Elisabeth was revising for the final Fellowship of the Faculty of Radiologists (FFR) exam. We had no furniture for the large sitting room, so the children roller-skated on the bare boards. One night, when the hall was still full of tea chests, I was woken by the doorbell. I went downstairs to be faced by a police constable. I thought it must have looked as though we were squatters, but in fact he had been sent to contact me by the surgical registrar on duty, as the phone was out of order.

We had thought that the allocation of bedrooms might be contentious, but in the event each child made a different choice: Andrew opted for the smallest, bedroom number two; Sally quirky number four and Clare bedroom three, which seemed to us the nicest room. Bedroom five was used for Andrew to create a large '00' gauge railway and bedroom six became a guest room. Gradually the house came together: the second tranche of kitchen units was delivered, and I installed them. The sitting room was furnished, ending the roller skating. I laid carpets upstairs, refashioning the ones from Launde Road, some of which originated in Sheffield.

A couple of years later, when we had the funds, the garage was rebuilt. It was originally one-and-a-half cars wide and one-and-a-half cars long but the back third was occupied by a concrete air raid shelter which had to be demolished. It was widened to take two cars and extended forwards to align it with the approach door in the hall, so that the linking structure could be added later. However, we decided that this was not necessary and preferred to retain outside access to the rear garden. For economy, the previous pitched garage roof was replaced with a flat one.

Once the sitting room was furnished, we noticed a dreadful smell of drains. Excavation showed that the kitchen waste (which had not been altered during our building works) was connected to a rainwater soakaway which also drained a gulley close to a ventilator under the sitting room floor. This required an additional chamber to connect the kitchen drain to the nearby foul drain, and that solved the problem.

THE GARDEN

I was glad to have a large garden, but it needed rearranging. The plot was tidy but dull, so gradually we modified it. A decrepit front fence was removed resulting in an open front garden, partially shielded by a row of silver birches along the boundary. We removed the single field gate and widened the entrance. On the east side of this was a large poplar and one day a couple appeared at our front door, shaking after a huge branch had fallen just in front of their car. Fortunately, they were not injured; we had the tree felled forthwith. Unwisely, we replaced it with an *x Cuprocyparis leylandii,* which rapidly grew to an enormous size. The worn-out rose beds and crazy paving in the front garden were swapped for curved borders and a lawn.

The west boundary was a privet hedge about nine feet high – difficult to cut even from a stepladder. The house on that side had been split into two flats. When the owner who lived in one of them died, it failed to find a buyer for a few years, becoming derelict. This enabled me to work from both sides of the hedge, to reduce its height. When the house was finally sold it was demolished, and a Leicester City footballer had a modern house built, with a large indoor swimming pool flanking our back garden. He agreed that the hedge dividing our front gardens could be removed and we jointly filled the bed with trees and shrubs.

The south-facing back garden had a large lawn on two levels, with a narrow border along each side, furnished with decaying poplars. Beyond this there were two clumps of conifers and a vegetable garden containing a few elderly apple trees and a huge pear tree. Too close to the south-east corner of the house was a large poplar which we dared not fell for fear of subsidence, so it was pollarded every few years. All but two of the apple trees were removed and I brought the vegetable garden into production. I created an asparagus bed and built a large fruit cage for raspberries and blackcurrants. The poplars along the borders were gradually felled and replaced with more interesting trees and shrubs.

Much later, in the year of our silver wedding, we modified the rectangular lawn by excavating a pond on the upper lawn. The area in front of the pond became a shaped bed, and behind it was a waterfall. The excavation and the installation of electricity for a pump could not have been achieved without Andrew's hard work. The vegetable garden was larger than we needed, so the front third was converted to an herbaceous border, separated from the vegetables by a *Lonicera* hedge.

MAINTENANCE

Over the following 30 years the house was slightly modified and various repairs were needed. I recruited a single-handed decorator, who had been admitted under my care with rib fractures after falling from a ladder. He served us very well for over 30 years, doing one room or redecorating half of the exterior each year and gradually bringing it up to standard. He made useful suggestions, such as removing hardboard panels to reveal the original Voysey-style bannisters and was happy to do minor plastering or carpentry jobs.

After we had been in the house for about eight years, we noticed water collecting on the windowsill in the playroom. An architect friend jabbed his penknife into the wooden mullion and water spouted out! The beam supporting the roof over the loggia had rotted due to leakage from the gutter and the rot had extended into the adjacent window frame. The roof of the loggia had to be supported while the timber was replaced. Then in 1987 we decided to make better use of the void where the servants' stairs had been, creating a large wardrobe off bedroom six and at the same time putting a window in the end wall.

In 1994, we had the kitchen redesigned and refitted to a traditional but more stylish design. This provided better seating for three or four people, and we subsequently used it for most meals, using the dining room only for weekend lunches or visitors.

We also had problems with damp. Like most houses of this age, ours did not have a proper damp course, just a layer of blue bricks. Damp first occurred in 1989 in the lounge hall, requiring an injection damp course and replastering to three feet. Then in 1999 damp affecting a corner of the dining room led to the discovery of wet rot in the floor timbers. Again, the wall was injected and replastered and the floor was rebuilt. I took the opportunity to do some rewiring (I was by then working only six sessions). I moved the power points from the skirting board to 15 inches up the walls and rearranged the wall lights. The bathrooms had been equipped as economically as possible when we moved in and looked dated. In 1999, we had these refitted and the downstairs cloakroom modernised.

Notwithstanding the various maintenance problems, The Gables was our much-loved family home for 42 years. We carried out some modifications after we retired and only decided to downsize when I was nearing 80 and the large garden began to feel burdensome.

17

PRIVATE PRACTICE

My priority was always the NHS. Nevertheless, there were two reasons for doing some private practice: the additional income was welcome and there was also a feeling among colleagues that a surgeon not doing private work was second class. I therefore opted for what was known as a 'nine-elevenths' contract. This permitted two half-day sessions per week to be devoted to the private sector, with a proportionate abatement of salary. The denominator of 11 sessions was a hangover from the days when Saturday morning formed part of the standard working week.

FACILITIES

I was fortunate to be offered consulting facilities at 23 De Montfort Street, filling the slot vacated by Donald McGavin, my predecessor. This was the most prestigious set of rooms in Leicester, accommodating five partners and about eight tenants such as me. There was one other house, in Princess Road, which ran on similar lines but was owned by one of the consultants and closed when he retired. There were also limited consulting facilities at the Leicester Clinic. Some consultants saw private patients at home, but I certainly did not wish to do so: I preferred to keep work and family life separate.

The private beds were a motley collection. The Fielding Johnson Private Hospital near the LRI was managed by the NHS, with minor waiting list surgery on the top floor. The St Francis Nursing home, on the London Road and on my way home, was run by nuns. The Leicester Clinic on Scraptoft Lane had opened in 1969 as part of the Nuffield Provincial Hospitals Trust; being on the east side of the city it entailed an additional journey.

The Fielding Johnson had a single antiquated operating theatre. Ken Wood used a swab on a stick to write 'this wall is dirty' high up and the letters remained for years. The St Francis was old fashioned. Admissions were arranged with the Mother Superior, who had bad knees, so bookings were often made in her bedroom. For theatre, one rolled up one's shirt sleeves and then scrubbed up, still wearing one's ordinary trousers. Both the latter hospitals lay on my route between home and the LRI, so I tended to favour them unless the patient preferred the Leicester Clinic.

DEVELOPING A PRACTICE

I started seeing private patients in January 1972. Initially, referrals came from two main sources: the Hinckley GPs and via the secretaries at De Montfort Street, who diverted impatient patients if the consultant to whom they had been referred was overbooked. Gradually I began to get referrals from other doctors. Many of the patients were not insured and used a private consultation to avoid the wait for an outpatient appointment, but then opted for any investigations or operations under the NHS.

Investigations were an awkward issue. The senior pathologist (one of the partners) would take blood samples at De Montfort Street, have them processed in the lab at the LRI and charge the patient for the consultation. No fee accrued to the NHS. Alternatively, I could take the blood and hand it in at the Infirmary, marking my secretary as the 'ward or department'. There was no mechanism by which I could get these investigations done at cost. Radiologists in private practice would arrange plain films and do contrast examinations, such as barium meals. They provided reports, but to view the films it was necessary to visit the Fielding Johnson or the Leicester Clinic where the examination had been done. Uninsured patients often expected to avoid the fee by having X-rays done in the NHS. Strictly they should then have been seen with the result in outpatients, but it was widespread practice to bring them back to the consulting rooms. Those who then opted for an operation in the NHS often expected priority; I minimised this pressure by keeping my waiting list short.

Colleagues had suggested that in general surgery it would be easy to duplicate my NHS earnings in the private sector. Analysis of my accounts shows that I never achieved gross private earnings of more than 85 per cent of NHS pay in the 1970s, falling to about 55 per cent in the 1980s. After 1990, the figure fell to 27 per cent, as merit awards boosted my NHS income and national surgical affairs began to take up much of my time. This may seem a mediocre performance in private practice, but I refused to let consulting expand beyond my one session, both to give appropriate priority to NHS work and to preserve time for home life.

PARTNER AT DE MONTFORT STREET

When the pathologist retired in 1978, I was promoted to be a partner in 23 De Montfort Street. This entitled me to have half a consulting session free of the service charge, but as this only applied to sessions exceeding one per week, I gained no financial benefit. I also continued to use the tenants' room, as the larger rooms were not free for the session when I was consulting and I didn't want to rearrange my timetable. I upgraded the furnishings and had a curtain rail installed around the examination couch. Only when Ken Wood retired did I graduate to a partner's room; again, I had to have a curtain fitted.

Socialists have often accused private practice of damaging the NHS, but the relationship is more complex. Of course, it was nice to have more time to talk to the patient, but if one is uncomfortable about differing standards of care then the solution is to endeavour to behave with NHS patients as one would 'in private'. A reputation for diligent care in the NHS must surely encourage GPs to make their private referrals to that consultant.

Later the rules were changed so that any consultant could have private practice earnings of up to 10 per cent of NHS income, without forfeiting one-eleventh of their NHS pay. As a result, several additional anaesthetists became available for private cases, and I noticed another effect. Some of them had been notorious for deferring patients on NHS operating lists for trivial medical reasons, to the great irritation of their surgeons. Once they were seeking private work this behaviour ceased.

NEW FACILITIES

In 1983 a meeting at the Leicestershire Club discussed a proposal to establish a new private hospital in Leicester but this came to nothing. Subsequently in 1989, BUPA opened a new hospital in Oadby, much nearer to home than the Leicester Clinic. The private beds at the Fielding Johnson Hospital were closed and the NHS sold the building. The BUPA Hospital[12] included a generous number of consulting rooms and was keen to attract the consultants from 23 De Montfort Street.

The five partners chose to stay put, but our tenants moved to the BUPA Hospital. Then in 1991, when two of the five had retired, we realised that it was not sensible to continue. I moved to the BUPA hospital (consulting there from 1st January 1992) and the other two joined the Leicester Clinic. The house was sold in 1992, for about £170,000 and the proceeds accrued to the five partners. As a memento of a very genial working environment, I purchased the antique Pembroke table that had stood in the hall.

Several of our former tenants considered that they were entitled to participate in the payout and took legal action to achieve this. However, after several exchanges of solicitors' letters they agreed to abandon their claim, provided we paid our own costs, to which we agreed. I let it be known that I was giving my windfall to support surgical activities, trusting that this would satisfy the critics. Half of the money went to provide a CUSA device for liver surgery at the LRI and half to support the development of a computerised system for trainee surgeons' operative logbooks nationally.

Consulting at BUPA had advantages: I concentrated my private operating there, which minimised travelling and it was easy to call back from home in the evening. Blood samples were taken by the nurses and analysed by the on-site lab; plain X-ray films were available immediately and the films from contrast examinations were to hand. My secretary from De Montfort Street moved with me, also working for other consultants, so the transition was seamless. With hindsight, we should have closed '23' sooner.

EXIT STRATEGY

Entering the 1990s, I was spending more time with national surgical organisations (see chapters 31 to 35), so I needed to reduce my commitments in Leicester. I decided that the easiest activity to cut was private practice, so I stopped seeing new private patients in 1993. The long-term follow-up work could then be contained in fewer consulting sessions and there was little operating apart from some follow-up colonoscopies. Finally in 1999, I withdrew from private practice altogether, passing on the remaining patients to colleagues. Private work had been of great financial assistance in the earlier

12   Now Spire Hospital.

years, enabling us to buy a lovely house, but as our combined NHS earnings increased (with merit awards) the additional income became unnecessary. Contributions made from private practice did provide a useful addition to my NHS pension.

18

BUILDING HOSPITALS

In 1962 Enoch Powell, as minister of health, launched a 10-year programme to rebuild the district general hospitals (DGHs). By 1970 some had been completed, for example Doncaster Royal Infirmary in 1968. However, no wards were built in Leicester until 1970, despite a plan – devised before the Second World War – to enlarge the LRI.

Founded in 1771, the original building was still in use in 1971, extended with three blocks, each of three Nightingale wards, plus a children's hospital, providing a total of about 550 beds. Four operating theatres had been built over the original casualty department and pathology laboratories were added over one ward block. A new casualty department and radiology facilities had been provided in 1958. Terraced housing was demolished to the west of the Infirmary to clear the site for the next phases. In 1970 a 144-bed maternity unit (phase I) was added to the north of the casualty block, replacing Bond Street Maternity Hospital, where Sally was born, which had occupied a row of converted terraced houses.

Besides the Infirmary, there was Leicester General Hospital (LGH), built by the city council in 1905 and Groby Road Hospital, built for infectious diseases in 1899, but now also providing cardiothoracic surgery. There were two large psychiatric hospitals, one for the city and one for the county. The original 'lunatic asylum' had become the first building of the University College in 1921. All these facilities served Leicestershire and Rutland, a total population of about 760,000.

In addition, there were small hospitals in the market towns, some originating as workhouses, others created by public subscription for Queen Victoria's Diamond Jubilee or as First World War memorials. As a result, Hinkley, Market Harborough, Melton Mowbray and Oakham each had *two* small hospitals though their populations were each only 15–50,000. These were supervised by local GPs, with outpatient and operating sessions by consultants visiting from Leicester. Loughborough, with a catchment of about 100,000, had a larger hospital (built in 1862) with a few junior doctors.

In 1970 Mrs Thatcher, as minister of education, announced the decision to site the third of the new medical schools in Leicester. It was believed that this decision aimed to kill two birds with one stone: the hospital development necessary for the medical school would also correct the historical underfunding of health services in the county, which stood at 70 per cent of the national average per capita.

LRI PROJECT GROUP

In 1974 there was a vacancy on the Project Group responsible for the redevelopment of the LRI. This chimed with my past idea of becoming an architect, so I put my name forward. I don't think anyone else wanted to do it, so I was appointed. The group of about 25, involving managers, architects and two hospital consultants, met quarterly to review the work of the smaller project team at the Sheffield Regional Hospital Board (RHB)[13]. It was an unwieldy body with limited influence. The architects were a large local firm, Pick, Everard, Keay and Gimson, which had been responsible for work at the LRI since 1899. Their original suggestion had been to construct a single 13-storey tower block, but the city council had ruled that it must be limited to six floors, plus a basement.

The site, resulting from slum clearance, was being used for staff parking, so as a preliminary a multi-storey car park was built. Many consultants argued that they should each have a designated space, but this would have been wasteful as most of them had sessions elsewhere, so the idea was overruled. There was no provision for patients to park on site.

By the time I joined the group, planning of phase II, a surgical block of about 500 beds had been completed. It had a three-storey podium, providing

---

13   The RHB became the Regional Health Authority (RHA) under the 1974 reorganisation.

outpatient clinics, 16 operating theatres (four to be mothballed pending building of the next phase), ICU, coronary care unit (CCU) and A&E. These were surmounted by a four-storey 'H'-shaped ward block with four wards on each level. The wards in the old building had been named after benefactors and one former matron, but those in the new maternity block were numbered one to six. The wards in phase II were therefore numbered seven to 22, 13 being omitted and the space used for the burns unit. The result was a total on the site of 1,050 beds. There was generous provision for teaching and research, with four seminar rooms and two research laboratories on each ward floor. No offices were planned for medical secretaries, so when the building was occupied seminar rooms were taken over for them.

Her Majesty Queen Elizabeth II opened phase II in 1979. As the time to occupy these excellent facilities approached, many surgeons expressed doubts about the move, questioning whether the 12 theatres could be staffed, but in the event the change went very smoothly.

The physicians were disappointed that, while the surgical specialties enjoyed new inpatient facilities in phase II, they were left in the old Nightingale wards. After pressure from the dean, the RHA agreed to upgrade the old wards, though this programme was never completed. The number of children's surgical beds in phase II was found to be over-generous, so medical paediatrics was able to move from the old Children's Hospital into two wards in phase II in 1982. The old Children's Hospital was then demolished.

The Project Group next had to plan the later phases. Phase III was for the area pathology service. Phase IV was to accommodate the remaining specialties from the old building, except for radiotherapy which was to have a new unit at Glenfield. A freestanding mental illness unit was proposed for the LRI site, but this plan was later abandoned.

DEVELOPMENTS AT LGH

Meanwhile, there had been piecemeal development at LGH. Four wards, ICU, CCU and two theatres were built from the 'Harness' portfolio of plans. That system offered standardised plans for wards, operating theatres and other departments, which could be joined together in the required proportions to fit a hospital site, reducing the cost of planning. A new block of six wards was constructed for geriatric medicine, to coincide with the closure of Hillcrest, the old workhouse hospital.

Later there was some upgrading of the Nightingale wards and the serial addition of more operating theatres and outpatient facilities. Finally, in the 1990s on Elisabeth's initiative, the LGH Trust built a new radiology department to replace the adapted and extended ward. These improvements were most welcome, but LGH never had a comprehensive plan for redevelopment of the site.

GLENFIELD HOSPITAL

Leicestershire needed more beds. There had been a plan to build a DGH in Loughborough, but the arrival of the medical school dictated that it should be in Leicester. In 1974 the decision was taken to build Glenfield Hospital, in the grounds of a former hospital for the mentally handicapped (as they were then called). The consultant staff would have preferred expansion on the two existing acute sites, but the Department of Health (DoH) had recently ruled that no teaching hospital should exceed 800 beds, so it was a third hospital or no expansion. This policy may have been influenced by dissatisfaction with the legacy of huge mental hospitals, which were by then being wound down. Twenty years later, as junior doctors' hours were reduced, the need to cover three acute sites caused much difficulty.

I was asked by the management to become one of the two consultant members of the Glenfield Project Group. The plans went through many stages: there was to be one 800-bedded phase the shape of an ocean liner; it was to be built in several phases; the design was to be according to the 'Harness' system (as described for LGH). No, this would not be satisfactory, but the design should nevertheless follow 'harness principles'. After all that discussion, phase I was to comprise 80 general medical beds and 120 surgical beds, which the planners assumed would all be for general surgery. In the event, on the recommendation of the Bed Allocation Committee (see chapter 28), general surgery was reduced to 60, an orthopaedic ward was provided, and a ward was added to the medical allocation.

Glenfield Phase I was completed in 1984, consultant staff were appointed, and I bowed out of the Project Group. The plan for later phases included the transfer of cardiology and cardiothoracic surgery from the nearby Groby Road Hospital and a maternity unit, the third in Leicester. But by the time building of phase II was about to start the latter was not needed. The space was adapted for cardiothoracic surgery, at considerable expense.

COMPLETING THE PLANNED DEVELOPMENTS AT LRI

Phase IV of the LRI was finally completed in 1992. Offices for the medical consultants and their secretaries had originally been planned for the same floors as their wards but were removed to reduce the size of the building and control the cost. The secretaries were then to be accommodated in an area on level two. However, by the time building was in progress that space was needed for the growing GI endoscopy service. Later, single rooms on some medical wards were cannibalised for offices!

The ICU in phase II had eight beds, approximating to one per cent of total beds, as then recommended in the DoH guidelines. Adjacent was an eight-bedded coronary care unit (CCU), far from the medical wards. The ICU provision proved inadequate, so a small high-dependency unit was converted from a seminar room. In the 1990s more high-dependency facilities were required, particularly to care for patients after very major surgery. A ward in phase IV was turned into a CCU, freeing the old unit to provide eight high-dependency beds.

The birth rate was falling at that time so there was room to move gynaecology into the maternity block. The ward released was converted to provide beds for ophthalmology. Ophthalmic theatres were created in the adjacent vacant ward, previously occupied by general surgery, but empty since the surgical allocation had been reduced for financial reasons. The 'temporary' building put up in 1918 and used for about 70 years for ophthalmology could at last be demolished.

Radiotherapy gradually changed its name to oncology as its staff were increasingly involved in chemotherapy. It had occupied the ground floor and basement of the 1771 building. The plan had been for it to move to new accommodation at Glenfield – an ideal arrangement as it is one of the few specialties that does not need to be represented on the A&E site. However, in the 1990s, the linear accelerator (the most powerful radiotherapy machine) failed, needing to be replaced urgently by two new ones. This precipitated the requirement for new accommodation for the oncology department. I suggested that this was the opportunity to move it to Glenfield, as originally planned, but the oncologists resisted this idea. The LRI Trust, enjoying its independence and competing with the other sites, built a new block beside the pathology departments, to include clinical haematology as well as oncology with its heavy equipment. This was just one example of the way the existence of three trusts could prevent proper strategic planning of major developments.

LATER CHANGES IN LEICESTER'S HOSPITALS

In 1997 an acute services review, attended by management and senior consultants, was asked to consider reconfiguration of the hospitals. This was prompted by a projected shortfall in revenue and the difficulty of maintaining cover on three sites, while complying with the New Deal on junior doctors' hours and the European Working Time Directive[14]. There was unanimous agreement that there should be two acute sites. One should be the LRI because it had the A&E unit, but there was no consensus as to which of the other hospitals should be reduced to a supporting role.

Following the amalgamation of the three separate hospital trusts into the University Hospitals of Leicester NHS Trust in 2000, just before I retired, an ambitious scheme was developed to concentrate acute activity at the LRI and Glenfield, with Leicester General Hospital having a lower profile, without out-of-hours medical staff. This was the Pathway Project, the planned cost of which gradually escalated from £350m to £760m and then to £910m, at which point it was abandoned. Meanwhile the Leicester Hospitals had suffered from planning blight.

This two-plus-one configuration would have involved the transfer of several specialties between sites. Their 'price' for agreeing was bigger and better facilities, which doubtless accounted for much of the increase in capital cost. The aborted project was acknowledged to have incurred £60m in planning costs. Some of us had said at the outset that the project was undeliverable, but we were ignored. From 2014 onwards, a modified two-plus-one option was again being considered.

The history of hospital development in Leicester exemplifies the difficulties resulting from a prolonged planning process. By the time building starts the requirements have changed; the only solution is for the design to be flexible enough to allow changes in the use of the facilities. A fundamental issue affecting Leicester was the arbitrary national policy limiting the size of hospitals, producing three rather than two and resulting in difficulties in junior staff cover as working hours were brought under control.

---

14   See chapter 29 on the limitation of juniors' hours

19

SURGICAL FACILITIES

W hen I returned to the LRI as a consultant in 1971, I found that little had changed since I was a registrar in 1962-4. Subsequently, with the opening of the phase II development in 1979, our beds transferred to modern wards, though over the following 15 years there was a gradual decrease in the number of beds for general surgery. In contrast, the number of operating theatres increased dramatically, and this improvement was sustained. By the 1990s these beds and theatres were shared by a growing number of consultants.

BEDS FOR ADULT PATIENTS

From 1971 to 1979 general surgery occupied four Nightingale wards, each containing 36-40 beds. Two wards, one for each sex, were designated for emergency admissions; the others plus a small ward of 12 beds were intended for elective cases, though the emergencies often overflowed. Extra beds could no longer be set up to cope with demand as had been the policy in 1962. Prior to the founding of the NHS the emergency wards were known as the house surgeons' wards, and etiquette put them out of bounds for the consultants! In mitigation, the house surgeons at that time commonly had the FRCS.

Before the opening of phase II, general surgery had about 160 beds. We were allocated four wards, each of 30 beds, in the new block and retained 40 beds in one of the old wards, again a total of 160. The new wards each had four six-bedded bays and six single rooms and so were suitable for dual sex occupancy. After negotiation with the nursing management, this arrangement was agreed, with two bays for each sex and the single rooms available to adjust for variation in the exact numbers. The great advantage from our point of view was that the patients of each of the four firms (each of two consultants) could be concentrated in one ward, which facilitated supervision.

Progressively over the next decade, our residual beds in the old building were transferred to other uses. The four wards in phase II were retained when Glenfield phase I opened in 1984, even though the number of firms had reduced from four to three. Then a budgetary crisis resulted in the closure of one ward, reducing the total to 90 beds. This caused great anguish – consultants regarded their beds as status symbols. However, by reducing lengths of stay we coped well. Nevertheless, we hoped that the missing ward would reopen but this possibility was finally lost when it was converted into ophthalmic theatres.

In summary, we went from 160 beds for eight consultants in 1979 to 90 beds for 10 consultants by 1999.

OPERATING THEATRES

The old hospital had three main operating theatres for general surgery and gynaecology. One smaller theatre was used only for ENT. There were separate facilities for orthopaedics and ophthalmology. The instruments were sterilised by boiling, within the theatre. If it got too hot the windows were opened. There was no recovery space; patients went straight back to the wards.

Phase II had 12 air-conditioned theatres, with the shells of four more to come into use when phase IV was built. The instruments were autoclaved in trays in the adjacent theatre sterile supplies unit. There was a large recovery area staffed by nurses and supplied with ventilators for use if needed. Two coffee rooms were provided, originally designated for doctors and nurses; but this was later changed to non-smoking and smoking for both professions, though the smoking room was mainly used by nurses.

The increased number of theatres had to accommodate orthopaedics and plastic surgery and two were designated for day cases. Gynaecology remained in the old building until phase IV was in use. The number of theatre sessions for the general surgeons was more than doubled, so twin theatre lists became possible, enabling an SR or registrar to operate in parallel with the consultant. Though this sometimes resulted in inadequate supervision, it was mostly satisfactory, given the experience of the juniors in the 1980s. There was still no designated daytime emergency theatre, a facility that was not even considered until the 1990s.

OUTPATIENT CLINICS

The outpatient department in the old hospital was primitive, comprising a large central waiting area and half a dozen consulting suites, one of which was for general surgery. The consultant and a registrar shared a long table, with a patient at each end; the cubicles were just large enough for an examination couch. This set-up had not changed since I was a registrar.

The outpatient suites for general surgery in phase II were palatial. Two surgical consultants' teams, each of up to four members, could work simultaneously, everyone having a consulting room with an examination room on either side. Each clinic had its own waiting area and receptionist's station.

DAY-CASE UNIT

A day surgery unit had been built in 1958 specifically for urology, then part of general surgery. Cystoscopies predominated, but the single theatre was also used by SHOs to remove superficial lesions such as lipomas and sebaceous cysts. There were a dozen cubicles with trolleys on which patients awaited their turn and recovered postoperatively. An on-site secretary managed the waiting list efficiently.

A generous day-case facility was provided in phase II. A 30-bedded ward communicated across a corridor with a pair of theatres at the end of the central operating department, permitting a rapid turnaround. Again, there were clerks to maintain the waiting lists and organise the operating sessions under the supervision of the theatre sister. Most patients were present for only half the day so there was spare capacity, which was promptly taken up for haematology. Later, when the latter moved to new facilities, a third theatre was created from a disused plant room adjacent to the other two. All the beds were then used for surgical patients – mostly general surgery and gynaecology, as other surgical specialties were reluctant to have separate day-case lists.

SECRETARIAL SUPPORT

When I was a registrar from 1962–4 the medical secretaries were managed as a 'pool', though in practice each consultant usually dictated to the same secretary. Letters were dictated face-to-face and taken down in shorthand. By 1971 the secretaries were in twos and threes in a series of small rooms on the main corridor (formerly overnight bedrooms for junior staff). Each consultant and his juniors now shared a personal secretary. Some consultants still dictated to a secretary while others used a Dictaphone. I wanted to be able to dictate letters during ward rounds. In 1973, at the suggestion of my registrar, I introduced a hand-held tape recorder, a technology which gradually spread around the hospital.

Each ward floor in phase II had five small offices which were shared among the consultants and a nursing officer. One seminar room on the general surgical floor was utilised for our medical secretaries and we found this a very convenient arrangement. Inpatient waiting lists continued to be run from a central office, though I think management within each surgical specialty would have been more efficient. When the LRI gained trust status in 1991 many of the arrangements for outpatients were modified (see chapter 28).

RESIDENT DOCTORS

In the 1970s the house officers were resident; each had their own bedroom though they were only required to be in the hospital when on duty. Most chose not to have any other accommodation; this was the traditional and easiest option for a single person in a six-month post. Similarly, nurses could opt to live in the onsite nurses' home. In parallel with the completion of phase II, multi-storey blocks of flats were built for resident staff on an adjacent site. On-call rooms were retained in the hospital for junior staff on duty, including the registrars on call for specialties with a large emergency workload.

However, in the 1990s the residential accommodation was disposed of, and the management expected doctors on duty to remain awake through the night even though they might have no work to do. The juniors objected and we managed to reinstate some on-call rooms. Concurrently, junior doctors' hours of work were being reduced. As a result, fewer doctors were on duty, but their workload increased, so there were less opportunities for sleep. These changes were associated with the demise of the junior doctors' mess as a social centre.

20

THE MEDICAL SCHOOL –
CLINICAL SUB-DEAN

I n November 1970 Margaret Thatcher, then minister of education, announced the establishment of a medical school in Leicester. Preceded by Nottingham and Southampton, it was the last of a tranche of three, after which no more were created in England until the millennium.

A distinguished committee was appointed to plan the medical school, chaired by Professor Sir Andrew Kay from Glasgow (formerly professor of surgery in Sheffield). They proposed a curriculum 'to be developed as a close-knit whole, avoiding too sharp a distinction between the pre-clinical and clinical parts'. In fact, it was conventional, comprising two pre-clinical years followed by three years of clinical work. The first intake of students was to be 48, increasing over the following four years to 96 and ultimately to 144.

A more integrated course might have been expected, but the plans were constrained by the timetable for the associated hospital building. Teaching of the basic sciences commenced in 1975, using temporary accommodation for the first year, until the Medical Sciences Building on the university campus was completed in 1976. Phase II at the LRI was not ready for clinical teaching until 1979, so the first entry had to start their third year confined to the old wards.

There was one innovative feature in the curriculum: 20 per cent of the time in the first two years was designated for 'Man in Society', comprising sociology, public health and a continuing attachment to a family with a long-term health problem. Students had the option of an intercalated year to do a research project for a BSc, usually between the second and third years and therefore generally in a subject from the pre-clinical course.

Professor Bill Crammond, a psychiatrist who had been working in Australia, was appointed as dean, but moved on to be principal of Stirling University two years later. By this time five foundation professors had been appointed, including Peter Bell as professor of surgery, with further posts planned. In April 1975 Professor Robert Kilpatrick became the dean and he guided the medical school through to maturity, leaving in 1989 to chair the General Medical Council. He had already completed his term as dean of medicine in Sheffield, where the post rotated at three-yearly intervals, as it then did in most medical schools. The intention was for a similar rotational arrangement to apply in Leicester once the school was well established but by 1989 medical school deans were being appointed by advertisement and often from outside the university. Accordingly, the next dean was Professor Frank Harris who had already served as dean, in rotation, in Liverpool. I had known him slightly when he was a lecturer in paediatrics in Sheffield and his wife was a research assistant in the Department of Surgery.

In 1976, after a medical staff committee meeting, Robert Kilpatrick asked me if I would take on the part-time post of clinical sub-dean. I had an idea of what the job involved from having met the holder of this position in Sheffield and I accepted promptly. Two half-day sessions per week were judged necessary and these were freed from my programme by dropping the day at Hinckley, where I was replaced by a senior lecturer in surgery. There was no reduction in my NHS salary and the university paid a small honorarium, initially £500 per annum. I visited the clinical sub-deans in Nottingham and Southampton to learn how they had tackled the role in a new medical school. As neither was a bed-holding clinician, I felt I had an advantage.

SETTING UP CLINICAL TEACHING

I was left to write my own job description, deriving this from the curriculum:

- Organising the introductory course in clinical methods, arranging pairings of physicians and surgeons to take groups of five or six students.

- Arranging clinical attachments for the third- and fifth-year students, in liaison with the professors of medicine and surgery.
- In the fourth year the respective university departments would manage the four nine-week specialty blocks, so my role was simply to allocate the students among the four groups.
- Planning for the nine-week elective in the fourth year, rotating with the other blocks.
- Establishing systems to assess students' performance in their clinical attachments.
- Counselling clinical students.

My first task was to secure the full support of the NHS staff. They already had enough committees, so I did not set up any new ones, preferring ad hoc meetings and informal discussions. The consultants had been keen to have a medical school, but many were apprehensive about teaching. However only one, a surgeon, declined to take part, pointing out that he had deliberately chosen a job in a district general hospital (DGH). Two physicians were not considered suitable, for specific reasons, and were excluded from student attachments.

We also had to reassure the nursing staff who had visions of long-haired men in dirty jeans defiling their wards, so study days were arranged for me to discuss their concerns with ward sisters and staff nurses. I emphasised to the students the need for a professional appearance; the male who had been wearing a dress reverted to trousers and several men had their hair cut. One contentious issue was whether female students should be allowed to wear trousers! To alleviate any public unease, I wrote a piece in the *Leicester Mercury* emphasising that the students would not be making any decisions about patient care.

THE THIRD YEAR

When working on the arrangements for clinical teaching in the third year, some practical issues arose, so the curriculum required adjustment. The original plan was to devote the afternoons during the first six months to lectures in pathology, followed by the 'topic teaching' course covering the whole of medicine, all provided on the LRI site. There was however a preference among clinicians to teach in the afternoons, so that when appropriate this could be extended into the evening to include more emergency admissions.

After discussion, the plan was reversed, with the lectures moving to the mornings. I also pressed for the provision of student on-call rooms at each hospital to maximise their experience of emergency work. Wednesday afternoons were reserved for sport or other leisure activities, as they were in the first two years.

The introductory course in clinical methods was shortened from 20 to 14 weeks, up to the natural break at Christmas. This comprised preliminary sessions, eight weeks with paired physicians and surgeons and four weeks' introduction to the specialties of orthopaedics, ophthalmology, mental illness, and obstetrics and gynaecology.

The remainder of the year comprised a rotation of five six-week clinical attachments, two each in medicine and surgery, together with a combined block which included an introduction to general practice (two weeks), cardiology and neurology (two weeks), A&E (one week) and urology (one week). The last two blocks, after the end of the topic teaching course in April, were full-time.

Six surgical firms – four at LRI and two at LGH – were to be involved in this teaching, but seven medical firms had been envisaged across these hospitals and Groby Road Hospital (GRH). Six of each would enable a much easier rotation of students, without the need to rearrange the groups, so the physicians were consolidated into six firms.

Of the first intake of 48 students, two had dropped out and nine were doing an intercalated BSc, so there were only 37 for the first year of clinical teaching. It was helpful that we could start with only three for each pair of consultants, later increasing to three for each one.

Based on my own experience as a student, I was keen to introduce choice into clinical placements. In the third year, students were in no position to choose firms, so I gave priority to them being able to form their own groups, which stayed together through the year, for the introductory course and their allocation to clinical firms. The rotations were balanced to equalise the time spent away from the LRI, which involved more travel. We did not provide transport between hospitals, as would be routine in later decades, but they always managed to get there.

THE FOURTH YEAR AND THE ELECTIVE

The fourth year was a rotation through five nine-week blocks. These comprised: obstetrics and gynaecology (O&G), paediatrics, psychiatry and a block split between general practice, anaesthetics, and orthopaedics; the fifth block was the elective period. The blocks were managed by the respective university departments. Allocation of students among the blocks was my responsibility; where a student started in the rotation was decided by the block chosen for their elective. There were specialty exams after O&G, paediatrics, and psychiatry; if a student failed, he or she could repeat the specialty during additional clinical practice at the end of the fifth year.

I was responsible for the arrangements for the elective. In many medical schools, the easy option was for a student to fix up an attachment at a DGH near home, but we wanted the students to experience a different environment. I offered the following alternatives:

- A clinical attachment in a different medical system, either abroad or in one of the outlying islands of Britain. Consultants were asked to suggest contacts who might prove helpful, and these were listed in the office.
- A clinical attachment in a specialty not included in the curriculum and away from Leicester, for example neurosurgery.
- A research project in a department in Leicester or elsewhere.
- Any student who had failed the pathology examination in the third year did further study to resit this in lieu of an elective.

These rules were accepted by the Faculty Board. Students had to gain my approval for their elective and once they had a letter of acceptance from their host they could book into the block of their choice, subject to there still being a place. Every student managed to find a suitable elective. Overseas electives involved significant travel cost, to help with which we set up a modest loan scheme. A few bursaries were also available, generously provided by a local pharmaceutical company and the Leicester Medical Society; these were allocated competitively, based on written proposals.

I was concerned about hazards in developing countries, but there were no serious problems apart from one case of toxicity from antimalarial prophylaxis. The hosts for the electives were asked to report and each student had to deliver a written account of the elective. A prize was given for the best report, judged by a small panel of consultants. For subsequent years we maintained a list of previous contacts, which proved of great assistance to the students.

THE FINAL YEAR

The original plan for the medical school had not envisaged links outside Leicestershire, but additional hospitals could offer useful clinical experience, while more pre-registration posts were needed for our graduates than were available in Leicester. Situated at the southern end of the Trent region, the only other hospitals officially allocated to Leicester were the DGH in Boston and a smaller hospital in Grantham, both in Lincolnshire. To add to these, Robert Kilpatrick contacted hospitals just over the border in adjacent regions: Peterborough DGH (East Anglia), Kettering DGH (Oxford) and George Eliot Hospital, Nuneaton and Walsgrave Hospital, Coventry (both West Midlands).

Negotiations resulted in a mutually advantageous package for these associated hospitals, including Boston. This comprised: final-year teaching in medicine and surgery, the allocation of their pre-registration posts to Leicester graduates, and the inclusion of some registrar and SHO posts in Leicester rotations. There was uncertainty about the adequacy of the teaching in these other hospitals, so a gradual introduction was judged advisable. I negotiated the details with helpful colleagues in these hospitals and followed up with visits once the students had started.

The final year was originally planned to provide 12-week senior firms in medicine and surgery, interrupted respectively by two-week detachments to ophthalmology and ENT surgery. I felt this would disrupt teaching on the firms and waste clinical material, so I persuaded the Faculty Board to accept an arrangement of three eight-week blocks, one each in medicine and surgery in Leicester. The third block comprised two weeks' ophthalmology, two weeks' ENT and four weeks in a DGH split between medicine and surgery. This arrangement enabled the size of firms to be limited initially to one student per consultant. We planned to expand the teaching in the DGHs once we were sure that it was effective.

Students were encouraged to express their preferences for senior firms. They were asked to give three choices in priority order for medicine and for surgery and to indicate which specialty was to be given preference. The administrator in the clinical sciences office at the LRI sorted out the allocation on the principles that both attachments could not be at the LRI (the most convenient site for students) and that a higher preference for one specialty might have to be balanced by a lower one for the other. It proved possible to accommodate all the students within their chosen options apart from a few exceptions, which I negotiated individually.

This freedom of choice was popular with the students, and it helped them in choosing pre-registration posts. It also provided valuable information about the teaching. After the first couple of years substantial differences emerged regarding the popularity of the various firms with three- or four-fold differences in the number of first choices. Of course, several factors influenced students' choices, not just the quality of teaching. Other influences might be geography and teaching styles, the latter ranged from challenging to gentle; different styles suited different students. Nevertheless, the variation in the popularity of firms provided a basis for advice to the less favoured consultants.

I wanted to extend clinical teaching to those specialties which did not have substantial student attachments, both to utilise their expertise and their patients and to broaden the students' experience. A total of 12 specialties (for example cardiology, haematology, radiology and rheumatology) were asked to offer four-week series of 'senior specialty rounds' during the senior firms. Students were invited to sign up for these weekly half-day sessions according to their interests and the limitations of the programmes of their firms. I suggested that two such series in any four-week period would be appropriate; some students followed these extra opportunities enthusiastically, others less so.

The teaching in the DGHs was much appreciated by the students and after two years I judged that we could move on to the inclusion of eight-week final-year attachments in Peterborough (the best organised of the associated hospitals). I was concerned that students might see these placements as less satisfactory, so I persuaded prominent individuals to be the trailblazers, with no adverse reports. Senior firms were subsequently added in the other associated hospitals. This enabled the number of students per consultant to be held at two or three, despite the medical school intake rising to 96. At this point the blocks were increased to nine weeks. The combined block then included dermatology and anaesthetics as well as ENT and ophthalmology.

ASSESSMENT

Consultants were asked to report on students' attendance and performance at the end of each attachment. Attendance was judged unsatisfactory if it fell below 80 per cent. Clinical skill and knowledge were rated from 'A' (very good) to 'E' (unsatisfactory). Understandably, consultants found it difficult to assess performance and tended towards being supportive, so there were few critical reports. These gradings were used for guidance but were not at that stage considered sufficiently robust to be incorporated in the marking for finals. I had informative conversations with the students, both when they called in at the office and more formally when presenting their plans for the elective. Twice a year I visited the associated hospitals to liaise with the consultants and talk to the students.

I had no responsibility for organising the final examinations in medicine and surgery, held in March. These were managed by the professorial departments and comprised written papers, traditional clinicals with long and short cases, and vivas. Most NHS consultants were involved as examiners.

At about that time academics from Dundee advocated an 'objective structured clinical examination' (OSCE) in which candidates progressed around a series of clinical stations, so that they all saw the same patients and were marked at each station by different examiners. This produced a more consistent result and, as a bonus, the marks could be analysed by station to detect topics on which the students were weak. I advocated the OSCE as an alternative to the traditional short case clinicals, but the Faculty Board would not accept the idea, on the grounds that it was 'too early to make any changes'. This contrasted with the opinion expressed by friends from other medical schools who often said how lucky I was to be in a new school, not bound by tradition! By about 2010 all medical schools were using OSCEs as part of their examinations.

Most students who had already passed the examinations in the fourth-year subjects did two periods of 'additional clinical practice' (ACP) in the remaining 12 weeks of the final year. They could choose from the two options:

- Allocation to a specialty in Leicester which does not otherwise have an attachment in the curriculum.
- An attachment in any major specialty in one of the associated hospitals or in general practice.

One subject failed in the fourth year could be repeated during ACP. Anyone who had failed in medicine or surgery or in a second subject from the fourth year had to resit, after further attachments, in November.

The original proposals included a 'final test of clinical competence' to be held in June, but no one could see how this would operate. Could a student fail at that stage, having passed all the examinations in the major subjects? This idea was abandoned, but diligent attendance in ACP had to be certified.

HOUSE OFFICERS

There were enough pre-registration posts in Leicester and the associated hospitals for all our graduates and a matching scheme was introduced, as in many other medical schools at that time. Very few chose to move to other areas. Each final-year student listed their three choices of post in order of preference and consultants gave their preferences among those who had included them. Most achieved a one-to-one match. Students usually chose consultants to whom they had been attached during senior firms. I often had a female house surgeon, at a time when only about one-third of the intake were women, in contrast to the 60 per cent in the 21st century.

This arrangement proved satisfactory; the new graduates knew what they were getting, and both parties had a personal stake in making it work. I was retained as a member of the pre-registration committee until the mid-1990s, when the dean insisted that a randomised allocation system should be used, 'in the interest of fairness'. I commented that consultants might then be less committed to their house staff and was condemned as advocating patronage. I then resigned from the committee.

INTERLUDE

On a lighter note, we lacked eccentricity among the staff. When I was a registrar, three senior consultants wore bowler hats, but now all we had was one monocle. Should there be financial incentives for pocket watches or gold-headed canes? There was only one consultant with a worthwhile nickname: 'Shifting Dullness' (for non-medical readers, this is a physical sign of a fluid collection in the abdominal cavity). One of my colleagues had suggested advice for GPs referring difficult patients to consultants. They could choose: Dr X for extensive investigation and then a prescription for Valium, Dr Y for a quick diagnosis of vitamin deficiency, or Dr Z for a nice friendly chat. Knowing the physicians concerned these were apt caricatures, but I didn't think we should provide these descriptions to assist students in their choices.

CONCLUSION

This brief account of the clinical course describes my involvement. It does not cover the details of the inclusion of all the specialties or of lectures given during the attachments in the fourth year. Minor adjustments were made in the light of experience and the number of students per firm increased as the intake expanded.

I was asked to continue for a second three-year period, enabling me to see the first two cohorts through to completion. My suggestions for a successor were then sought. I felt that the person should be a clinician, not be drawn from any one specialty and he or she should not again be from the LRI. I put forward three names, one surgeon and two physicians; all three served, sequentially.

It was a great privilege to have this role in the setting up of a new medical school and it was satisfying to find that the arrangements continued substantially unaltered for about 15 years. By that time changes in hospital practice and the increasing subspecialisation within general medicine and surgery rendered the firms used for teaching in the third and fifth years unsuitable for their original prolonged attachments. Surgical patients were no longer admitted the day before operation, which had allowed time for student clerking and for teaching. As new subspecialties developed, and individual consultants limited the scope of their elective work, six or eight weeks attached to a 'general' firm no longer offered a broad experience of medical or surgical conditions. Shorter attachments to multiple units with different interests could solve this problem, but with a loss of the continuity in relationships between students and all grades of the medical staff. Such familiarity provided more than just instruction, adding mentorship and informal advice.

The solution developing in the 1990s was for concurrent attachments to two or more consultants from diverse specialties; for example, I was linked with an ENT surgeon and an anaesthetist. I found it difficult to coordinate the times when I had the students with the best teaching opportunities. To try to ensure coverage of a wide range of illnesses, students were given a list of core conditions that they should have seen, but agreement on what to include was hard to achieve. More of the teaching needed to take place in outpatients but this was constrained by the number of patients to be seen in the limited time. In 1994 a student wrote to the dean, complaining that surgical teaching at the LRI was subject to frequent cancellations. This did not surprise me as the competing pressures of the hospital's contracts and the reduction in junior staff support was stretching us to the limit. By 1995, because of these trends, my enthusiasm for student teaching began to waver.

143

I believe that since I retired in 2000 the change to shift working for junior staff must have further weakened the value of clinical attachments. More didactic teaching is being offered to compensate for this, but I suspect that clinical skills are suffering. However, simulation and skills laboratories are at last providing a proper introduction to practical procedures such as intravenous cannulation, catheterisation and suturing. Inevitably, some teaching methods that served us well for so long have been displaced by changes in hospital practice; it must be challenging to provide good clinical teaching in the current environment.

21

CONSULTANT RADIOLOGIST

The radiologists in Leicester welcomed Elisabeth. They had only one substantive post for a trainee – a senior registrar (SR), rotating with Sheffield – and naturally wished for more. Norah Hudson, who became a close friend as well as a colleague, was already training as an SR under the centrally funded training scheme for married women, working part-time, and a further post of this type was promised for Elisabeth.

We assumed that our move to Leicester would coincide with the start of the school year for all three children, so that we would require only minimal cover for childcare. Four-year-old Clare had been at primary school in Sheffield in the summer term of 1971, so we had expected that she would be able to continue in Oadby. Unfortunately, the Leicestershire policy was not to accept children under the age of five and as her fifth birthday was on 2nd September, she couldn't start school until January. We thought this delay would be disruptive for her and make it too difficult for Elisabeth to start her post on time. We went as far as to appeal to the chief executive of the county council (the husband of a cardiothoracic surgeon whom I knew slightly) but to no effect. Thus, Clare missed a term of school and Elisabeth had to delay starting as an SR until January 1972.

By 1973, she was ready to sit the examination for the Fellowship of the Faculty of Radiologists (FFR)[15]. This coincided with our move to Knighton

---

15 When the Royal College of Radiologists was established in 1979 this became the FRCR.

Rise, where we were camping in a few rooms while work on the house was completed. Despite revising amidst the chaos, Elisabeth passed at the first attempt, opening the way to a consultant post, subject to a further two years as a trainee to comply with the regulations. Training was defined by duration rather than competence and there was argument about whether a half-time trainee had to take twice as long.

Meanwhile, Norah Hudson had completed her training and was appointed in 1974 to work partly at LGH and partly to do cardiac radiology at Groby Road Hospital. She had surprised the appointments committee by saying that the two sessions vacant from a maximum part-time post would be spent with her two children rather than in private practice.

Elisabeth wanted a six-session job and she effectively had a choice of hospitals. She felt that LGH offered the best opportunities, and she was appointed there in 1976. At that time, the radiology department at LGH had not developed beyond barium studies and intravenous pyelography (IVP). More complex procedures were done at the LRI, but with the start of the medical school and the appointment of new consultants, for example in nephrology and urology, the hospital's needs were changing.

Over the next few years Norah and Elisabeth developed arteriography at LGH and set up a lymphography service for Leicester. This investigation involved the cannulation of frail lymph vessels in the foot for infusion of oily contrast to demonstrate deposits of malignant tumours in lymph nodes deep in the abdomen. It was important at the time, though later superseded by computed tomography (CT). They introduced arterial interventions to correct narrowing and blockages, procedures requiring close cooperation with and the trust of clinical colleagues. As a consultant, Elisabeth taught both medical students and trainees in radiology. She chose not to do private practice but later, at the request of surgical colleagues, she did occasional arterial procedures for private patients in the department at LGH, donating her fees to departmental funds.

DIVERSIFICATION AND TECHNOLOGY

Diagnostic ultrasound began to have a role beyond its use in obstetrics, so both the LRI and LGH appointed consultant radiologists specifically to develop this. However, neither did so, the colleague at LGH saying that he preferred 'steam radiology'. Undeterred, Elisabeth decided to teach herself ultrasound. In due course she was joined by one of Leicester's former trainees who had exceptional ability in this very operator-dependent subspecialty. Then the hospital was allocated a gamma camera, housed in a side ward; but who was to supervise it and report the results of radioisotope imaging? Elisabeth took this on, did a diploma course in London and achieved considerable expertise, particularly in nephrology. Along with these special investigations she did her share of the routine reporting of plain films. She also took responsibility for the radiography at Rutland Memorial Hospital, paying a twice-yearly pastoral visit.

Through the 1980s and 90s the range of radiological interventional (treatment) procedures increased, starting with balloon dilatation of narrowed arteries. Patients with an obstructed kidney were managed initially by percutaneous insertion of a drainage tube under ultrasound control, often needing to be done out of hours. This approach was extended to insert tubes large enough to enable a urologist to extract stones, so Elisabeth went to the Middlesex Hospital to observe this technique. Intussusception in infants was reduced by insufflation of barium (and later air) into the colon under radiological control. Narrowing of the renal arteries, as a cause of hypertension, was dilated with a balloon catheter passed from the groin. Conversely the renal artery could be blocked by insertion of a metal coil prior to operations to remove large tumours of the kidney, so reducing bleeding. Patients who had suffered repeated pulmonary emboli had a filter placed in the inferior vena cava to prevent further emboli reaching the lungs. Often these complicated procedures were needed during the night, so that by the 1990s Elisabeth was as likely to be called out as I was.

In parallel with the development of these advanced procedures by the radiologists, the senior radiographers were encouraged to develop skills in performing and reporting barium enemas and IVPs. To handle the increased workload the total staff had expanded from five in the 1950s to about 50. Under Elisabeth's leadership, the medical staff, radiographers, secretaries, nurses and porters all worked well together.

Collaboration with clinical colleagues also resulted in joint authorship of papers, particularly on topics related to renal failure and transplantation. A surgical colleague was due to read one such paper at the Association of Surgeons' meeting in Edinburgh but was unable to get there because his wife had gone into labour. Elisabeth was accompanying me to the conference and agreed to deliver the paper. In his introduction, the chairman of that session remarked: 'Women doctors are often accused of having to miss medical commitments on account of childbirth, but in this case the reverse is true'.

HOSPITAL MANAGEMENT

When Norah Hudson decided to concentrate on cardiac work and therefore spend all her sessions at Glenfield, Elisabeth effectively became the senior member of the department. At about this time she increased her formal commitment to eight sessions, though she often worked more. Management changes in 1990 called for a Hospital Board which included clinical directors. One directorate was for the 10 clinical support services, which ranged from radiology and pathology to physiotherapy, dietetics, social work, electrocardiography and the mortuary. There were two obvious candidates for clinical director: Elisabeth and the senior pathologist. Elisabeth was chosen, continuing in this role from 1991 to 1996. To help with this she did a part-time course in 1994 at the University of North Staffordshire, resulting in a Diploma in Health Services Management. She worked hard for the diverse departments and played a full part in the workings of the Board.

A NEW DEPARTMENT

Housed in a converted ground-floor Nightingale ward, with extensions, the X-ray department was inconvenient and too small. When the LGH became a trust in 1993, Elisabeth argued for a new department to include the gamma camera and for the first time provide computed tomography (CT). The addition of magnetic resonance imaging (MRI) was envisaged. With support from Hugh Ross, the chief executive of the trust, and after intense debate at the Board, her plan was approved, and a two-storey block was designed and built.

Elisabeth was also keen to introduce digital recording of the images to replace film. This had been done at only two sites in the UK: in Hammersmith Hospital at a cost of some £18 million and in Hastings where the coverage was incomplete. She persuaded the board to seek contractors for this modern system and it was achieved for only about £2 million – the first use of this system in Leicester. With the picture archive and communications system (PACS) the images could be viewed on monitors distributed around the hospital.

The development of the building, its equipment and the introduction of the digital system required a project manager. Fiona Barnaby, one of the superintendent radiographers, offered her services and with Elisabeth's support was appointed. The project was successfully completed on time and on budget. Fiona then went on to a career in the design of X-ray departments and the installation of radiographic equipment. Digital recording of radiological images became universal.

Elisabeth was glad that at last LGH had CT, but with retirement approaching she decided not to tackle this, in addition to her ultrasound, interventional radiology and radioisotope work. The task fell to younger colleagues who had had the appropriate training in cross-sectional imaging.

A GREAT CAREER

In April 1998 Elisabeth announced her intention to retire in the following April. Despite the 12 months' notice, a successor was not appointed until over a year after she left. She'd had an amazing career, helping to bring radiology at LGH into the modern age, while in conjunction with colleagues she had published 15 papers. Her contribution had been recognised by a 'C' and then a 'B' distinction award. And somehow, she succeeded in combining this with running our household. Fortunately, the changes in radiology ran in parallel with the needs of our family. In the earlier years, when the children were at home, emergencies were few. By the late 1980s, when the children had grown up, the interventional work developed and was often needed at night or during the weekend.

A career such as Elisabeth's was rare – if not unique – among the wives of the consultants when we moved to Leicester. A few were medically qualified, but only one, an anaesthetist, was a consultant; another was a principal in general practice. Several had trained as nurses, but few continued working. The vast majority had no paid employment; some did charity work, while the most active ones became magistrates. In contrast, by the time we retired most of the younger consultants' spouses had jobs. The medically qualified ones were GPs or consultants (and of course there were many other female consultants), others were teachers or lawyers. Such couples often had twice the income of a single consultant, so that for many private practice became less important.

22

CHANGES IN THE CARE OF SURGICAL PATIENTS

In addition to the changes in operative surgery, there were parallel advances in postoperative management during my 29 years as a consultant. Prophylactic measures markedly reduced the incidence of wound infection, thrombo-embolism and wound breakdown. Pain control improved, and the effectiveness of intensive care increased. Consultants had tended to limit their involvement to the patients admitted under their care and any others specifically referred to them. This gradually changed to a more cooperative pattern and later to the introduction of multidisciplinary teams, particularly for cancer patients. Senior supervision of care on the wards was enhanced; from 1992 we had daily consultant-led ward rounds on our firm. Lengths of stay shortened, and more procedures were undertaken as day cases.

PROPHYLAXIS

Wound infection is liable to occur after contamination from bowel contents during gastrointestinal operations. When I was a house surgeon a week's course of antibiotics (usually penicillin and streptomycin) given by intramuscular injection was prescribed postoperatively, and then administered a few hours later by the ward nurses. It did not reduce the number of infections. Two insights were needed to achieve this.

First, there was the recognition that the optimum time to defeat wound contamination is during the operation, before the bacteria have time to multiply. Prophylactic antibiotics were therefore given at induction of anaesthesia, without necessarily being continued postoperatively. Secondly, specimens from infected wounds began to be cultured in anaerobic (oxygen-free) as well as aerobic conditions, demonstrating the importance of anaerobic organisms. It followed that the antibiotics should also be active against these bacteria. The result of these prophylactic measures was a great reduction in wound infection following operations ranging from appendicectomy to large bowel resection.

In the 1970s a pulmonary embolus (due to a blood clot travelling from a leg to the lungs) was a common event, typically occurring about a week postoperatively. Sometimes the patient died within a few minutes. We did our best to diagnose deep vein thrombosis (DVT) before embolism could occur. The only means of suspecting a DVT were finding ankle swelling or calf tenderness or noting a spike of temperature. The patient would then be anticoagulated: a surgical ward would often contain one such patient. Initial treatment with intravenous heparin and then adjustment of the dose of warfarin, taken orally, could extend a patient's stay by 10 days. However, most of the tragic deaths from a major pulmonary embolus occurred without prior signs of thrombosis. In the 1970s, two young women suffered fatal pulmonary emboli following appendicectomy in the LRI in the same week; both had been taking an oral contraceptive.

The problem persisted despite various prophylactic measures, which included calf muscle exercises, compression stockings and a mechanical device to keep the ankles moving during the operation. Trials of these methods were monitored by intravenous injection of radioactive labelled fibrinogen, followed by daily scanning of the lower limbs. The prophylactic measures reduced the incidence of thrombosis provided they were in force during the operation. Then in the 1980s, controlled trials showed that low-dose subcutaneous heparin, started just before the operation, drastically reduced the incidence of DVT without bleeding complications. Furthermore, in large trials, there was a great reduction in fatal pulmonary embolism. Intermittent compression to the lower limbs using inflatable leggings during the operation also proved moderately effective. The combination of low-dose heparin, started preoperatively, and inflatable leggings was synergistic. This became standard practice for patients at significant risk. By the 1990s postoperative

DVT and pulmonary embolism were rarely seen on our general surgical wards.

In theatre, before making the first incision, I used to confirm the identity of the patient, the procedure to be done and check that heparin and antibiotics had been given. These topics are now covered in the recommended 'time out' for the whole theatre team, as proposed by Atul Gawande in *The Checklist Manifesto* in 2009. I was doing this solo rather than as a team effort, so probably less reliably, though I never operated on the wrong patient or the wrong side.

WOUND CLOSURE

Up to the mid-1970s the emergency theatre list often included the repair of a 'burst abdomen', when a recent vertical abdominal incision suddenly gave way. This was most alarming for the patient, as the intestines appeared, with little warning other than a slight pink discharge from the suture line. Various policies were advocated to minimise this risk: the overlapping layers of a paramedian incision; interrupted sutures; a continuous suture; non-absorbable sutures or deep tension sutures (comprising a large 'bite' of skin, muscle and peritoneum) but the problem persisted. Then in 1976, the Guildford surgeon TP Jenkins showed a dramatic reduction in burst abdominal incisions by incorporating all the muscle and aponeurotic layers in a single continuous non-absorbable suture. This 'mass closure' became standard practice and thereafter the burst abdomen almost never seen. However, this policy did not reduce the incidence of subsequent incisional hernias.

Skin incisions were traditionally closed with non-absorbable nylon or Prolene sutures, requiring removal at seven to 10 days. Alternatives were skin clips or staples, but these likewise needed removing. When I was a student, and over the following few years, patients stayed in hospital until the stitches (or clips) had been taken out, a procedure often dreaded by the patient, though not so bad when the time came. As lengths of stay were shortened, this duty was passed to the district nurse. The next stage of evolution was to use a continuous subcuticular Prolene suture, secured with a bead and a clip where it emerged at each end of the incision; this aimed to minimise scarring. By 1990 we had moved on to using a dissolvable subcuticular suture, which did not need to be removed, thus saving a district nurse's visit. Patients who feared the removal of their stitches could be reassured that this would not be necessary. The disadvantage of these methods was the difficulty of draining a wound abscess, so when contamination had been significant (for example, after the removal of a perforated appendix), I still preferred interrupted sutures.

POSTOPERATIVE MANAGEMENT

The standard method of postoperative pain control had been injection of morphine or pethidine, prescribed four-hourly PRN (*pro re nata*) and given at the nurses' discretion. Later, these drugs were often given as a patient-controlled infusion. Additionally, infiltration or irrigation of the wound with local anaesthetic provided short-term relief postoperatively. A spinal epidural catheter could deliver repeated doses over several days. However, the supervision of the latter was at first deemed to need a bed on a high dependency unit (HDU) and such beds were in short supply.

In the 1970s, it was usual practice to insert a nasogastric tube for patients having abdominal operations of the magnitude of cholecystectomy and above. The oral fluid intake was limited until the hourly volume of fluid aspirated reduced. The rationale was to avoid the complication of a paralytic ileus, which comprised absence of peristalsis and dilatation of the gut. I surmised that the presence of the tube itself inhibited normal gut activity. I increasingly dispensed with it after elective operations, without any increase in ileus.

It took a while for the anaesthetists to accept that I did not wish them to routinely insert a nasogastric tube, even though this saved them a procedure that, in the anaesthetised patient, was awkward and sometimes traumatic. Gradually this policy was widely adopted, and it formed one part of the enhanced recovery programme introduced in 2000, for open abdominal operations, by Professor Henrik Kehlet from Copenhagen.

Originally, consultants did two comprehensive ward rounds per week, not necessarily following their days on take. Otherwise, the junior staff of the firm provided weekday medical care. Until 1988, night and weekend cover for the general surgical inpatients at the LRI was by a second on-call house surgeon. He or she only visited in response to requests from the nursing staff. Some calls were for patients who were deteriorating, but most were for analgesia, replacement of a canula or to extend the prescription for intravenous fluids. This arrangement did not provide a routine review of the patients at weekends, which was achieved in a variable manner by SR or registrar ward rounds and visits by individual consultants if they were worried about a patient. In 1992 the number of consultants on our unit increased from two to three and we then agreed a policy of a daily ward round by one of us at 8am each weekday and on Saturday and Sunday mornings. That was by no means universal for other firms at that time. I feel this arrangement provided better care, occasionally identifying a serious complication earlier than would otherwise have happened. It also reduced lengths of stay by deciding about the discharge of patients more promptly, especially at weekends.

INTENSIVE CARE
The care of patients immediately after the most major operations increasingly involved artificial ventilation and adjustment of fluid replacement, monitored respectively by repeated blood gas measurements and central venous and sometimes pulmonary artery pressure recording. This level of support required a bed in an intensive care unit. Whereas I had been deeply involved in ICUs as a trainee and in setting up the training of specialist nurses in Leicester, these developments left me behind, the patients being managed by intensivists from an anaesthetic background.

The ICU had been built with space for eight beds, just short of the NHS norm of one per cent of the total beds in the hospital. There was increasing pressure on the unit, for patients following major trauma (especially major head injuries), unstable patients after emergency operations (particularly ruptured aortic aneurysms) and ward patients who had developed major septic complications. There were also medical patients, often overdoses. An increasing number of elective operations for aortic aneurysm and the introduction of epidural analgesia also added to the need for ICU beds. These elective operations frequently had to be cancelled because the unit was full of emergency admissions. The problem was relieved by the addition of a small high dependency unit (HDU) for patients who did not need artificial ventilation. In about 1990 I advised the chief executive that the number of ICU/HDU beds would need to be doubled. Adjacent to ICU was an eight-bedded coronary care unit (CCU). When the new phase IV was opened in 1992, the CCU was transferred there, and the space vacated provided eight more HDU beds.

Throughout my career, patients undergoing oesophagectomy or anterior resection of the rectum did not routinely qualify for ICU, and just returned from the recovery area to the ward. Anastomotic leakage was one major complication occurring in these patients and would not have been prevented by a few days in ICU, but they were also liable to respiratory problems which would be better handled on ICU. Admission to ICU has become almost routine after such operations; if no bed is available the operation is deferred.

ON THE WARDS

This whole complex of advances in the care of surgical inpatients, associated with markedly reduced lengths of hospital stay, increased the intensity of activity on the wards. Whereas in earlier years the more mobile patients could help to take the teas round, there were now no such patients. A much greater proportion were on intravenous drips, while fewer were drinking tea. The nurses' workload increased and, partly as a response to its increasing complexity, the enrolled nurses (SENs) were encouraged to convert to SRN. Then later, in the 1990s, all nurse training led to a university degree. This inevitably resulted in a service gap for the more basic nursing procedures, filled by a new cadre of health care assistants – really the old SEN grade under a new name. The nurses' increasing use of computers for record keeping could lead to them spending more time at the nurses' station and less in patient contact. Good leadership was required to correct this trend.

STOMA CARE

Large bowel operations may involve the creation of an artificial opening, either an ileostomy from the small intestine or a colostomy from the colon. The patient then manages the effluent using a stoma bag, originally held in place by a belt. This may be for only a few months or lifelong. The output from an ileostomy is liquid and contains enzymes capable of digesting the nearby skin. Soon after I arrived, I was forcefully reminded of this when a patient was admitted with horribly excoriated skin around an ileostomy, performed some years previously. She had never had any form of appliance to collect the efflux, just using masses of cotton wool to soak it up. It took many weeks of nursing care to heal the skin before a bag would adhere. The Ileostomy Association[16] had been founded to help patients with a stoma and I became its local chairman.

In the 1960s, the appliances industry produced adhesive plastic bags to apply to stomas but the effectiveness of these depended on careful preoperative siting of the stoma away from bony prominences and deep folds in the skin.

---

16 Now the Ileostomy and Internal Pouch Association, having extended its remit to include patients who have had a restorative proctocolectomy.

This required the surgeon to do a dummy run with a bag preoperatively. In the mid-1970s, Brendan Devlin, a surgeon from North Tees, cooperated with a nursing sister to introduce the role of stoma care nurse. He spoke about this at a postgraduate meeting at the LRI and we managed to get our first stoma nurse appointed in 1978. She counselled patients preoperatively, marked out the site for the stoma and provided ongoing support postoperatively. In due course, each hospital had a stoma care service.

MULTIDISCIPLINARY TEAMS

All decisions about the management of surgically treatable cancers were traditionally made by the consultant surgeon, with subsequent referral when appropriate to a radiotherapist who might also arrange chemotherapy. From about 1990 however, the alternative modes and sequencing of these modalities of treatments multiplied. We were urged to introduce multidisciplinary teams (MDTs) to consider all the treatment options. As a minimum, the MDT would include surgeons, radiotherapists, medical oncologists and diagnostic radiologists but other allied professions might also be involved. An NHS website now lists 15 participants for one type of cancer. Curiously, at a time when the patient's involvement in decisions is being emphasised, he or she is not included in these group discussions.

Before I retired, I had limited experience of an MDT, for colorectal cancer. It was quite demanding in terms of staff time. In principle, it should improve care but I don't think it influenced the decisions about treatment other than for unusual cases. The opportunity cost of involving so many members of staff is significant.

DAY-CASE SURGERY

I have always been enthusiastic about day surgery. In 1972 I started doing circumcisions and hernia operations for small children, using a vacant session in the GU theatre when there was a fifth Monday in the month. Phase II at the LRI included a 30-bedded surgical day ward with two adjacent theatres, allowing development of day surgery. With the enthusiastic support of the sister in charge, I started to do stripping for unilateral varicose veins and then inguinal hernia repairs in selected adults under general anaesthesia. I explained the day-case option in the clinic and found that many patients were enthusiastic.

In the mid-1980s, I adopted the Canadian Shouldice Hernia Hospital's multi-layered repair for inguinal hernias and followed their example of offering local anaesthesia (LA). After these operations under LA, I encouraged the patients to get off the operating table and walked back with them to the day ward, to emphasise an early return to light activity. They had already received a dose of an anti-inflammatory drug (diclofenac) and took home with them a few days' supply of this, and an oral analgesic. As assessed at a follow-up visit this provided good analgesia and I recommended a return to all but heavy exercise by two weeks, permitting a return to work as soon as they felt comfortable enough. The adoption of the latter policy was patchy: one patient, still off work at six weeks, maintained that he could not go back until he'd finished tiling the bathroom! By the early 1990s I was repairing 90 per cent of unilateral hernias as day cases, mostly under LA.

Meanwhile, repair of inguinal hernias with a large piece of Prolene mesh (the Lichtenstein repair) was introduced. This was simpler to teach so, in agreement with my colleagues, I adopted this method for training juniors. Subsequently my younger colleagues began to do laparoscopic inguinal hernia repairs and then cholecystectomies as a day case. The day-case unit also enabled me to accommodate the often poorly prioritised conditions of pilonidal sinus and ingrowing toenail. In addition, I launched a day-case service for the drainage of superficial abscesses (see chapter 23).

COMMUNICATIONS

Over the years, I attended various meetings to discuss how the hospital might be improved. Invariably, one of the main conclusions was that we needed to improve our communications, but this was in relation to the management of the hospital.

However, I was equally interested in improving communications about patients, especially with the GPs. Patients discharged from hospital were supposed to take with them an interim discharge letter, to be handed to their GP. This was often written at the last minute, commonly by the on-call house surgeon who knew nothing about the patient. It was followed by a typed discharge letter or discharge summary. The grade of 'registrar' originated in teaching hospitals in the 1930s specifically to 'keep the register', which included producing discharge summaries. When I was a house surgeon the SR and the registrar did just that. When I was a registrar, I produced succinct discharge letters rather than detailed summaries. As a consultant I found that the registrar's letter was often delayed by several weeks. Meanwhile the case notes travelled via 'coding' to a pile in the secretary's office and then waited until the registrar had time to deal with the backlog.

In 1973, my registrar introduced me to the new hand-held Dictaphones, and I promptly purchased one. I proposed that the letters should be dictated on the ward rounds and typed forthwith, eliminating the often-inadequate interim letter. Once the backlog had been cleared there would be no extra work for the medical secretary and fewer telephone queries from the GPs. For many patients, a confident prediction of their discharge date was possible a few days in advance. Indeed, for routine operations the letter could be dictated in theatre at the end of the operation. For patients with malignant disease, or if a major complication occurred, sending a typed interim letter before the discharge date was settled could be useful to the GP in answering relatives' queries.

This ambitious scheme was never fully functioning. It was difficult to define who in the unit was responsible for dictating the letter about each patient; I suggested that it should be the operating surgeon, but junior staff rotating from other units found it hard to adapt to this system. Also, we never worked out who was responsible for letters about patients admitted as an emergency but who did not require an operation. Unfortunately, the medical secretary whom I shared found it difficult to keep up, so the letters were late and interim discharge letters were still needed. I suppose a voice recognition system might solve that problem in the 21st century.

As junior doctors' hours were reduced, they had less time for dictation, and I often spent Saturday morning doing those letters that had not been dictated before discharge. This incidentally gave me a good overview of the management of the patients and the quality of the case notes.

EVIDENCE-BASED CARE

Did I practise evidence-based medicine? Previously, policies for the treatment of serious conditions were based on expert opinion. Through the 1970s and 1980s I did my best to research the best treatments, reading extensively and following the recommendations in review articles and editorials. For lesser surgical disorders, one could only identify the most convincing clinical report or occasionally a controlled trial. For example, I adopted Peter Lord's 'bloodless' operation for hydroceles and chose my operation for piles from the Leeds trial of four types of haemorrhoidectomy. There was evidence but it was patchy and by modern standards of mediocre quality.

During the 1980s 'evidence-based medicine' was discussed, but only in the context of population-based policies. Later from 1993, the Cochrane Collaboration began to publish systematic reviews of treatments, grading the quality of evidence from double-blind randomised controlled trials down to retrospective case series. Then in 1996 David Sackett at McMaster University in Canada described the application of evidence-based medicine in education. Gradually it became the ideal, but it does not always help in unusual situations or in the presence of multiple morbidities. Then we still rely on experience and logical consideration of the problem.

The systematic reviews underpinning this movement depended upon computerised search engines to identify all the trials of an investigation or treatment. The statistical technique of meta-analysis was developed to combine the results of multiple trials. In the 1990s these methods provided superior quality information regarding many aspects of surgical care. Only then could we begin to follow what has become the gold standard of evidence-based medicine.

23

EMERGENCY SURGERY IN LEICESTER

Emergency surgery merits a chapter of its own for it had long been neglected. When I was a registrar, hospitals were run as though surgical emergencies were quite unexpected, even though they amounted to half of the total admissions in general surgery and accounted for most of the fatalities. Nationwide, until the last decade of the 20th century, there was no specific provision of medical staff or operating theatres. At the LRI emergency admissions in general surgery averaged 10 per day, with a range of three to 17, and the average of three emergency operations had largely to be done after 5pm. Only after the first CEPOD Report in 1987 (see chapter 32) did these deficiencies begin to be addressed.

Throughout my years of training, the care of patients admitted as emergencies was left to the SRs and registrars. A few consultants willingly helped when asked to advise on a difficult problem, but out of hours most expected to be called only for patients who were members of staff. I suspect that some of the older ones had lost confidence in coping with emergencies. I recall taking one senior consultant to see a lady with abdominal pain, about whom I was in great doubt whether to operate. He advised: 'Do a haemoglobin and a blood urea and then decide.' Another time, seeking advice about intravenous fluids, I was told: 'Dr X [the chemical pathologist] is better at that sort of thing'; in fact, Dr X always advised: 'More normal saline' regardless of the circumstances.

The next consultant ward round was not necessarily on the following day and certainly not at the weekend. Consultants did not like to find patients admitted with possible appendicitis who had not been operated upon, nor other unresolved diagnoses. The dictum of Sir Zachary Cope, earlier in the century, that 'It is better to look and see than wait and see', held sway. But with developments in supportive care, a delay in operating, even if it eventually proved necessary, carried less risk than formerly. In uncertain cases this altered the balance of advantage between early operation and conservative management, unless the patient was critically ill.

By the time I became a consultant I had substantial unsupervised experience of emergency surgical admissions. As a measure of this, I had records of 65 operations for abdominal injuries and 66 operations for upper gastrointestinal bleeding. These figures exceed the experience of modern trainees by a factor of about 10 times. I found the uncertainties in the assessment of emergencies challenging and interesting.

HOW EMERGENCY SURGERY WAS ORGANISED IN LEICESTER

Arriving back in Leicester in 1971, I was keen to achieve better control of the management of emergencies under my care. On call with a registrar but no SR cover I think I managed this, often going in to supervise the more difficult procedures. As the medical school developed, the number of SRs increased, so I was then on call one day in six with both an SR and a registrar. The former was usually well experienced and often he (it always was a male) seemed to resent my 'interference' in the care of emergencies. Such was the culture of SR independence but, in fairness, the results were generally good.

No theatre was reserved for emergencies during routine lists, from 9am to 5pm, on weekdays. For the most urgent cases – abdominal injuries, ruptured aortic aneurysms and perforated ulcers – it was accepted that a routine list might have to be interrupted. All other emergency operations were deferred until the elective lists had finished and there was then only one theatre available for all the specialties apart from orthopaedics, so emergencies often ran on through the night. It was not uncommon for some patients then to be left over until the following evening. On Saturdays and Sundays, the emergency theatre was open throughout the 24 hours.

The availability of investigations was limited to routine blood tests and plain abdominal X-rays. Ultrasound and whole-body CT were not yet operational and when they did arrive in the early 1980s they were provided only during normal working hours. By the latter part of the decade CT was being used to assess severe acute pancreatitis but we were slow to apply it to other abdominal problems and it could only be obtained by a direct consultant appeal to a consultant radiologist and then only during routine hours.

There was no scope for diverting emergencies out of the county, so the Leicester hospitals had to cope with however many patients were referred. Until the millennium, about 70 per cent of emergency admissions in Leicestershire were referred by GPs, more than in some large conurbations. The other 30 per cent presented in A&E. The GP contacted the house surgeon on duty, who in principle could decline the patient, but only did so if an alternative (such as an early outpatient appointment) could be agreed. In 1974, Frazer and Patterson surveyed 166 requests for admission from 18 practices in Leicestershire and found that 89 per cent were accepted immediately, nine per cent reluctantly and only three per cent were rejected. Patients presenting to the A&E department and needing admission stayed at the LRI. Referrals from general practice were allocated to LRI or LGH according to a calendar. Both hospitals had a trickle of surgical referrals from other specialties, chiefly general medicine. It was therefore necessary for each hospital to have a duty firm even when it was not on take for GP referrals.

When Glenfield Hospital opened in 1984, the allocation of GP cases was altered, at my suggestion, to match the new complement of beds and surgeons in the three hospitals. To support the A&E department the LRI took emergencies every day, while LGH and Glenfield alternated. Emergency admissions were distributed to give a ratio of six: four: three, among LRI, LGH and Glenfield, reflecting the number of consultants at each. This was managed by routing the GPs' requests for admission through the bed bureau, which was already in existence for the more numerous medical emergencies. The patients were allocated in a planned sequence to the two hospitals on take. Admissions from A&E to the LRI counted towards its quota. Very rarely, a hospital asked for a variation because of extreme difficulty in finding a bed.

From 1995 a separate rota operated for vascular emergencies. In 2004 after I had retired, the new contract removed GPs' responsibility for out-of-hours cover. All emergencies were then routed through a 'common portal of entry' in the A&E department and distributed between the LRI and LGH, the latter involving an ambulance transfer. The 'general surgeons' at Glenfield had become breast specialists and did not admit emergencies, though they still provided first-line cover for inpatient referrals.

MAJOR INCIDENTS

I participated in two critical incidents, one internal and the other a major accident involving an airliner.

One evening in the mid-1970s, before we moved into phase II, I was on call and received a message from the LRI switchboard saying that the hospital was on fire. I was the first consultant to arrive, found that I was in charge, and had to organise my colleagues as they came in. Four fire engines were already at work on a fierce blaze in the stairwell of the end block. The smoke extended along the main corridor on each of the three levels. The nurses on the three Nightingale wards had acted promptly to evacuate the patients via the fire escapes but patients on the ICU had to be wheeled, with their ventilators, along the first-floor corridor through the smoke to the middle block. The electricity supply had failed in the four wards affected, so they were in darkness and the internal phone lines were disrupted so information could only be obtained by sending a runner. It took a while to establish that all the patients and staff were safe.

The major damage was limited to the stairwell, where the fire brigade estimated that it had reached a temperature of 3000°F. The wards suffered only smoke damage and were cleaned and back in use within a few days. Subsequently it was established that the fire had been started in a basement kitchen storeroom by a porter who was disgruntled that he had been denied holiday that week; he had only been in the job for a month. The fire had burned through the electrical supply to that block; there was separate emergency wiring, but it followed the same route and was likewise interrupted. There were no fire doors at the stairwell or on the corridors; these were installed soon afterwards.

One evening in 1989 I saw on the television news that a twin-engine airliner was in trouble on the way to East Midlands Airport; I and several others made our way to the LRI before the switchboard called a major incident. We sat in a group waiting for the first patients to arrive and decided how to deploy the surgeons. Later we learned that the plane had developed a fire in one engine, but the other engine was inadvertently shut down first and would not restart. The plane glided towards the airport but struck the far bank of the M1 motorway, breaking its back. Fortunately, no one travelling on the motorway was injured. The accident was equidistant from the LRI, Queen's Medical Centre in Nottingham and the Derbyshire Royal Infirmary. A&E staff from all three arrived on the scene and the ambulances distributed the injured among the hospitals.

Twenty-one patients were admitted to the LRI. Those with abdominal or chest injuries were distributed among the three general surgical teams. All recovered apart from one very severely injured patient who died in the A&E department despite heroic efforts to operate and control the bleeding. The ability to distribute the injured among three hospitals meant that none was overwhelmed.

IMPROVEMENTS IN FACILITIES FOR EMERGENCY SURGERY

In 1987 the Confidential Enquiry into Postoperative Deaths[17] (CEPOD) drew attention to the lack of facilities for emergency surgery. There was frequently a lack of consultant supervision by both surgeons and anaesthetists. Most surgical deaths occur among the emergency admissions; of course, these are often higher-risk patients, but senior staff should be involved to maximise their chance of recovery.

Following this report, hospitals were urged to provide dedicated daytime emergency theatres and senior staff were to be actively involved. Nocturnal operating was to occur only when urgency demanded it. There should always be a consultant-led 'post-take' ward round the following morning. These changes were gradually implemented in Leicester and nationally, encouraged by the comments of visitors from the royal colleges and the specialist advisory committees (SACs). However, pressure to meet elective waiting list targets often resulted in the loss of daytime emergency sessions.

When junior doctors' hours were reduced in the 1990s, there was only one specialist registrar on duty at the LRI; on half the days some of these doctors might have only limited experience. As a result, I needed to go in for an evening ward round, and to supervise most operations apart from appendicectomies. By this time, we had two emergency theatres out of hours, but we were competing with orthopaedics, plastic surgery and gynaecology. Priority for the emergency theatre was determined by a combination of the order in which patients were added to the theatre list and the judgement

---

17 For CEPOD see chapter 32

of the theatre nurses and anaesthetists. I formed the impression that to be waiting in person in the coffee room improved the chances of my patient being sent for, so over the years I spent many hours dozing there in a chair. The alternative was to go home to bed and be called when my turn came, but this increased the risk of the case not getting to theatre before the next day's routine lists began and the patient being shunted into the next evening.

Patients with superficial abscesses were among the common emergencies. Drainage of these was often left to the end of the overnight emergency list on the grounds that they were less serious and might infect others. They were liable to be put off to the next night and the same thing might happen again. The delay of up to 48 hours was distressing for the patients and legitimately the subject of complaints, and we needed to solve the problem. Emergencies had never been considered for day-case surgery, but after discussion we set up a system whereby these patients, on referral from a GP or A&E, were asked to attend the day ward at 8am for operation at the end of that morning's list. As these patients are usually free of serious comorbidity (apart occasionally from diabetes) and not elderly, this system worked well. It solved the problem of the lengthy delays and saved beds. I believe this was the first published example of emergency operations managed as day cases[18].

In 1996, we designated two six-bedded bays on one general surgical ward as a surgical assessment unit. GP referrals were admitted directly to it without passing through A&E and transfers from A&E were accepted promptly. This reduced congestion in A&E and kept all our adult emergency admissions together for ease of initial assessment and review. It was made clear to patients (and relatives) that, once a diagnosis had been made, they might not need to stay overnight. If an operation was needed, patients normally returned to one of the main surgical wards. Those not operated upon were transferred once it was clear that their admission would exceed 48 hours. This system worked well: patients were in beds rather than waiting on an A&E trolley, and frequent review by more senior staff was facilitated. Disturbance in other wards due to night-time admissions was avoided and the early discharge of those who did not need to stay in was easier. It was occasionally necessary to mix the sexes in one of the bays, but in the circumstances, patients seemed philosophical about this. Many hospitals have followed a similar policy, but we were one of the first.

---

18   Loftus IM, Watkin DFL. The provision of a day case abscess service. *Ann R Coll Surg Eng* 1997; 79: 289-90

When I was president of the Association of Surgeons of Great Britain and Ireland in 2001, I made Emergency Surgery the theme of the annual conference. It remains an area of concern, and in recent years, there have been national initiatives to improve the care of surgical emergencies.

24

TRAINING SURGEONS

When I was an SHO in Bristol, I was well supervised by the SR for my first few operations for appendicitis, hernias and varicose veins. A consultant urologist oversaw me doing cystoscopies and parts of retro-pubic prostatectomies and I did one cholecystectomy under the watchful eye of Professor Milnes Walker. While a registrar in Leicester, I received valuable operative training from James Hadfield, the SR.

Thereafter, the number of operations for which a consultant directly supervised me could be counted on the fingers of one hand! It was a matter of watching the consultants, reading up on the operations and then doing them. Apart from my time in Bristol I had no systematic teaching except for attending occasional courses. I was very experienced but under-trained. As a consultant, I was determined to provide better training.

OPERATIVE SURGERY

Once I was established, I began to take both my registrar and my SHO through appropriate operations on elective lists. I carefully controlled what they did when I was absent by booking my own waiting list admissions, a task usually delegated to juniors. I had only two half-day theatre sessions per week at the LRI, which limited the scope for taking SHOs through operations. A weekly list at Hinckley and District Hospital, comprising mostly hernias and varicose veins, provided a useful opportunity for teaching them. I also took a direct interest in the emergencies, with out-of-hours ward rounds and support in theatre for major cases. I decided that the single SR, who was always on call covering the registrars, need not do so on my days on duty. This policy was designed to relieve the SR of some of his onerous hours, but it also meant that the registrar was directly under my charge – an opportunity for instruction.

These arrangements changed as we acquired more SRs so that there was one for each firm of two consultants. Then, when we moved into phase II (see chapter 19), I acquired a twin theatre for one of my two sessions. The benefit of twin theatres is that they enable trainees to operate with help available from the consultant next door, although this can be difficult to provide when engaged in a major case. Senior registrars who needed experience of major operations often had less supervision than would have been desirable, because I was in the other theatre teaching the registrar or an SHO.

In the 1990s we needed to appoint additional consultants, and to provide facilities for the newcomers the twin theatres were lost. On balance, I felt this improved the supervision of trainees, but we had to be careful to give them enough operative experience.

During the 1980s, the SR provided the emergency cover for the registrar, and he was sufficiently experienced to do this, other than for exceptional cases. In my last decade at the LRI, the Calman changes (see chapter 33) and the limitation of junior doctors' hours meant there was either an SR or a less experienced registrar on duty, not both as previously. Coupled with rising public expectations and the increasing incidence of litigation, consultants became increasingly involved in emergency operations. By 1995, when the more junior specialist registrar was on duty, I went in to supervise any emergency operation more serious than an appendicectomy.

CLINICAL TRAINING

There is much to training apart from operating. Ward rounds are the obvious example, but it is difficult to combine talking to the patients with instruction for the various grades of juniors and the students. Ideally these three activities would be separated, but there wasn't time to do this, so I did my best to combine them. As a result, my routine ward rounds were considered to last too long! One of my most important roles was, on occasion, restraining enthusiastic SRs from operating when there was a better alternative, such as 'wait and see' or occasionally interventional radiology.

In outpatient clinics, it was difficult to decide the relative roles of consultant and juniors – I usually had three others working in my clinic. Should the consultant see all the new patients, leaving others to deal with subsequent visits, often with the results of investigations and the need for a decision? Or should the same doctor see the patient throughout? I was always on hand to give advice, but often it was not sought. With up to 70 patients attending a clinic I was busy, making it difficult to supervise the two or three trainees as well as teach my students. Furthermore, there was an inevitable tendency for juniors to play safe by bringing the patient back another time, thus swelling the numbers. One of my colleagues laboriously went through the case notes before the session, allocating them to individuals. I didn't think this helped with training; it was more likely to leave the trainees seeing only routine follow-up patients.

In the 1990s, as additional consultants were appointed, there was some reduction in the number of patients at each outpatient session, and fewer juniors were present. Also, we were trying to organise the clinics to minimise the time patients waited. Traditionally, the nursing staff had allocated patients among the various members of staff to keep the clinic flowing, but individuals had no incentive to keep to time. This all required reorganisation. I introduced a policy for each doctor to have a schedule of timed appointments for new and follow-up patients. When a further appointment was specified the grade of surgeon was to be indicated. With the help of my efficient clinic clerk, these arrangements worked better.

Informal chat, over a cup of coffee, also contributes to training. We discussed clinical matters, career plans, research projects and current hospital issues. This was facilitated by the 'firm' structure, which gave stability in personal relations over periods ranging from three months to a year. Following the subsequent change to shift working I believe this has been lost.

TRAINEE ROTATIONS

When I arrived in 1971, the 'peri-FRCS' registrars were often appointed having passed the primary but not the final FRCS. They rotated around the Leicester hospitals, including posts in cardiothoracic surgery and urology. In the late 1970s registrar posts in Peterborough, Boston, Nuneaton and Kettering were included as part of a deal to place final-year medical students in these hospitals.

Achieving a Balance was introduced in 1987 (see also chapter 30), aiming to relieve the bottleneck at progression from registrar to senior registrar. It made a distinction between career registrars (CRs) eligible for promotion in the NHS and visiting registrars (VRs) who were to be recruited from overseas and were time limited. All registrars were to have the same training opportunities, with the effect of mandating inclusion in the teaching hospitals' rotations.

Once these changes were applied in 1990, the career/visiting registrar rotation was purely in general surgery and the FRCS was required before appointment. All registrar posts in DGHs then had to be incorporated in rotations with teaching hospitals.

The SRs in Leicester originally rotated in a fixed sequence through six firms, including the urological unit. This did not take any account of the developing special interests of the trainees so, in the mid-1980s, I suggested a flexible scheme to allow choice. My colleagues all argued that this would prove too difficult, but when I undertook to organise it, they accepted with alacrity! I asked each SR to give his order of preference for the next year. If a firm was oversubscribed, I gave priority to the more senior trainee. Shortly afterwards the SR post on the urological unit was recognised for training in that specialty and so was detached from the general surgical rotation.

We were fortunate to gain an arrangement with the RAF for one of their trainees to spend a year in Leicester, bringing his salary with him. This enabled one of our SRs to seek an attachment in a specialist unit elsewhere in the UK or abroad (mostly in Australia). This was easily arranged because the trainee carried his salary with him. It proved popular; indeed, I often had to adjudicate between SRs who wished to take advantage of it. It also eased problems in the choice of placements, as the RAF surgeon could be allocated to whichever firm was least sought after for that year.

The Calman changes were implemented in 1995, amalgamating the CR/VR and SR grades as specialist registrars (SpRs). Each firm then had one SpR in the later years of training and one in the earlier years, the former rotating annually and the latter six-monthly.

FORMAL TEACHING FOR TRAINEES

Soon after I arrived, I started a series of early evening tutorials for FRCS candidates and was rebuked by the postgraduate dean for not going through the proper channels. Later we began biannual week-long courses for the exam, including mock clinical and viva sessions.

In 1983 Peter Bevan in Birmingham published his experience of running 'anastomosis courses', using animal material. The next year I set up similar teaching for SHOs, using a seminar room in the Clinical Sciences building. I had no funding for this and aimed to run it at only a nominal cost to the trainees. One of the research registrars agreed to assist and he was tasked with obtaining the bowel and blood vessels from the abattoir. The staff there were happy to oblige in return for a bottle of whisky. I borrowed sets of instruments and begged sutures from theatres. At that time SHOs had adequate experience of knots and suturing skin, so we covered bowel anastomosis and arterial suturing on three successive Saturday mornings. These sessions proved popular with the result that when a trainee had the opportunity to do an anastomosis under supervision in theatre, that went more smoothly.

I continued to run these courses for over 10 years, until a training facility was developed at LGH. This happened in the 1990s when the Regional Health Authority (RHA) agreed to fund simulation for laparoscopic surgery, and we were able to use the purpose-designed facility for basic skills training. As the opportunities for hands-on training in theatres came under pressure from the hospital contracts, the Royal College of Surgeons introduced basic surgical skills courses. These started with surgical knots, and skin and abdominal wall closure using models, plus excision of skin lesions from a pig's foot, concluding with bowel anastomosis using commercially prepared material. I thought the basic suturing skills should be taught right at the start of surgical training, while anastomosis would preferably come later when manual dexterity had improved, but we had to abide by the RCS syllabus. This course was supervised by a colleague from LGH and managed by the nursing sister responsible for the unit. I continued to teach on the course after retirement, along with other consultant volunteers, until I was 70.

The early courses cost participants £5 for three sessions, to pay for whisky for the abattoir staff, biscuits and coffee. By 2017 they paid £695! I doubt whether the economical arrangements that I established in the 1980s would be permitted now.

FEMALE TRAINEES

There were few female consultants in surgery; the first was not appointed in Leicester until 1984 and she remined the only one until the late 1990s. The proportion of women among our surgical trainees diminished from SHO to registrar and we never had a female SR in general surgery until the 1990s. The reasons were multifactorial but included prejudice among consultants. However, there were then two trailblazers in Leicester.

A female peri-FRCS registrar in Leicester married and started a family. She moved to a part-time research job in Nottingham and obtained an MD. It then proved possible to employ her in Leicester as a supernumerary SR on six sessions, using funds reserved for this purpose (as had been the case for Elisabeth in radiology in the 1970s). This was the right solution for her, but it did raise problems over her placements. If she was additional to the substantive post, would this exceed the SAC ratio of trainees to consultants? Alternatively, she could fill a vacancy while another SR was seconded elsewhere, with his salary, but then the unit was understaffed, particularly for emergency duty. We used each of these solutions at various times, while she often did more than her half share in the emergency rota. She completed her training in Leicester, passed the exit exam (see chapter 34) at the first attempt and was appointed to a consultant post as a colorectal surgeon in a teaching hospital.

Another woman, with two children, was originally appointed as a VR working full-time. Following a revolution in Nigeria, her husband was imprisoned, and she became a political refugee, and so was eligible to become a CR, and then a specialist registrar (SpR) under the Calman reorganisation, working full-time throughout. She too became a teaching hospital consultant. It was unusual at that time for female trainees to progress to surgical consultant posts. These two were incredibly determined and were well supported by most of my colleagues.

RESULTS OF TRAINING IN LEICESTER

How can the effectiveness of surgical training in Leicester be assessed? One measure is how the trainees progressed in their careers. The SHO posts attracted a good field of applicants, and most became registrars in a variety of specialties. Some decided that surgery was not for them, because they found operating too stressful or they couldn't face the need for research and publications; most of these went into general practice. For the first 20 years an important hurdle for SHOs was the primary FRCS exam in the basic sciences, which some failed to pass, indicating a lack of determination to proceed in surgery. I think one of the functions of the SHO grade was to help young doctors decide what they wanted to do.

The peri-FRCS registrars mostly passed the final FRCS but found it difficult to progress thereafter in general surgery. There were too many candidates for the SR vacancies and research for an MD thesis became virtually a prerequisite. Some trainees could be fitted into research posts in the professorial department or as transplant fellows; others found similar posts elsewhere. Two managed to complete a thesis while working as registrars. Others moved into a less over-populated surgical specialty, while some went into general practice. In about 1990, the reorganisation under *Achieving a Balance* corrected the disproportion between the numbers of registrar and SR posts. This improved the prospects for registrars but moved the bottleneck to SHO level.

During the early 1980s some of our SRs had difficulty securing consultant posts, two being SRs for five or six years, compared with a requirement of four years, but all were finally placed in good jobs. A substantial minority were appointed to posts in Leicester. On reflection, there should have been more of a mix with outside candidates. Into the 1990s, expansion of the number of consultants resulted in a national shortage of candidates, so all trainees were placed promptly. A disproportionate number of our trainees found consultant posts in teaching hospitals, which suggests that they were good candidates.

Since the introduction of the Intercollegiate Exam in 1991, another measure of success is the proportion who pass this exit exam at their first attempt. Up to the year 2000, only two of ours had to resit and both passed the next time. I had access to the results for all the other training schemes, many of which had lower pass rates. I tried to interest the Specialist Advisory Committee (SAC) in using these figures as part of the assessment of regional training schemes, but they would not take up the idea.

THIRTY YEARS AS A SURGICAL TRAINER

I thoroughly enjoyed training individual surgeons at the various levels, though this was often made more difficult by the time pressures, particularly in theatre. There was a serious lack of simulation aids, helped a little by the start of the anastomosis courses. Laparoscopic surgery particularly lends itself to simulation, but we only acquired facilities for this in the mid-1990s and then there was little uptake, other than in formal courses, because it was sited away from the main theatres.

As a member, and later chairman, of the SAC and as an examiner for the Intercollegiate Board, I gained a broader view of training nationally. My involvement in the preparation of the first two versions of the curriculum for higher training in general surgery and its subspecialties prompted conversations about what should be included. I hope that in these activities I made a small difference.

25

WHATEVER HAPPENED TO GENERAL SURGERY?

When acquaintances asked what I did, I replied that I was a surgeon at the Leicester Royal Infirmary:

'What sort of surgeon?'

'A general surgeon.'

'You're not a specialist then?'

This led me to explain that following the development of various surgical specialties (for example orthopaedics or ENT), what remained was a specialty known as general surgery, which in the 1970s comprised 'guts, glands and arteries'. That was indeed the scope of my practice when I started as a consultant, together with basic urology, neonatal surgery and occasionally primitive neurosurgery for trauma. Over time, this changed. Michael Johnstone arrived to take care of the neonates. CT scanning facilitated the transfer of appropriate head injuries to the neurosurgeons in Nottingham. A urology unit was established at LGH, so prostatectomy no longer figured in my lists. Increasingly the professorial unit provided for arterial surgery, though it was 1995 before there was a formal rota to manage ruptured aortic aneurysms and other arterial emergencies.

The surgery of the gastrointestinal (GI) tract was my main interest, and this too was changing. Peptic ulcers – a major part of my work in the 1960s – were being diagnosed endoscopically and treated with drugs to control the secretion of acid. At the other end of the gut a 'new coloproctology' developed in the 1970s, much of it initiated by Sir Alan Parks, at St Mark's Hospital in London. He devised procedures to control faecal incontinence, and pouch operations to avoid the continuous effluent from an ileostomy after pan-proctocolectomy for ulcerative colitis. Bill Heald, from Andover, introduced the concept of total meso-rectal excision (TME) for rectal cancer, reducing the incidence of pelvic recurrence, which had been a problem in my practice. The use of stapling devices facilitated oesophageal and low rectal anastomoses and a surgical stapling society was started with the backing of the industry, but it was short-lived due to overlap with other organisations. Others refined the surgery for anal fissure, fistula and rectal prolapse, while physiological investigation of the anal sphincter began to rationalise the management of disorders of defaecation.

All this was a challenge for surgeons. I was busy with the work of clinical sub-dean and then in hospital management, so did not have the time to acquire all these new skills. For patients with colitis who chose 'restorative proctocolectomy', I relied on colleagues to do the 'pouch operation', avoiding an ileostomy – a Birmingham-trained senior lecturer and then a surgeon from Peterborough. We arranged for one of the academic staff to set up an anorectal physiology laboratory.

Another development in gastrointestinal surgery was the introduction of procedures to promote weight reduction for morbid obesity. The first method, in the 1970s, was small bowel bypass. It was adopted by a colleague in Leicester but the effects were often too drastic nutritionally. Operations to reduce the capacity of the stomach followed in the late 1980s, and after discussion with Professor Alan Johnson in Sheffield, I carried out a small number of 'vertical banded gastroplasties'. A variety of other operations, open or laparoscopic followed, so establishing bariatric surgery as another subspecialty.

GASTROINTESTINAL ENDOSCOPY

While I was a lecturer in Sheffield, the unit acquired its first flexible fibre-optic gastroscope. It had a feeble incandescent bulb at its tip and was side viewing and so was suitable only for examination of the stomach. By the time I moved to Leicester an end-viewing oesophago-gastro-duodenoscope

(OGD) was available. It had more powerful lighting delivered by optical fibres from an external source. With a diameter of 12mm, it was a little difficult to manoeuvre through the pylorus into the duodenum.

A medical colleague suggested that we make a joint application for an OGD, and this was successful. However, there was nowhere to use it other than in the operating theatre or a side ward. When phase II of the LRI was being commissioned we managed to take over the seminar room on the new day-case unit, and this served as the endoscopy room for the next dozen years. Dr David Carr-Locke, a medical trainee and subsequently a consultant, then drove forward the development of endoscopy in Leicester. He introduced colonoscopy, enabling biopsy of large bowel lesions and the removal of polyps. With difficulty, I learned colonoscopy and included it in my weekly endoscopy list.

Then he developed endoscopic retrograde cholangiopancreatography (ERCP) which gave X-ray images of the bile ducts and the pancreatic duct. Endoscopic division of the sphincter at the lower end of the bile duct released stones. I wondered about taking up ERCP, as a surgical colleague at LGH was doing. However, after attending a course at the Middlesex Hospital, I concluded that I didn't have the time for the long learning curve.

In 1983 endoscopes were introduced with a small video camera at the tip, which enabled the image to be viewed on a television screen. This was less tiring and enabled other members of the team to see, and to assist in complicated procedures. Training was facilitated. As a fibre-optic bundle was no longer involved, the diameter of the OGD could be reduced to 8mm, which allowed the examination to be performed under much lighter sedation or even none.

In 1992 we moved into a purpose-designed endoscopy unit in the new phase IV building. In many hospitals gastrointestinal endoscopy was the prerogative of medical gastroenterologists but the surgeons in Leicester were keen to continue it as a shared activity and to include it in training in general surgery. I believe access for GI surgical trainees remains a problem.

BREAST CANCER

My practice included breast cancer for two-thirds of my years in Leicester. Local excision of the lump combined with radiotherapy had been shown to be as effective, for selected cases, as simple mastectomy. For lesions suitable for either treatment I discussed the alternatives and tried to discern the patient's priority. Some, particularly the younger ones, wanted to retain a breast; others, often the older subjects, had a desire to 'get rid of it all' by mastectomy. Then I would angle my advice towards their choice so that they did not feel a burden of responsibility for it. I adopted adjuvant hormonal therapy with Tamoxifen for all patients and chemotherapy for those with spread to the sampled axillary lymph nodes.

In 1986 the *Forrest Report* recommended screening mammography for women aged 50–70 and this was rolled out as a national programme over the following two years. As the consultant member of the executive of the Leicestershire District Health Authority, I was present when the district medical officer said that 'obviously' this service would be based at the LRI. As this site had the only A&E department, it was under intense pressure. I therefore urged that mammography should be at Glenfield and this was a rare instance in which I influenced a development. Once the screening unit was based at Glenfield it followed that surgery for breast cancer should also be concentrated there. This was the first subspecialty of general surgery to be formally separated in Leicester. I stopped seeing patients with breast conditions and concentrated on GI surgery, which had always been my principal interest.

LAPAROSCOPIC (KEYHOLE) SURGERY

Gynaecologists had been using laparoscopy for many years, for diagnostic examinations within the abdomen and to carry out simple operations such as clipping the Fallopian tubes for birth control. A telescope is inserted into the peritoneal cavity through a small abdominal incision and the abdomen is inflated with carbon dioxide to create space for viewing. What facilitated more complicated procedures was the arrival of miniature video cameras that could be mounted on the laparoscope. The field of view is presented on screen. Instruments introduced via separate small incisions can be manipulated effectively and all members of the team can assist appropriately.

In 1990, Professor Alfred Cuschieri from Dundee won the Association of Surgeons' video competition with a film of laparoscopic cholecystectomy (removal of the gallbladder for gallstones). The other judges and I were completely bowled over by this and it made a great impression when shown at the annual conference. Following this, surgeons around the country were keen to adopt the procedure but it did involve a capital outlay for the equipment. I made a proposal to our chief executive at the LRI for expenditure of £30,000 on laparoscopic instruments and the associated video system. Unsurprisingly, there was no money! Soon afterwards, an entrepreneur advertised a package that included a laser. I reapplied, in partnership with the gynaecologists (who would also use the laser), and with this modern-sounding addition the money was found, despite the price having risen to £70,000. Thus, my colleagues and I could start doing laparoscopic cholecystectomies. The laser was found to be unnecessary (and a little dangerous for this purpose) and languished in a cupboard; many hospitals were similarly taken in by the salesman.

The story of the introduction of laparoscopic cholecystectomy deserves further discussion. Surgeons in the USA and Europe were already experienced in it and some British surgeons attended their short practical courses. But most of us just did it! I followed a policy of explaining to patients that this was a new procedure, with the advantages of smaller incisions, less pain and a more rapid recovery but that for safety I would convert to a conventional open operation if I met with difficulty. That was indeed the result in three of my first 10 attempts, but once I was familiar with the procedure I very rarely needed to convert.

Manipulating the long instruments, while watching the operation on the television screen, is quite different from an open operation. However, I was used to snaring polyps colonoscopically, managing the process on screen, and this helped me adjust to laparoscopic operating. Fortunately, I did not have any serious complications, but others did, sometimes with fatal consequences. The way that laparoscopic cholecystectomy was adopted in Britain was subsequently heavily criticised and it was decided that comparable new operations would no longer be allowed without a properly organised training programme, such as was established for laparoscopic operations for bowel cancer.

It is remarkable that this important innovation attracted little interest from academic surgical units. In the UK only those in Dundee and Leeds reported early experience of it. Then a controlled trial of cholecystectomy was conducted in Sheffield, with blinded aftercare to compare the recovery period with that for the open operation. Interestingly, this showed no significant difference in the length of hospital stay. It averaged four days in both groups, longer for laparoscopic operations than in most other hospitals, probably due to caution in the care of the Sheffield patients.

Over the next few years surgeons explored the use of laparoscopy for other abdominal operations. The most suitable appeared to be those in which a long incision had been needed for a small procedure within the abdomen, for example adrenalectomy (when the gland was over acting) or operations to correct gastro-oesophageal reflux (to relieve heartburn). I left these advances to my younger colleagues.

LAPAROSCOPIC HERNIA REPAIR

Another development was the laparoscopic repair of hernias. The rationale was not just a reduction in postoperative pain and avoidance of the scar in the groin, but the mechanical advantage of placing a 'patch' on the inside, where intra-abdominal pressure would help to hold it in position. The analogy is that a bucket should be patched on the inside rather than the outside. Some of my colleagues adopted this method and in 1992 I went on a two-day hands-on course in Guildford. I found the technique difficult and concluded that the learning curve would be prolonged and that it would therefore not be sensible to embark on this as I was approaching retirement.

Subsequently, the published trials showed only a small advantage for laparoscopic hernia repair as measured by a modest reduction in pain and a shortened recovery time. These advantages must be set against a higher cost for the equipment (and disposables) and very infrequent but serious complications, due to damage to intra-abdominal organs during insertion of the laparoscope. Both open and laparoscopic repairs of groin hernias can be done as a day case; the open repair has the additional advantage of the practicability of local anaesthesia. The merits of these two approaches remain delicately balanced with laparoscopy preferable for bilateral groin hernias and for recurrences after open operations. It is therefore appropriate to discuss these options with the patient.

FURTHER APPLICATIONS OF LAPAROSCOPY

Gradually, through the 1990s, laparoscopic methods were devised for most abdominal operations. One limitation is the retrieval of a resected specimen. For splenectomy, 'morcellation' within a plastic bag provides material which is acceptable for histological examination, but colonic cancers require an abdominal incision for removal of the specimen. Some procedures are facilitated by the insertion of a hand through a small incision, with a sealing collar around the wrist to maintain inflation. Bowel anastomosis is achieved by using miniaturised stapling devices. One useful laparoscopic application is in live donor nephrectomy for kidney transplantation. On the other hand, the suggestion of a laparoscopic operation for abdominal aortic aneurysm has not been adopted because the endovascular technique is easier.

The development of robotic equipment added another dimension. Strictly, this is robot *assisted* surgery; the operator controls the laparoscopic equipment from a virtual reality console. This is technically a triumph, but its real advantages may be limited to two situations: where access to the site of the operation is restricted or for very small-scale manipulation, when magnification of hand movements in the controlling console is helpful, for example when joining small blood vessels.

VASCULAR SURGERY

The techniques involved in arterial surgery are quite different and most general surgeons of my generation had not had adequate training. I soon withdrew from elective arterial work, leaving this to Professor Bell's unit. I continued treating varicose veins both surgically and using compression sclerotherapy, until the vascular surgeons separated.

During the 1990s vascular surgery in Leicester began to diverge from general surgery, providing a separate emergency rota from 1995. The evolution of treatment for abdominal aortic aneurysm is discussed in chapter 39. In due course vascular surgeons took over the treatment of varicose veins, which previously they had eschewed. There were two reasons for this: varicose veins provide suitable operative experience for junior trainees; and there is scope for private work, whereas arterial surgery requires more supporting services than may be available in private hospitals.

NATIONAL TRENDS

These changes in the practice of individual surgeons were occurring, with local variation, throughout the country. Surgeons were excited by the possibilities and subspecialty societies encouraged sub-specialisation. The serious emergencies in vascular surgery led to separate rotas for these, resulting in vascular surgeons being in dual jeopardy, having responsibility for this in addition to their general on-take commitment. In larger hospitals, additional surgeons were appointed to cover a separate vascular emergency rota.

Newly appointed breast surgeons, extending their repertoire to include reconstruction after mastectomy, were doing little elective GI surgery and felt uncomfortable with abdominal emergencies. Gradually they and the vascular surgeons withdrew from the general emergency rotas, so additional GI posts were necessary to provide an acceptable frequency of on-call. This process was exemplified at the LRI as discussed in chapter 28.

During the 1990s gastrointestinal surgery began to differentiate into upper GI, hepatobiliary and colorectal surgery. This process is considered from the perspective of the Association of Surgeons in chapters 31 to 35, with its implications for staffing, training and the provision of the emergency service.

26

MEMORABLE PATIENTS

I particularly remember patients in whom errors led to serious complications or death and a few of these are summarised below. Most operations are uneventful and therefore much less instructive. One can also get into trouble with the law, as in 'The case of the stolen heart'. Surgeons tend to want to operate, but the decisions *not* to do so are equally important and examples of non-surgical alternatives are described in the last section.

SELECTED DISASTERS

Foreign bodies. In the early 1970s, patients were frequently referred to us from Leicester Prison (which is across the road from the LRI), having swallowed objects such as nails. These normally passed through the gut without incident. The prisoners were observed in hospital until then, granting them a break from prison.

One day, a prisoner was admitted having swallowed two razor blades. He seemed well and X-rays of chest and abdomen showed that they were in the rectum, whence the registrar on duty removed them. Thirty-six hours later the patient became ill and a repeat chest X-ray showed fluid in the right chest cavity. The razor blades had slit the wall of the gullet, which had leaked only after an interval. Despite an operation to repair the oesophagus he died of sepsis. We should have taken this variety of foreign body more seriously and had his oesophagus examined radiologically. After this incident there were no further admissions of prisoners who had swallowed objects; the inmates must have realised that it was not a safe pastime.

Heparin. When I first adopted low-dose heparin prophylaxis against thromboembolic complications (see chapter 22), I made an exception for abdominoperineal excision of the rectum (AP) for rectal cancer, fearing that there was a risk of bleeding from the pelvic cavity. Then a patient had a massive and fatal embolus after an AP, leading me to reverse my policy, which had not been based on evidence. Interestingly, a few years later I received a phone call in the middle of the night to tell me that a patient for whom I had done an anterior resection for a cancer of the rectum was bleeding from an abdominal drain 'and would need reopening' to control the blood loss. I said that we should first try omitting the next dose of heparin; the bleeding stopped, and reoperation was avoided.

Closed-book packing. A 17-year-old girl was admitted following a car crash. She had a closed abdominal injury, with massive blood loss from a deep split in the liver near its midline. My efforts to control this by packing the cavity failed to control the bleeding and sadly she died on the operating table. I was not then aware of the recently described alternative policy of 'closed-book' packing, using large gauze packs either side of the liver to push the sides of the tear together. Her father was terribly angry, both with me and the young man who had been driving the car far too fast. Some months later, he asked to see me to thank us for our attempts to save his daughter; I did not confess that closed-book packing might have made a difference – I should have done.

Ruptured aorta. A middle-aged man, injured in a road accident, was referred from A&E draining blood from a tube inserted in his left chest cavity. The loss amounted to about 1.5 litres and was continuing. On opening the chest, I found that he was bleeding from a tear in the upper part of the thoracic aorta. This injury is often contained for a while within the surrounding tissues, allowing time for transfer to a cardiothoracic unit. However, in this case it was already leaking into the capacious pleural cavity. A cardiac surgeon responded rapidly to my call for help, but without the availability of a heart-lung machine he was unable to gain control and the patient died in theatre. He might have had a better chance of survival if the drainage tube had been clamped while transferring him to the cardiothoracic unit at Glenfield

Hospital. I was wrongly influenced by the recent experience of a colleague, who had a patient with similar bleeding into the *right* side of the chest and proved to have rupture of the large azygos vein (which only exists on the right side). The ends were ligated, and that patient made a full recovery.

Two other patients of mine with incomplete aortic injuries (not yet bleeding into the chest cavity) were diagnosed, transferred to the thoracic surgical unit, and had their aortas successfully repaired. (I had only one other patient who died on the operating table. He had both abdominal and head injuries and died of the latter while I was dealing with the accessible bleeding in the abdomen.)

Ultrasound misdiagnosis. A 70-year-old patient had an ultrasound diagnosis of cancer of the gallbladder, confined within its cavity. A routine preoperative ECG showed an abnormality of rhythm, but the medical registrar's advice was that this was not significant. In view of the possible malignancy, I chose open cholecystectomy rather than the laparoscopic approach. The operation was completed uneventfully but while in the recovery area she developed a severe arrhythmia and died in ICU shortly afterwards. No carcinoma was found in the gallbladder. With hindsight, I should have asked for a repeat of the ultrasound, which might have disposed of the cancer diagnosis, so avoiding the operation. Before going ahead with the procedure, I should also have obtained a more senior opinion on the ECG.

Hands-on help. While mobilising an awkwardly placed cancer at the junction between the duodenum and the upper jejunum I met profuse bleeding from a tear in the inferior vena cava (the large vein draining the lower half of the body). I could control the bleeding by finger pressure on the vein, but this left no hands free to repair it. I called an SR who had vascular experience and sent for the vascular instruments. He sutured the defect while I controlled the vein, and after removal of the tumour the patient made an uncomplicated recovery. This was an understandable accident, when dissecting in unfamiliar territory. The important lesson is to call for help when it is needed.

THE CASE OF THE STOLEN HEART

In 1979, Sir Terence English started the heart transplant programme at Papworth Hospital, Cambridge, and appealed for donors. In January 1980, a young woman was under my care following a moped accident. She had suffered a severe head injury and after ventilation for four days on the ICU was declared brain dead. She carried a donor card and we approached her parents regarding kidney donation. Her father told us she had previously said that in the event of her death she would like *all* her organs to be available for donation. Accordingly, I discussed this with Sir Terence, who was keen to proceed.

Our transplant fellow obtained verbal approval from a pathologist who was acting on behalf of the coroner. The heart was collected and successfully transplanted – among the first 10 such operations done at Papworth. This attracted interest from the press and the district administrator called a press conference, which focused on the diagnosis of brain death and the family's consent.

The next day I was visited by two very senior detectives enquiring into 'The theft of the heart', at the request of the coroner. The Leicester coroner at that time was unhappy about organ transplantation and had already made difficulties with the kidney transplant programme, which had been initiated by Professor Bell. It transpired that the pathologist had given approval for transplantation, but the inclusion of the heart had not been specified. I was given a very rough ride in the coroner's court, despite the Medical Protection Society having sent a barrister to assist me. The press was more even-handed, and the police decided that no crime had been committed. Subsequently, approval by the coroner's representative had to be in writing.

As a final twist, a member of the public wrote to Sir Terence, with a copy to the Minister of Health, complaining that to have transplanted this heart into a man with a criminal record was improper. He was told that medical ethics do not discriminate against law breakers.

AVOIDING SURGERY

Letting nature take its course. A thin, severely demented elderly lady was transferred directly to theatre from A&E with a diagnosis of a ruptured abdominal aortic aneurysm. She was in circulatory shock with a soft, diffusely tender abdomen but I could not feel an aneurysm. I considered that she was suffering from failure of the blood supply to the small intestine. Ordinarily on making this clinical diagnosis, a confirmatory abdominal exploration would follow, though with little chance of saving life. In this case, I phoned her son (who did not live locally). He said that her dementia had indeed reached the point at which she had no quality of life and we agreed that she should be allowed to die with dignity. She was moved to a ward and passed away peacefully a couple of hours later.

Interventional radiology. A serviceman was injured in a road accident in Lincolnshire while on leave. He was admitted to a small DGH with retroperitoneal bleeding and required transfusion of two pints of blood daily to maintain his blood pressure. After this had continued for four days, he was transferred to the LRI for investigation to determine the site of the bleeding, because arteriography was not available in the DGH. On examination, he had pain in the right flank, with a rapid pulse and extensive bruising down the whole right side of his trunk. The arteriogram showed active bleeding from a small artery on the right wall of the pelvic cavity.

The SR, whose special interest was vascular surgery, proposed that we should do an abdominal operation to stop this, but I thought that the bleeding point would be difficult to locate in the large haematoma and that we might then have to settle for ligating the internal iliac artery supplying it. This was in the early days of interventional radiology. I watched our expert radiologist introduce a catheter into the femoral artery, manipulate it close to the bleeding point and then insert a blocking coil. I was relieved to see the bleeding stop instantly. The following morning the patient was pain free with a normal pulse rate and he returned to his unit in Portsmouth, though the bruising would take weeks to resolve. I should have anticipated the possibility of control by embolization and involved the expert radiologist for the first arteriogram.

Ultrasound triumphs. A middle-aged man, of Pakistani origin, was admitted with gross ascites (an accumulation of fluid in the abdominal cavity). The differential diagnoses were tuberculous peritonitis, cirrhosis of the liver or disseminated intra-abdominal cancer. However, ultrasound showed only one vein (of the normal three) draining the liver, with dilatation of the portal vein (carrying blood from the intestines to the liver), making a diagnosis of Budd-Chiari syndrome. This condition, due to occlusion of the hepatic veins, is rare in the UK but occurs in parts of Africa. In South Africa it has been attributed to drinking a variety of 'bush tea'.

One of my radiological colleagues passed a catheter up a vein from the groin to demonstrate narrowing of the opening of the one remaining hepatic vein. He was then able to dilate this using a balloon catheter, following which the ascites was reabsorbed. The patient's job involved stirring an open vat of chemicals to produce a special adhesive. I wondered whether inhalation of chemicals from this might have caused the occlusion of the veins and his employer agreed to alter the procedure. Long-term anticoagulation with warfarin and follow-up ultrasound examinations, together with repeat dilatations, maintained him in good health.

As a postscript, many years later he presented with a narrowing in the transverse colon, thought radiologically to be cancerous, which proved histologically to be tuberculous.

Boerhaave syndrome. Spontaneous rupture of the oesophagus was first described in 1724. It classically results from violent vomiting. Without treatment it is universally fatal. Even with prompt operative repair the mortality is around 25 per cent.

In 1985 a 70-year-old woman was admitted following 24 hours of central chest pain that started after vomiting. Her circulation was stable, and a chest X-ray was normal. The next day endoscopy and a contrast swallow showed a haematoma in the wall of the oesophagus and a small leak into the right chest cavity. In view of the time that had elapsed and her good condition she was treated with antibiotics, intravenous nutrition and insertion of a drainage tube into the right pleural cavity. After three weeks, the oesophageal defect had healed but a CT scan showed a persistent abscess in the lower, posterior, part of the pleural cavity. Part of a rib was removed to allow insertion of a large bore drainage tube, following which the cavity closed and she made a good recovery.

By coincidence, another patient of mine was in the ward at the same time recovering after an early operative repair of an oesophageal rupture. In my whole career, I had six of these, with two fatalities.

Fuss about nothing. A man aged 56 was admitted as an emergency with abdominal pain. He had a history of a back injury and the scar of a previous abdominal operation, but he did not know what had been done. The abdomen was soft, with only a little tenderness. With reassurance, he became pain free over the next 24 hours.

He had voluminous LRI case notes and with those from LGH there were records of 17 similar admissions over the last three years. Sometimes the diagnosis had been sub-acute intestinal obstruction and on other occasions it was diverticulitis. I reviewed the case notes and X-rays; there was no objective evidence to support either diagnosis. The episodes seemed minor, even to the patient. It appeared that each time he complained of pain he was sent into hospital because of the diagnosis made at his last admission. After explaining this to him and in a letter to his GP, he was not admitted again.

OTHER ODDITIES

These are only a small sample of the unusual conditions that I encountered during my 40 years in surgery. Others included a patient with AIDS, when this was a new diagnosis, a paracetamol overdose presenting as 'cholecystitis', and a patient, recently returned from India, with an amoebic abscess in the abdomen. Most of these memorable patients were admitted as emergencies; I loved the variety of the problems seen 'on take'.

27

MY EXPERIENCE OF
DUODENAL ULCER

The management of duodenal ulcer (DU) is an example of the profound changes in medicine during my working life. When I started as a consultant, surgery for DU was my particular interest, but by the late 1980s elective operations had ceased and there were fewer emergency procedures. Duodenal ulcer also impinged directly on my career at several points.

Duodenal ulceration was first described in 1830 by John Abercrombie but was rarely mentioned until the late 19th century. From 1900, the incidence among young men increased, and by 1910 it had reached 'epidemic' proportions. At first, surgical treatment applied only for the closure of perforated ulcers; (surgery for the other emergency of bleeding ulcers did not start until the 1930s). Elective surgery began with the recognition that gastric juice was damaging the duodenum. The latter was bypassed by anastomosis of the stomach to the upper jejunum (gastrojejunostomy). In 1905 Sir Berkeley Moynihan, the leading British surgeon, opined that this was 'The greatest surgical advance of the century'. John Buchan's *Greenmantle*, set during the 1914–18 war, had John S Blenkiron suffering from a DU; later his symptoms were completely relieved after gastrojejunostomy. Interestingly, Buchan wrote his earlier novel, *The Thirty-Nine Steps*, while hospitalised due to a DU.

Following gastrojejunostomy, many patients found that their symptoms recurred a few years later, because of ulceration at the anastomosis. In response, acid secretion was reduced by partial gastrectomy, removing about two-thirds of the stomach. Reconstruction by gastrojejunal anastomosis completely bypassed the duodenum. The results in terms of cure of the ulcer were better, though ulceration could recur at the anastomosis. The side effects of fullness, bilious vomiting and 'dumping' (sweating and faintness after eating) were common.

Attempts to reconcile cure while avoiding side effects showed that the more of the stomach that was removed, the greater the cure rate, but the more prominent were the side effects. Despite this, throughout the 1940s and 1950s partial gastrectomy was widely practised. Indeed, it came to be regarded as the measure of a general surgeon's competence: Norman Tanner in Balham was reputed to perform the operation under local anaesthetic in 45 minutes! When I, as a very inexperienced registrar in Leicester, sought advice about a patient with a bleeding ulcer, I was asked: 'Are you an ace gastrectomist?' My answer was 'No.'

VAGOTOMY

In 1943 the Chicago-based surgeon Lester Dragstedt, aiming to reduce secretion without the disadvantages of gastrectomy, divided the vagus nerves supplying the stomach. About a third of his patients developed impaired emptying of the stomach, so a routine 'drainage procedure' of gastrojejunostomy or pyloroplasty was added. Initially only a few surgeons in the UK adopted vagotomy and pyloroplasty (V&P), while many resisted it. This dispute was exemplified at LGH, where the senior surgeon, Terence d'Offay, was an ardent gastrectomist, while his colleague, Davis Beatty, published one of the first British series of vagotomies. So unpleasant was this confrontation that the latter emigrated to Canada. Shortly afterwards, d'Offay moved to the Seychelles for personal reasons.

Apart from the vagus, the other stimulus for gastric secretion is gastrin, a hormone secreted by the mucosa of the gastric antrum. The antrum is incidentally removed in partial gastrectomy, but the significance of that had not been recognised. In 1968, JC Goligher and colleagues from Leeds and York reported on a controlled trial of operations for DU, comparing partial gastrectomy, vagotomy plus antrectomy, and vagotomy with gastrojejunostomy. The result was inconclusive: gastrectomy had a slightly lower recurrence rate but vagotomy had fewer side effects. This may have been the first example of a randomised controlled trial to compare surgical operations.

As a student at the Westminster Hospital, I was unaware of vagotomy until Harold Burge gave an invited lecture. He described his invention of an electrical device used at operation to confirm the completeness of vagotomy. If the intra-gastric pressure rose he would search for missed vagal branches. The device was never widely adopted. As a house surgeon I saw only one vagotomy and that was done for bleeding from an ulcer at the gastrojejunal anastomosis after a previous gastrectomy. Then on arrival in Bristol as an SHO, I found that vagotomy was well established, with ongoing research into the mapping of acid secretion in the stomach. Likewise, in Leicester: in 1962, vagotomy and pyloroplasty was the standard surgical treatment for DU and I learned to do the operation.

Additionally, registrars at the LRI had pioneered vagotomy and pyloroplasty (V&P) as the definitive treatment for perforated DU (rather than simply suturing the perforation). About 10 years earlier, AGR Lowdon in Newcastle had suggested partial gastrectomy as the treatment in these circumstances. Surgeons in the USA had published a series of cases of perforated DUs treated by vagotomy, the perforation being incorporated in the pyloroplasty. This policy had not been followed in the UK.

MY FIRST PUBLICATION
The perforated DUs treated at the Leicester Royal Infirmary from 1959 to 1963 provided an opportunity for my first publication. During this period 177 operations were performed. Before 1962, all those by one firm were simple closure of the perforation (the traditional method). On the other firm, the registrar James Hadfield (an SR by 1962) used vagotomy and pyloroplasty if the ulcer was deemed chronic. This policy was followed by all firms from 1962.

The postoperative mortality in the vagotomy series was three in 61, similar to reported series of simple suture. I followed up 93 per cent of those who had had their operation more than two years previously. Only 10 per cent of the V&P series had experienced further serious symptoms compared with 60 per cent after simple suture. I was encouraged to present these results at a meeting of the East Midlands Surgical Society in Sheffield in April 1964, where it was well received. I feel sure that this contributed to my appointment later that summer as an SR in the Sheffield Regional scheme. James Hadfield and I had published the study in the *British Medical*

Journal on 4th July, just before the SR appointment committee, at which I also described how I employed V&P and under-running of the ulcer bed for a bleeding DU.

THE INSULIN TEST

In 1968, on appointment as lecturer in surgery in Sheffield, after four years as an SR, I was set the project of reinvestigating the significance of the insulin test of completeness of vagotomy. Hollander had introduced this investigation in 1948. Intravenous-insulin-induced hypoglycaemia, which in turn caused an increase in acid secretion, mediated by the vagus nerves to the stomach. The concentration of acid, aspirated via a nasogastric tube, was monitored over the next two hours. A rise of more than 20mEq/l within the first hour was interpreted as 'early positive' evidence of an incomplete vagotomy; a rise in the second hour was a 'late positive' insulin test. The test was being performed routinely about 10 days after V&P. A chart on the wall of the department showed the results for each surgeon. Patients with symptoms suggesting recurrence of the DU, years later, were also tested and if they produced a positive test, reoperation, aiming to complete the vagotomy, was advised.

I suspected that the good correlation between the result of the insulin test and the recurrence of a DU might be biased because of changes in the response over time. Patients with negative tests in the early postoperative period might become positive a few years later as function recovered. I repeated the test in a group of 40 patients at two and six months after vagotomy. In the interpretation of the results, I abandoned Hollander's binary criterion of a 20mEq/l rise in the concentration of acid, and his comment that 'There are no degrees of vagality'. Instead I used the actual figures for acid concentration in the analysis. This showed that the distinction between 'early' and 'late' positives merely reflected the magnitude of the response. Many patients produced more acid in the tests at six months, while a few produced less.

I then repeated the insulin test results in patients seen in the long-term follow-up clinic and compared the results with their tests done soon after the operation. A group of 15 patients with clinical evidence of recurrence had a significant average increase in acid concentration. Sixty patients without symptoms of recurrence had no increase. The probability of recurrence increased sharply with increasing peak acid concentration in the delayed insulin test[19]. An objective means of identifying recurrence would have been desirable, but barium meal examinations proved difficult to interpret after pyloroplasty, while endoscopy of the duodenum was not yet available.

IMPROVING VAGOTOMY

Meanwhile, attempts to reduce the incidence of side effects (particularly diarrhoea) after V&P focused on making the vagotomy more selective. But preserving branches to the liver and the coeliac plexus did not reduce the side effects. Then in 1970, two surgeons – David Johnston in Leeds and Eric Amdrup in Denmark – independently theorised that destruction of the pylorus was responsible for the side effects of V&P. They introduced 'highly selective vagotomy', preserving the nerve supply to the antrum and pylorus, so retaining the normal mechanism for emptying the stomach. Pyloroplasty was not then needed. This did avoid the side effects. However, the operation was technically demanding, so not all surgeons achieved their low rate of recurrence. In 1982, TV Taylor from Manchester sought the same objective by preserving only the branches of the anterior nerve to the pylorus. He divided the posterior vagal trunk and incised the outer layers of the anterior wall of the stomach adjacent to the lesser curvature to interrupt the branches of the anterior vagus supplying the body of the stomach. This technically simpler operation preserved innervation of the gastric antrum and the pyloric sphincter but was not widely adopted.

MEDICAL TREATMENT

During the 1970s, histamine H2 receptor-blocking drugs were developed (starting with cimetidine), providing a 70 per cent reduction in acid secretion and relief of symptoms. Fibre-optic endoscopy demonstrated healing of the ulcer, but maintenance treatment was needed to prevent recurrence. Later, the protein pump inhibitor omeprazole proved even more effective.

Although this medication clearly shifted the balance away from operative treatment, surgeons continued to do vagotomies. From 1972 to 1983 the number at the LRI fluctuated between 46 and 107 per annum, with no downward trend. However, of 59 vagotomies in 1983 I was responsible for only one, confirming my recollection that by then I rarely recommended the

---

19   Duthie H, Watkin DFL. The delayed insulin test and recurrent duodenal ulceration. *Br J Surg* 1971; 58: 775-80

procedure. Thereafter, the number of elective operations for duodenal ulcer fell precipitately and by the 1990s they had ceased.

A LASTING TREATMENT FOR DU

Another revolution started in 1984 when Barry Marshall, in Australia, showed that a bacterium, *Helicobacter pylori*, colonising the gastric mucosa, was the main cause of DU. The ulcer could be cured permanently by a course of an appropriate antibiotic. This treatment came into routine use in the early 1990s. It was so reliable that procedures for bleeding needed only to control the bleeding point, leaving the antibiotics to cure the ulcer. Was the rising incidence of DU in the late 19th century due to the arrival of *Helicobacter pylori* in the population? It seems unlikely that we will ever know.

PERSONAL EXPERIENCE

Ever since performing insulin tests in Sheffield, from 1968, I'd had recurrent episodes of what I thought was ulcer pain. I controlled them with the available medication, self-prescribed. Then in 2000 I almost fainted while running up the escalator at Piccadilly Circus. I could not feel my radial pulse and initially thought I had an arrhythmia. I recovered sufficiently to go on to a planned meeting at the Department of Health, but cancelled my immediate commitments with the Association of Surgeons in London and travelled home to Leicester for cardiological investigation. Initially this indicated sick sinus syndrome, and I was judged fit to travel.

Three days later I was due to fly to Chicago for the meeting of the American College of Surgeons, representing the ASGBI. Immediately after my return, I was scheduled to attend a conference of the South African Association of Surgeons to speak on 'A Modern Hernia Service'. I fainted on getting up, cancelled my travels and was admitted to hospital. My haemoglobin was found to be only seven grams per 100ml – half the normal value. A blood count had been requested when I saw the cardiologist, but the result had not been noted. Only then did I notice that I was passing altered blood. Endoscopy showed a DU with evidence of recent bleeding. I needed transfusion with a total of eight pints of blood, narrowly avoiding an emergency operation. I was then treated to eradicate the *Helicobacter* and have had no symptoms since.

Reflecting on my 32-year involvement with duodenal ulcers, I wonder whether I may have acquired *Helicobacter* when doing gastric secretory tests on patients with a DU in Sheffield. I know of a colleague who was involved in tests of gastric secretion who required an operation for a DU.

Research projects measuring gastric secretion in relation to operations for DUs were a large part of the activity of academic surgeons in the 1970s; it is chastening to realise that all that effort was irrelevant.

LOCAL MANAGEMENT

28

HOSPITAL AND DISTRICT MANAGEMENT

Hospital management was reorganised repeatedly during my consultant career, and I was duly swept up in the process. When I arrived, the LRI and LGH were managed by the Leicester No 1 Hospital Management Committee. There were separate HMCs for Groby Road Hospital (and the cottage hospitals) and for each of the two psychiatric hospitals. All were under the control of the Sheffield Regional Hospital Board. This structure had not changed in the 23 years since the foundation of the NHS.

Additional consultant posts were limited by annual national specialty-specific quotas, distributed to regions in small numbers. This effectively controlled expenditure but limited development of the service. Hospital medical staff committees, comprising the whole body of consultants, could offer advice, but were kept at arm's length from the management. As an SR I had attended management courses at The King's Fund and in the Sheffield region, and I realised that consultants had a responsibility to engage with the managers. This chapter describes how local hospital management was modified during my career and my involvement in the process.

THE FIRST REORGANISATION

The *Cogwheel Reports* in 1967, 1972 and 1973 made many sensible comments on hospital management. They proposed a more focused medical contribution, by way of specialty divisions and a medical executive committee. As the most recently appointed consultant, I was made honorary secretary of the Division of Surgery, which covered all the hospitals in Leicester.

The 1974 reorganisation of the NHS implemented the Cogwheel recommendation in the hospitals. On an area and district basis it also aimed to integrate public health, hospitals and general practice, but this was not achieved for the latter. Regional Boards were renamed Regional Health Authorities (RHAs) and for the first time the teaching hospitals were included in their remit. All the health professions were represented at each level of management and decisions were by consensus.

An Area Health Authority (AHA) usually encompassed more than one district. Application of this model to the Leicestershire (and Rutland) area produced three districts, each with a DGH (Glenfield in the NW district was yet to be built). The two psychiatric hospitals were allocated to the Eastern and SW districts and the cottage hospitals were included in the geographical sectors. There was an Area Hospital Medical Staff Committee (AHMSC) on which all the specialty divisions were represented, and Elisabeth and I took our turns in that role. I was elected as one of the consultant representatives on the SW District management team. These meetings generated a lot of paper, but I cannot recall any substantial achievements.

BED ALLOCATION

In 1975, as phase II of the LRI was approaching completion, the AHMSC set up an area Bed Allocation Subcommittee. The chairman decided that it needed a 'cutter', and I was asked to be the surgical member. Our first task was to advise on the allocation of wards in phase II when it opened in 1978. Most of the surgical specialties were to occupy the new block while medicine, gynaecology and ophthalmology expanded in the 'old' wards, which were due to be upgraded.

It proved possible to meet the requirements of the various groups, subject to using the fifth new children's surgical ward for adults and retaining the existing ophthalmology unit in its single-storey block. We were told that it was necessary to demolish the latter 'for fire access', but when we challenged the management to produce support for this from the fire service it was not forthcoming, so the ophthalmology ward was retained. All the specialties were then satisfied.

The surgeons wished to minimise the number of wards in which each firm had patients, achieving this by combining the sexes in each ward. After discussion, particularly with the nursing management, this was agreed, placing males and females in separate six-bedded bays. The six single rooms provided flexibility. At that time, these mixed-sex wards proved entirely acceptable to patients, hitherto accustomed to the large Nightingale wards. The issue, however, rumbles on to this day.

REORGANISATION IN 1982

Following one of the recommendations of the Royal Commission on the NHS (The *Merrison Report*, 1979), AHAs were abolished in 1982, with districts (DHAs) taking over their functions. Generally, these were the pre-existing districts, but the staff in Leicester thought that a single district, corresponding to the old area, would be preferable. Thanks to vigorous lobbying by the dean, Robert Kilpatrick, this was achieved.

In 1983, Roy Griffiths, a director of Sainsbury's, conducted an inquiry into management in the NHS. He visited Leicester and I was among those he interviewed. Griffiths confirmed the structural changes recommended by Merrison but his main conclusion was the need for 'general management'. He is often quoted as saying: 'If Florence Nightingale were carrying her lamp through the corridors of the NHS today, she would almost certainly be searching for the people in charge.' A less well remembered remark was: 'The NHS is so structured as to resemble a mobile, designed to move with any breath of air, but which in fact never changes its position and gives no clear indication of direction.'

Griffiths recommended that all day-to-day decisions should be taken at unit level, with a general manager in charge of each unit. Functional management, with representation of each profession at every level, was abolished and the requirement for consensus was reduced. In Leicester, each of the three general hospitals acquired a general manager, two of them external candidates. The AHMSC became the DHMSC, continuing to include representatives of all the specialty divisions, but more important was the establishment of a District Medical Advisory Committee (DMAC), with five representatives from each of hospital consultants, general practice and public health.

DMAC CHAIRMAN

The new District Medical Advisory Committee had become the key source

201

of medical influence in the district. I was asked to chair this for four years starting in 1986. I was a member of the District Management Team (DMT) and attended the monthly meetings of the District Health Authority (DHA). Altogether these meetings occupied at least 10 hours per month, with much additional time spent reading documents at home.

To raise funds, we discussed the closure of pre-convalescent homes and the sale of surplus buildings and land. We considered the centralisation of paediatrics, the development of day-case surgery and the number of obstetric units. By 1988, it was apparent that the third maternity unit, planned for Glenfield, was not required. There would have been time to alter the plans for phase II, but at a meeting between the DMT and the representative from obstetrics, it was decided not to do so for fear of losing funding for the whole project. Then, on completion of the building, the maternity unit was converted, at considerable cost, to house cardiothoracic services, which then transferred from Groby Road Hospital. What a waste! Should I have blown the whistle when the decision was made to build the maternity unit?

In November 1986, the DMT travelled to the House of Commons to urge our local MPs to press for the district's percapita funding to be brought up to the national average. I had not been there before. On entering the lobby, we found ourselves in a lofty Gothic chamber with supplicants, many of them disabled, seeking audience. It was all very suggestive of a mediaeval court. We then convened in a smaller room where we received a sympathetic hearing, but I don't think the funding improved. The mission was repeated annually for three years, then was abandoned. Another reward of office was being invited with our wives to dinner at Quorn House, the historic family home of the chairman of the DHA. Simultaneously I was doing my best to keep an undiminished clinical commitment going, but was not keeping pace with developments in coloproctology. It was a fascinating and busy four years.

In 1989 we attended a meeting in Nottingham at which Kenneth Clarke, then secretary of state for health, outlined plans in the white paper *Working for Patients*. These included the 'internal market' and the proposal for hospitals to become NHS trusts. This would give them new freedoms and offered financial incentives, at least in the short term.

BACK TO BEDS

I was elected chairman of the Bed Allocation Subcommittee in 1982. It became apparent that children's surgery had more beds in phase II than were needed, so it proved possible to transfer medical paediatrics from the old children's block into this floor. A few years later, it was suggested that paediatrics should be centralised at the LRI, closing the single ward at LGH. This would facilitate the development of subspecialties within medical paediatrics, but it had implications for other specialties. General, urological and orthopaedic surgeons at LGH would no longer be able to treat children and it would be more difficult to support the special care baby unit there. After much argument, centralisation was finally achieved in 1989. There remained the exception of paediatric cardiology at Glenfield, where it was linked to adult cardiac surgery.

There were arguments over the provision of beds for urology and dental surgery, which the RHA considered to be part of the general surgical quota. The gynaecologists claimed that their allocation should increase to half the number of obstetric beds, many more than were currently provided. All these discussions were against a background of national specialty 'norms', which often exceeded what was available in Leicester. It was also a time when lengths of stay for many procedures were shortening and some operations were moving from inpatient to day case, so reducing the need for beds, particularly in gynaecology.

NHS TRUST
The NHS and Community Care Act 1990 introduced the 'internal market' within the NHS, with the option for hospitals to become NHS trusts. These would have a board responsible directly to the Department of Health (DoH), bypassing the RHA. They could set their own management structures, employ their own staff (including consultants), buy and sell assets and borrow capital, subject to limits. In each of the Leicester hospitals there was vigorous debate before the decisions were taken to become trusts in 1991. Chairmen and boards were appointed, and the changeover went remarkably smoothly, eased by the financial incentives. The existing unit general managers became chief executives.

At the LRI, Peter Homa, the chief executive, set up clinical directorates, each with a consultant 'clinical director' and a manager, responsible for the budget. The clinical directors met with the senior managers at the management board. When the trust's medical director was to be appointed some of my colleagues suggested that I might seek to do this job. However, I felt sure that another member of staff was better qualified for this. He was indeed selected and proved most successful. I was made clinical director for a combination of general surgery and the smaller specialties of ENT, plastic surgery, maxillofacial surgery and ophthalmology. Each of these specialties then had a head of service, with whom I liaised. I was supported by an excellent manager and a senior nurse, and together we steered the directorate through some troubled waters. I attended my first meeting of the hospital board in 1991; it functioned better than its predecessors.

GETTING DOWN TO BUSINESS

In 1993 the trust held an away day at Belvoir Castle for non-executives, senior managers and clinical directors to discuss the transformation of the LRI. There was discussion about how we should respond to the internal market and the associated contracts. I spoke about the wasteful repetition in aspects of administration, the relationship of waiting lists to contracts and the limitations posed by staffing problems in theatres. Regardless of the specifics, the day served to increase the medical staff's commitment to the necessary changes.

A business plan followed, identifying many strengths, weaknesses, opportunities and threats. A list of 17 items for development was proposed including: a high-dependency unit, an increase in the number of elective theatre sessions on each weekday from two to three (but how would these be staffed?) and major capital projects such as a new oncology department. Apart from the three-session theatres, most of these developments were achieved over the following five years. Without trust status, it would have been impossible for the hospital to carry out these plans on its own initiative or on such a rapid timescale. There was also a short-term improvement in the funding for new and replacement equipment. However, some proposals were never progressed, for example the creation of a neurosurgical department or a patient hotel to facilitate discharges.

Our general surgeons were now in competition with LGH and Glenfield. The other specialties in the directorate were monopolies but we had to plan to maximise our share of the general surgery in the district. The vascular unit was one obvious strength. We envisaged that it would provide the service for the whole district and increasingly attract outside referrals. However, it would need additional consultant staff, by the transfer of posts from LGH. For gastrointestinal work and other procedures, such as the repair of hernias, the plans were more matters of detail: a one-stop service for rectal bleeding, separate hernia clinics and, in conjunction with the medical gastroenterologists, open-access endoscopy for GPs.

RE-ENGINEERING

In 1994 the LRI trust proposed the engagement of management consultants to advise about improvements in the effectiveness of the hospital, at a cost in the order of £1 million. I attended the presentation by our chairman and chief executive to the NHS Executive at Quarry House, Leeds – an impressive building with a 50-metre swimming pool in the basement for the staff. The 'Re-engineering' proposal was received favourably and was supported financially by the DoH.

Members of staff, of all professions, attended numerous meetings with the management consultants. There were some improvements. Making an outpatient appointment was shown to involve 17 stages and this was streamlined by attaching an individual clerk as coordinator for each consultant's clinics. In outpatients, simple blood tests, chest X-rays and ECGs were often requested, the patient returning a week later for the results. A 'test centre' was set up next to the outpatient department, equipped with automated machines for blood counts and simple biochemistry, a room for chest X-rays and an ECG machine. The patient could then return to clinic with the results, all in the same session.

In the central operating department (COD), a holding area reduced time wasted in waiting for the next patient to arrive from the ward. An 'arrivals lounge' was created next to the COD, eliminating prior admission to a ward for patients having minor operations. Theatre staffing shortages were alleviated by amalgamating the roles of nurses and operating department practitioners (ODPs, formerly ODAs) so that the latter took on 'scrubbed' duties. In due course, the person in charge in a theatre might be from either profession. However, I do not think the management consultants produced the hoped-for amount of transformation.

STAFFING ISSUES IN THE SURGICAL DIRECTORATE

In 1995 one of the two dental surgeons was offered a research job in the anatomy department and retired early. His colleague had already bought a retirement home in Wales and planned to retire soon. The specialty had morphed into maxillofacial surgery, which was developing fast. It was inevitable that the dental surgeons' replacements would wish to do a much wider range of work (including the parotidectomies that I had hitherto included in my repertoire). A minimum of three consultants would be needed to provide an acceptable out-of-hours rota for emergencies. It would take about a year to negotiate replacement appointments, but we needed help immediately, especially to cover facial fractures. A retired surgeon from Cumbria was available as a locum but insisted on enhanced payment for little work. We had no option but to agree.

In another specialty, one consultant repeatedly arrived in the hospital under the influence of alcohol and despite warnings he persisted in this behaviour. He could not be allowed to continue but the trust would not dismiss him for fear of a prolonged and expensive legal battle, so he was retired on health grounds. Interestingly, he died only a few years later.

One year, an activist house officer organised his colleagues to record the occasions when they finished work after the planned time and coordinated a group claim for back pay. We had to concede this, but it seriously overstretched the directorate's budget. From then on, the hours arising from late finishing were offset by an extra half-day. We also had to cope with staffing problems due to the separation of vascular from general surgery as well as ongoing financial constraints exacerbated by the reductions in junior doctors' hours (see chapter 29).

EMERGENCY COVER FOR GENERAL SURGERY

From 1990 the reductions in junior doctors' hours increased general surgical consultants' workload, particularly as there was now either an SR or a registrar on duty for general surgery, rather than both. The less experienced registrars needed much more frequent consultant presence out of hours. Simultaneously, specialisation was evolving within general surgery. It was apparent both locally and nationally that a considerable increase in the number of consultants was required. The Association of Surgeons had identified a target of one consultant general surgeon per 30,000 of population and Leicester fell far short of this with 15 against a target of 26. I pointed this out to the district medical officer, who said there was no budget for additional consultants.

However, in 1993 the DoH recognised the problem by providing funds to the regions for the salaries of additional consultants to support the reductions in the juniors' hours. Initially, one post in general surgery was offered to the LRI. After discussion, two additional consultant posts were advertised later that year, half funded by the DoH and half by the trust, with interests respectively in vascular and liver surgery. This enabled the consultants' emergency rota to be relaxed from one-in-six to one-in-eight, reducing the impact of the increasing emergency involvement. There was no increase in facilities, so the existing theatre lists had to be redistributed, abolishing the parallel lists staffed by juniors.

DOUBLE JEOPARDY FOR CONSULTANTS

Two problems of double jeopardy then emerged. The vascular surgeons had set up a city-wide rota, on call one-in-six, in addition to their inclusion in the rota for general emergencies. The vascular emergencies were often ruptured aortic aneurysms, needing a consultant for this high-mortality operation. Their proposed solution was withdrawal from the general rota.

Neonatal surgery and emergencies in small children were covered by two general surgeons, each on call for alternate weeks, while also taking their turn in the general rota. Other teaching hospitals already had teams of specialist paediatric surgeons to whom neonates were referred from district general hospitals. Nationally, general surgical trainees were not involved in neonatal surgery, so when our two part-paediatric surgeons retired (the first due to do so in about 2000), it would not be possible to recruit replacements with dual training. We devised a sustainability plan for the gradual introduction of specialist paediatric surgeons, the first of whom was appointed in 1994.

In 1995 the three vascular surgeons at the LRI gave 12 months' notice of their withdrawal from the general rota. This would leave the remaining five surgeons on duty one-in-five. The two consultants involved in the rota for neonates declared that in that case they would become pure paediatric surgeons. Our youngest colleague could potentially have found another post in hepatobiliary surgery, and I could have retired aged 60, leaving just one surgeon for the rota! There was a real risk that the general surgical emergency service might collapse.

I had substantial commitments to national organisations and had become concerned about the number of days that I needed to spend away from Leicester. I offered to reduce my contract to six sessions, contributing part of my salary and facilities to an additional consultant post, while continuing to take a full part on the emergency rota. The management could scarcely refuse the offer, and a consultant with a colorectal interest was appointed, which made for an acceptable one-in-six rota.

I finished my term as clinical director in 1996, just as these arrangements were completed, and then ceased to have a management role locally. Subsequently a further general surgical consultant was appointed, with an oesophago-gastric interest. Michael Johnstone then shared the neonatal work with the recently appointed pure paediatric surgeon and withdrew from general surgery. Later, additional paediatric surgeons were appointed.

BECOMING A MEGA-TRUST

In 1999 the government decided that in cities with two or three acute trusts these should be amalgamated. Accordingly, the University Hospitals of Leicester NHS Trust was formed on 1st April 2000. This avoided wasteful competition between the hospitals, which had sometimes duplicated specialist services, for example liver resection. On the other hand, the trust management inevitably became remote from the shop floor. I never worked in this set-up, so am not qualified to comment further, but I have included reflections on the current NHS in chapter 41, among my comments on life in retirement.

29

JUNIOR DOCTORS' HOURS

Since I qualified in 1959 there had been dissatisfaction about the long hours worked by junior doctors. In my first pre-registration house officer (PRHO) post at the Westminster, I was resident and on duty for six months continuously, apart from one weekend when the registrar filled in for me. The working hours were long because (unlike the modern PRHO) I had to be present for all the operating lists, which displaced routine ward work into the evenings.

However, I was on duty for only the firm's own patients, averaging about 30. They were on the unit of two 14-bedded wards and two single rooms, plus a few elsewhere in the hospital, because patients remained in the ward to which they were first admitted. Turnover was low – a straightforward hernia repair resulted in a week's stay and many of the patients were up and about. One night in three I was responsible for emergency admissions, but as the hospital was in an area with a dwindling resident population there were few of them, so I usually had a full night's sleep. The basic salary (£420 per annum) was deemed to cover all out-of-hours work, regardless of whether the specialty involved much or little of it. After deduction for compulsory board and lodging, the salary amounted to approximately £5 per week, less than that of a dustman.

Moving on to posts away from London teaching hospitals, I found more considerate arrangements, usually being on duty for nights and weekends one-in-two or one-in-three, but with responsibility when on duty for all the patients in my specialty and with larger numbers of emergency admissions. I was resident when on duty until I became a senior registrar (SR) in 1964 and was then on call from home. In Sheffield, the emergency work was distributed among more units, so I was officially on call for emergency admissions only one-in-four, but my consultant at the Royal Hospital expected me to deal with the patients he sent in from domiciliary visits on any day. Then as a lecturer I was second on call to the registrar, on a one-in-four basis.

Arriving in Leicester as a consultant in 1971, I was supported by one of the three surgical registrars. The arrangement was that the sole SR would cover the registrar every night. I decided unilaterally that I would covert my registrar directly, giving the SR one night off in three. In 1969 extra duty payments, or units of medical time (UMTs), were introduced for junior doctors, at one-third the basic hourly rate, though as a university lecturer in Sheffield I was not eligible. Thus, trainees had a financial interest in maximising their UMTs, though this involved the disruption of working the extra hours. I never discovered whether the SR whom I had informally relieved of one-third of his on-call still claimed UMTs for this time.

In the late 1970s, after the medical school opened, Leicester gained three additional NHS surgical SRs and two lecturers, who functioned as SRs. By then there were three firms at the LRI, each of two consultants, sharing an SR and a registrar, so that these junior staff were on duty one-in-three.

The LRI originally ran a joint rota for the two PRHOs and three SHOs, each being on duty one-in-five for emergency admissions and a further one-in-five as second on call for existing inpatients. After it became a teaching hospital the complement increased to provide a PRHO and an SHO on duty with the firm on take for emergencies and a third, who might be of either grade, on call for the wards. Their calculated 84-hour week was a liberal arrangement in that era, but the basic working day often overran, so the weekly hours averaged about 90. There was no substantial change until the 1990s.

NATIONAL CHANGES

The first official mention of the need for reform was in *The Short Report on Medical Education* in 1981. Among far-seeing suggestions was a limit of 80 hours per week, but the report had no teeth, so nothing happened. Then in 1991, *Junior Doctors: The New Deal,* negotiated by the BMA, introduced targets to reduce junior doctors' hours, initially to 83 and then to a maximum of 72 hours per week by December 1994.

In 1993 the position was complicated by the *European Working Time Directive* (EWTD). This stipulated limiting doctors' working hours to 48 by 2009 but aimed for earlier implementation. The EWTD was enacted into UK law in 1998. The rules differed from the *New Deal* in the details of permitted continuous hours and timing of breaks, so the combined application of both sets of regulations was complex. A judgement in a Spanish court ruled that time on call at home counted as hours worked, regardless of the incidence of calls. This restricted arrangements for middle-grade cover.

CHANGES AT THE LRI

In the LRI Trust, discussions about implementation were complicated by the involvement, in addition to consultant and junior colleagues, of the Regional Task Force, the deanery, and the medical staffing office. First, we agreed to abandon the role of second call HS. A survey had shown that 70 per cent of calls were simply for drips or drugs[20], so it was practicable for this work to be included in the duties of the firm on take. There was pressure from management to put the PRHOs and SHOs on a 'partial shift' system, each doing one week in 12 on duty from 11pm to 8am, while the others finished at midnight when on take. This was tried for six months but the juniors did not like it, so we reverted to a one-in-six rota for both grades with a half day off to keep within the 72 hours.

The rotas for the registrars and SRs were more contentious, but we finally settled for having only one of them on duty so that each was on a one-in-six rota. As a result, when only an inexperienced registrar was on duty, the consultant was often called in. However, the *New Deal* did facilitate the appointment of additional consultants. All the trainees were then on a one-in-six rota for nights and weekends, calculated to be an average of 61.3 hours per week, though the basic weekday often overran the nominal eight hours. The structure of these rotas ensured that members of the junior staff on duty for emergency admissions were still working with others from their own unit. We regarded this as important.

Later, when the vascular consultants withdrew from the general rota, their

---

20 Astill JL, Watkin DFL. What does a house-surgeon on call for the wards do? *Lancet* 1987; 1:1363-5

juniors continued to participate in it. This helped to maintain the service and broadened their training, but it disturbed the integrity of the surgical teams. To minimise the disruption, I devised a complicated rota, cycling over 72 weeks! At that stage, the surgical staff still managed the duty rotas.

AFTERTHOUGHTS

After I retired, the tightening of the hours worked – to an average of 48 hours per week – dictated that all grades of junior staff moved on to 'full shifts'. The organisation of the rotas passed from the consultants to hospital managers, who inevitably were less concerned with how well the firms functioned. The differing numbers of staff in the various grades resulted in an almost random selection of the group on duty, with serious disadvantages in the loss of continuity of care and for training. When working with unfamiliar colleagues, juniors may be diffident about seeking help from seniors who they do not know. Senior colleagues in turn may not know how competent the juniors are.

Increasingly, cross cover between surgical specialties added to the pressure of work for the more junior grades – fewer hours but greater intensity. The firm structure was weakened, undermining mentoring for trainees. Gaps in shifts because of study leave or illness are filled by short-term locums. They are often present for a single shift, recruited from outside the trust and unfamiliar with the hospital. Their total hours in different trusts should not exceed the limit but this rule is not observed. I am glad that I did not have to practise in that environment.

These latter changes resulted from a wish to avoid tired doctors, out of concern for patients' safety and the health of the medical staff. Ask a patient whether they want to be treated by a tired doctor and they will say 'no'. But this may not be a sufficiently subtle question. Would they rather be treated by a rested doctor who knows nothing about them or their condition or by a slightly tired one who is familiar with their problem? The answer might well be different. The hours worked historically were clearly wrong, but in my view the compromise reached in the 1990s was better than the later outcome.

30

REGIONAL AFFAIRS

In 1987 I was elected to represent the region's general surgeons on the council of the Association of Surgeons of Great Britain and Ireland (ASGBI) and shortly afterwards as regional adviser, a college appointment. The combination of roles gave me a clear perspective of how the region functioned surgically.

The Sheffield Region was created at the start of the NHS in 1948, extending south to Leicestershire and eastwards to cover Lincolnshire. Many of the hospitals lay close to a north-south axis, later connected by the building of the M1 motorway. This elongated shape resulted from a decision that each non-metropolitan English region should contain one undergraduate teaching centre, in this case Sheffield. Later, additional medical schools opened in Nottingham (1971) and Leicester (1974). Then, under the 1974 administrative reorganisation, the Sheffield Regional Board was renamed Trent Regional Health Authority. The plan was to move its headquarters from Sheffield to a more central location in Nottingham, but for financial reasons this never happened.

The region was originally responsible for consultant and SR appointments, with a regional postgraduate dean based in Sheffield. The two new medical schools insisted that they should have their own postgraduate deans and make their own appointments. As a compromise, one of the three deans acted for the region. The region was shared out for teaching purposes, with

Leicester acquiring south Lincolnshire and Nottingham taking in most of Derbyshire and Lincolnshire.

EAST MIDLANDS SURGICAL SOCIETY

In my early years as a consultant, I played no part in regional affairs, apart from regular attendance at the biannual meetings of the East Midlands Surgical Society, which largely comprised general surgeons. These meetings lasted one day (originally a Saturday) and rotated among the general hospitals in the region. The programme for each meeting was devised by the local surgeons, but over the years consultant contributions tailed off and it became more a forum for trainees to present their research. The reduced interest from consultants reflected increasing specialisation and the growing number of national postgraduate meetings.

REPRESENTING THE REGION

Soon after I was appointed, I enquired about joining the Association of Surgeons of Great Britain and Ireland (ASGBI), but membership had been restricted until recently and I was advised to wait. I finally joined as late as 1986. Then in 1987, Professor Alan Johnson, from Sheffield, phoned to say that his three-year term as Trent representative on the council of the ASGBI was ending and he had to arrange the election of his successor. He felt, rightly, that this job should move around the region. He had identified a candidate from Nottingham and had asked Peter Bell, who had declined; would I be interested? By then our children were grown up and I was ready to branch out, so I agreed to be a candidate. I did not confess that I had been a member for only one year. As I had worked in three of the four major centres in the region, and so knew many of the consultants, it was unsurprising that I was elected. My involvement in the ASGBI is described in chapter 31.

Shortly afterwards, in 1989, Clifford Talbot, a surgeon in Sheffield, whom I'd first met when he was an SR in Bristol, wrote to all the surgeons in the region seeking candidates to replace him as regional adviser in surgery. Historically this post had been held by a general surgeon (including for many years Ken Wood from Leicester). There was a parallel orthopaedic adviser, but all the other surgical specialties were covered by the 'general' post. The duties had comprised approval of the contracts for advertised consultant posts and attendance at periodic meetings at the Royal College of Surgeons of England (RCS). The adviser had a low profile in the region and didn't seem to be involved in organising training. I thought this was something I could develop, in conjunction with my role in the ASGBI. A younger colleague from Leicester showed an interest but was dissuaded and the ballot was between me and a surgeon from Nottingham (the same one as in the ASGBI election), with the same result.

As regional adviser I concentrated on general surgery. The small regional specialties of cardiothoracic, paediatric, plastic and neurological surgery were only in the teaching hospitals and were tightly managed by the region. Urology and some neonatal surgery were provided in DGHs by general surgeons with those interests, while dental surgery in the DGHs had yet to mutate into maxillofacial surgery. I should have taken an interest in ENT, which was represented in each DGH.

I decided to visit each city or town to meet the general surgeons, with two main topics in mind: establishing a separate urology service and reorganising the registrar posts, as required under *Achieving a Balance*. Urology, defined by the skills of endoscopic resection, was emerging as a distinct specialty, supported by a long-established organisation, the British Association of Urological Surgeons (BAUS). The teaching centres each had a urological unit while in each DGH there was one (or sometimes two) general surgeon/s with a major interest. I encouraged the DGHs to move towards specialised urology. The obstacle was that those consultants with a urological interest were still members of the general surgical emergency rota and so would need to be replaced by an additional general surgeon. A single urologist would need a consultant colleague, requiring a net increase of two in the establishment of the hospital. Nevertheless, this change was achieved rapidly in Derby and Chesterfield, and more gradually in the other DGHs.

ACHIEVING A BALANCE

The government had accepted the report *Hospital Medical Staffing: Achieving a Balance* in 1987, designed to improve the career structure. I remembered that back in about 1960 *The Observer* had run a campaign on the scandal of 'time expired SRs', who had been in post for as long as 12 years, as compared to a target of four. By 1968 a Joint Professional Advisory Committee (JPAC) had been set up to manage the number of SR posts to match the predicted number of consultant vacancies and this had controlled the bottleneck at this level. The bulge then moved down to the registrars. Predictably, the number of registrars in the acute specialties had expanded to provide 24-hour cover, exceeding the number of SR vacancies.

Many of the registrars were from overseas, appointed with the expectation that they would take their training home with them, rather than competing for SR posts. They were mostly working in district general hospitals (DGHs). In practice, many had reasons for preferring to stay in the UK. They had married here and had children at school. Facilities in their home countries were often not as good and the jobs there were often filled by those with influence. A few achieved consultant posts in the UK but many became stuck as associate specialists or staff grades. The increased output of UK graduates, who then occupied a greater proportion of the registrar posts, intensified concern about the limited prospects of progression to SR.

Achieving a Balance proposed an increase in consultant posts, a reduction in the number of registrars and, crucially, a clear distinction between 'career' registrars (CRs), appointed for three years and entitled to residence in the UK, and 'visiting' registrars (VRs). The latter would be recruited directly from overseas (including the RCS's scheme) or by advertisement. Their time in post would be subject to a residency limit of four years. The training received by the two categories of registrar was to be equal, implying rotation between DGHs and teaching hospitals. The JPAC expanded its role to include controlling the number of CR posts. The personal 'training numbers' would be limited to exceed the SR vacancies only slightly.

My task was to implement this change in the region. I reconvened the Trent Regional General Surgical Training Committee, which had not met since 1987. It comprised a general surgeon from each city or town with one or more general hospitals receiving emergencies, together with the three professors of surgery. There was a total of 54 registrar posts in general surgery, which had to be whittled down to the JPAC allocation of 22 CRs, plus VRs. Those in post who had the FRCS and were judged likely to achieve consultant status had already been given temporary CR training numbers.

The next stage was to decide which posts fulfilled the criteria of the Specialist Advisory Committee for General Surgery (SAC) and to arrange these into rotations between the teaching hospitals and the DGHs. The SAC criteria required posts to be in hospitals serving a population of at least 150,000, to work for two consultants and to be on a rota for emergencies. If a registrar post was lost it was to be replaced by another member of staff – either a consultant or a senior house officer (SHO).

Analysis of the 54 registrar posts demonstrated differences among the teaching centres. In Sheffield, single-consultant units had an SR, a 'post-FRCS' registrar and a 'peri-FRCS' registrar. The latter posts were akin to SHOs in the newer teaching hospitals and accordingly were converted to that grade. Nottingham and Leicester had no designated post-FRCS registrar positions. It was appropriate to convert half of their peri-FRCS posts to CR/VRs and half to SHOs. In general, DGH registrar posts became CR/VRs.

Members of the regional committee visited each hospital, in pairs, to assess the suitability of the registrar posts for inclusion in the new arrangements. This resulted in a total of 40 CR/VR posts; the region had been allocated 22 CRs and the remaining 18 would be VRs. As there were three deaneries it was agreed that training would be organised in three sub-regional schemes, each centred on a medical school. The committee agreed to allocate the CR posts in approximate proportion to the total posts in each deanery – Sheffield: nine; Nottingham: eight; Leicester: six. The detailed management of training would be the responsibility of three sub-regional committees. This resulted in much smaller and arguably more personal training schemes than in other health regions. The transition was completed in 1990.

IMPLEMENTATION IN LEICESTER

I was already managing the flexible Leicester SR rotation, and I was asked to organise the South Trent CR and VR training as well. Outside Leicester and within the region we were allocated only the two posts in Boston, but in connection with student teaching we had already included posts in Peterborough, Nuneaton and Kettering (each in a different region) in our registrar rotations. It was helpful to those adjacent regions to have fewer DGH posts to incorporate in their rotations, so they readily agreed that we should retain these posts in the South Trent scheme.

In Leicester three peri-FRCS posts were replaced by additional consultants. Non-EEC trainees already in post in the DGHs became VRs. A professor in Warsaw offered to send a series of young surgeons for a two-year placement. With one exception they all returned to Poland – in contrast to the other VRs who often managed, by one means or another, to stay in the UK. Other VRs were recruited by advertisement.

After three years, I handed the sub-regional South Trent chairmanship on to a colleague and then my five-year term as regional adviser ended, passing the regional training committee to my successor. This period had been invaluable preparation for my time on the Specialist Advisory Committee in General Surgery. Subsequently, the Calman policy amalgamated the registrar and senior registrar grades as 'specialist registrars' (SpRs), as described in chapter 33.

REPRESENTING THE COLLEGE

As regional adviser, I received requests from the Royal College for nominees to take part in investigations in other regions, under the 'rapid response' service. Hospitals could request this following a complaint or when consultants became concerned about the performance of a colleague. The visiting team comprised two surgeons, one nominated by the college and the other by the BMA. They would spend a day or two interviewing the individuals concerned and then submit a report to the college for transmission to the hospital. I used to do two of these each year myself and found suitable consultants from our region to do the other one or two.

The responses were *not* rapid; finding a date when both the visitors were available commonly took about three months. When we got there the staff were cooperative, though some nurses proved reticent. The problems uncovered varied: poor communications, surgeons operating beyond their personal experience, inadequate monitoring of sick patients and rudeness all contributed. The reports were not a preliminary to, nor did they preclude litigation, but I think they may often have avoided the latter. Sometimes a consultant was advised to modify the scope of his practice.

At about this time, I began to be asked to represent the RCS on consultant appointment committees. The formal role of the 'college assessor' was to ensure that the person appointed met the training requirements, but he could also give his opinion on the candidates. Applicants were generally well qualified, and only once did I rule that one of those shortlisted should not be considered (he was subsequently appointed elsewhere but got into difficulties). On another occasion, I strongly supported an excellent candidate, despite his training technically falling short of the subspecialty criteria. The officers of the subspecialty association complained to the College and asked that I should never again be the assessor for one of 'their' posts. But the deed was done, and the surgeon enjoyed a stellar career.

MANAGING MULTIPLE ROLES

These five years as regional adviser were varied and interesting. They ran in parallel with my time as regional member of the council of the ASGBI (chapter 31), membership of the SAC (chapter 33), examiner for the Intercollegiate Board (chapter 34) and my role as clinical director for surgery at the LRI. This was a heavy workload but there were synergies. I attended regular meetings of advisers and tutors at the college and made good contacts there. This was all excellent preparation for my final job as president of the ASGBI.

NATIONAL ACTIVITIES

31

THE ASSOCIATION OF SURGEONS

During my early years as a consultant, I never imagined that I would have any role in national surgical affairs. My horizon was limited to attendance at conferences (particularly the Surgical Research Society) and publishing an occasional clinical paper. In the mid-1970s I was asked if Elisabeth and I would like to come as guests to a meeting of a well-known surgical travelling club, with a view to membership. We considered it but felt that, in the current state of our finances, the cost involved in membership, especially for the annual overseas visit, would have displaced family holidays. I politely declined the offer.

In about 1980, I applied to observe the vivas for the FRCS in London. I did this for the benefit of our trainees preparing for the examination but found that my visit was interpreted as a preliminary to applying to become an examiner! There was no tradition of consultants from Leicester being examiners but following this prompt I considered applying. However, I learnt that Professor Peter Bell was also thinking of doing so and it seemed unwise to have two applications from Leicester, so I did not proceed. In fact, Peter Bell did not apply either.

Early on I had enquired of my colleagues about joining the Association of Surgeons of Great Britain and Ireland (ASGBI) but was advised that I should leave this until I was well established. The limit of 600 on the number of fellows had only been abandoned in 1970, at which time there were about 900 consultants in general surgery, and membership was still seen as a privilege. As a result, I did not join until 1986.

In January of the following year, Professor Alan Johnson, from Sheffield, phoned to ask if I would stand for election to replace him for a three-year term as the Trent representative on the council of the ASGBI. This sounded interesting, involving four meetings per year, normally at the Royal College of Surgeons in London, so I agreed. I only discovered that I had been elected when at the ASGBI Annual Meeting in Liverpool in April. At that stage, I had no inkling of where it would lead.

COUNCIL

The Association of Surgeons was founded in 1920 on the initiative of Sir Berkeley Moynihan (later Lord Moynihan). He had already established the first surgical travelling club and the *British Journal of Surgery*. The members were general surgeons, though initially there were a few orthopaedists.

When I joined the council it comprised regional representatives, including one for Eire, a representative from the armed forces and two members of the mono-specialist general surgical committee of the *Union Européenne des Médecins Spécialistes* (UEMS). The Association's five nominated members of the SAC (see chapter 33) and a trainee attended as observers. The Association's paid staff comprised only a secretary and one assistant, and the premises were two small offices in the Royal College of Surgeons of England. The president, who might be one of the great and the good or a long-standing servant of the Association, was elected by the council for a term of one year, culminating in the annual scientific meeting in the spring, usually held in his home city. Some presidents also arranged a smaller autumn meeting, often overseas.

At my first council meeting, there was whispering of 'Who is he?' at the head of the table. A contentious issue was whether there should be an intercollegiate examination to mark the completion of training in general surgery. Other surgical specialties had become dissatisfied with the coverage of their subjects in the FRCS examinations of the four surgical Royal Colleges, which was taken early in training. In response, specialty 'exit' examinations were being set up. Logically, general surgery should follow suit but there was opposition.

Consultants, when they passed the English FRCS examination, had been told at the awards ceremony that they had achieved 'the highest qualification in surgery'. Trainees did not relish having to sit another exam. The consultants in Derby (where I had been SR and whom I knew well) were particularly vociferous, so in 1988 the president, Norman Addison, and I as regional representative, went to meet them. Over an amicable lunch they were persuaded that if general surgery did not have such an examination, it would render the specialty second class. After that the council at least knew who I was! My later membership of the Intercollegiate Board for General Surgery (ICB), which ran the exam, is described in chapter 34.

I attended the annual meeting in 1988 at a conference centre in Harrogate. The location was chosen by the president, a surgeon from Bradford. It marked a deviation from the usual use of university facilities. The centre served very well and paved the way for a general decision about venues in 1991. Elisabeth came too and enjoyed the accompanying persons' programme, and the council dinner in a nearby stately home. In November, the Association took us to Amsterdam to meet jointly with the Netherlands Association of Surgeons. This very enjoyable event was attended by about 30 surgeons from the ASGBI, accompanied by many of their wives, including Elisabeth.

Eddie Ashby, who had suggested that I apply for the SHO rotation in Bristol, and had followed me as a registrar in Leicester, later joined the council, representing the South-West Thames region.

TREASURER

During my third year, the treasurer asked whether I would be interested in succeeding him and I agreed. I don't know whether anyone else had been approached but there was no interview or election. The officers comprised the president, appointed two years in advance as vice-president elect and then vice-president, the honorary secretary, and the treasurer; the latter two were appointed for five years. This group functioned as an executive. The treasurer was responsible for general financial advice, signing all the cheques and managing the Association's substantial reserves, invested on the stock exchange.

The major expenditure was on the annual meeting, which had usually been held in university facilities near the president's base. By 1991 the increasing size of the event, coupled with a desire for more appropriate facilities, prompted a move to conference centres. There were a limited number of adequate size and they had to be booked far in advance. The linkage to the president's city was therefore abandoned. The conference in 1993 was to be at the International Convention Centre in Birmingham. We negotiated the terms while it was still under construction and secured a good deal as one of the first users. We then aimed to book each venue at least two years in advance.

In 1991, I was invited to one of the Buckingham Palace Garden Parties as a representative of the ASGBI, of which the Duke of Edinburgh was patron. At that time, besides spouses, unmarried daughters under the age of 25 were included, so Clare, our younger daughter, came with us. The duke's invitees were organised into parallel lines in alphabetical order, so we were placed between the Association of Cricket Umpires and the Auto-Cycle Union. Prince Philip spoke to each group; when he reached us, he concentrated on Clare, to her delight. When the royals had completed their progress along the avenues, we all broke up for tea.

I received a further nomination three years later from the NHS but believing that one was not to be invited twice, I declined and someone else went instead. Then in 1997, I was again nominated, by the Regional Health Authority; I repeated my belief that I could not attend twice but was assured that this did not apply to a recommendation by a different organisation. The inclusion of daughters had by then been abandoned, but Clare was over-age anyway.

COUNCIL BUSINESS

I can only pick out a selection of the matters considered by the council over these six years. There was discussion of the first *National Confidential Enquiry into Perioperative Deaths* (NCEPOD) report, a project which the ASGBI had supported. That prompted consideration of surgeons' involvement in clinical audit. I expressed interest in this and represented the Association on various national audit projects (see chapter 32). With the president, I had to represent the Association before the Monopolies and Mergers Commission, which was investigating whether private medical practice was a cartel – they decided that it was not.

In 1989, the proposal for the formation of an association of coloproctology raised concerns about the potential break-up of general surgery, which proved well founded. To document the extent of subspecialisation, Barry Jackson (the hon sec) and I sent questionnaires in 1991 to all 946 fellows of the ASGBI, of whom 85 per cent responded.

Fifty-one per cent were appointed as general surgeons, without a specified interest. Overall, 84 per cent expressed one or more current subspecialty interests while five per cent described themselves as pure specialists: only 11 per cent claimed to be generalists. Vascular surgery was the most popular interest, offered by 147 surgeons, of whom one-third expected it to become a separate specialty within 10 years. Ninety-four surgeons were still engaged in urology but most predicted that this would separate, as indeed it did over the following few years. Upper and lower gastrointestinal interests were often combined, while a cluster of surgeons had various combinations of interests in breast, endocrine and oncological surgery. Twenty-two per cent offered two interests and a few as many as five, surely making them generalists. All, except the pure specialists, took part in the general surgical emergency rota.

The council members realised that these findings suggested the likelihood of future fragmentation of general surgery and were keen to retain the subspecialties under the umbrella of the Association.

SUCCESSION

Barry Jackson was due to complete his term as hon sec in 1991. When the officers were considering who among the council should replace him, I suggested Bernard Ribeiro, a surgeon in Essex who hailed from Ghana, and this nomination was agreed unanimously. He subsequently became president of the Association and then of the Royal College of Surgeons. He was later made a life peer.

In 1991 the council was looking for a replacement member on the Specialist Advisory Committee in General Surgery (SAC), responsible for the supervision of general surgical training. I offered my services and was appointed. Subsequently in 1995, when I was elected chairman of the SAC, I resigned as treasurer of the ASGBI, a year short of the full term and handed over, at my suggestion, to Tony Giddings, who had been a registrar when I was in Sheffield.

As one of the Association's representatives on the SAC, I continued as an observer at council meetings until 1998, at which point I was, to my amazement, elected by council to be president for 2000/1. As a result, I attended council meetings continuously for 13 years. My year as president and many ongoing issues concerning training and surgical manpower are described in chapter 35.

32

SURGICAL AUDIT

Medical audit is not a new idea. Appalled by the high hospital mortality in the Crimean War (1853–5), Florence Nightingale improved hygiene and demonstrated reduced mortality in an early example of the audit cycle. Surgical audit was first advocated by Codman (1869–1940), who kept track of his patients for up to a year postoperatively using 'end-result cards'. Working at Massachusetts General Hospital, he instituted the first morbidity and mortality (M&M) meetings. Then in 1914 he put forward a plan for the evaluation of individual surgeons' competence, but this was not acceptable to his colleagues. As a result, he moved to set up his own 'end-result hospital'. Among 337 patients discharged, Codman reported 123 errors, an extraordinarily high rate.

In 1966 Donabedian, from the University of Michigan, wrote *Evaluating the Quality of Medical Care*, describing three phases of an audit study: structure, process and outcome. This seems to have attracted little attention until his further publication in 1988, *The Quality of Care. How can it be Assessed?* Then in 1989 the white paper *Working for Patients*, which was mainly about hospital trusts and the internal market, included as item seven 'The concept of clinical audit'.

In 1975 I had tried to establish a database of my cancer cases. Each surgeon in Leicester ran a fortnightly or monthly cancer follow-up clinic. Most patients attending were free of recurrence, while few or none at each session had evidence of further disease. Surgeons were encouraged by these favourable 'statistics', forgetting those who had already died. I wanted to have a record of all patients operated upon for malignant disease, grouped by the site of the primary tumour and updated at each review. I had kept copies of all the pathology reports and my university secretary had spare capacity at that early stage of clinical teaching, but we failed to establish the system due to pressure of other tasks. It would anyway have been difficult to maintain the record before computer databases became available.

SURGICAL AUDIT AT THE LRI

In 1980, Clive Quick, our SR, produced a plan for surgical audit, to record the basic details of diagnosis, operation and complications for all inpatients, using a personal computer. We jointly applied to the regional research committee for the modest funding needed. Our application was turned down because 'Members felt that there is as yet little evidence that surgeons are amenable to submit their work to audit'. However, in the Lothian region of Scotland, surgeons commenced a comprehensive computerised surgical audit in 1982 and this was sustained for 15 years until it was subsumed into a national programme. So, in Scotland at least, surgeons were prepared to audit their work!

In 1982, my colleague David Fossard suggested that the general surgeons at the LRI should hold a regular M&M meeting. A weekly session was held at 8am and all the surgeons, apart from our most senior colleague, participated. Each surgeon's SHO was responsible for a list of the patients admitted two weeks previously, giving diagnoses, operations and complications. The lists were circulated at the meeting and each firm mentioned patients of interest, particularly in respect of problems. Anyone, junior or senior, could ask questions and suggest improvements in management. The one-hour session proved valuable, but it lacked a longer-term view. Complications tended to be treated as one-off events and those responsible were reassured that 'it could happen to anyone'.

COMPUTERISING THE LRI M&M MEETINGS

We needed a record of the data, so that repetitive events could be flagged up. Fortunately, computers were becoming cheaper, offering the means to accumulate and analyse the information. In 1984, Clive Quick and then Leslie Boobis (both SRs) and I devised a system for entering the basic information submitted by the SHOs. I wanted each week's data to be compact enough to present at the meeting on three sheets of A4 paper. This required codes for diagnoses, operations and complications, with each patient's data occupying only one line. The codes had to be comprehensible to those attending the meetings without recourse to a code book. The official numeric International Classification of Diseases codes did not meet the latter requirement, nor did SNOMED (Systematised Nomenclature of Medicine), favoured by pathologists, nor the later Read Codes.

We decided to create abbreviations of the full terms in up to six characters, with a capital at the start of a word. Thus, appendicitis became *AppxIt*, colonoscopy was *ColSc*, total gastrectomy was *ToGasX* and wound infection was *WounIn*. Well-known acronyms such as *DU* (duodenal ulcer) and *RIH* (right inguinal hernia) were included. Following these rules, a code could be created for any new item.

The staff rapidly became familiar with the common codes. Rarities occasionally needed explaining, sometimes resulting in hilarity. The lists also gave the first six letters of the patients' names (to help those present to identify them) and their hospital registration number, sex and age. This was long before the Data Protection Act.

Initially I applied the codes myself, inputting the data into a BBC computer with an external hard disc; the list was printed for the meeting and revised afterwards. Later, a dedicated part-time secretary was trained to do the coding, with advice when uncertain, and we upgraded to a PC with an internal hard disc. This pattern of M&M meetings continued up to and beyond my retirement. The data files enabled us to produce, for example, mortality rates for appendicectomy and strangulated hernia and the ratio of recurrent to first hernia operations (eight per cent) as a measure of the hospital's recurrence rate. Boobis and I presented this system at a meeting on surgical audit at the Royal College of Surgeons in 1988.

CONFIDENTIAL ENQUIRIES INTO PERIOPERATIVE DEATHS

In 1982 Lunn and Mushin had published, on behalf of the Association of Anaesthetists, *Mortality Associated with Anaesthesia*. The surgical specialties had declined to be involved. However, the surgeons later relented, and a group led by Brendan Devlin, a surgeon at North Tees General Hospital, and Dr John Lunn, an anaesthetist, initiated a Confidential Enquiry into

Perioperative Deaths (CEPOD). They had finance from The King's Fund and the Nuffield Provincial Hospitals Trust, and the backing of the Royal College of Surgeons and the ASGBI. The first report was published in December 1987, describing perioperative deaths in three English NHS regions and making the following comments:

- Many surgeons do not hold M&M meetings.
- Some deaths followed operations in which juniors didn't seek consultant advice at any stage; the supervision of trainees should be reviewed.
- Time should be allowed for the resuscitation of emergencies; some are operated upon too soon.
- Decisions to operate (or not) on sick elderly patients need consultant input.
- The out-of-hours work in a district should be concentrated on a single site.
- The availability of emergency theatres needs to be improved.

This report was the catalyst for the nationwide introduction of surgical audit. CEPOD was accepted and rebranded as NCEPOD (National Confidential Enquiry into Patient Outcomes and Death). It conducted annual surveys on various aspects of surgical treatment. The council of the ASGBI strongly supported the report and the concept of audit and in December 1988 a subcommittee (of which I was a member) produced a report giving guidance and suggesting how computerisation could facilitate the process. The Royal College of Surgeons issued *Guidelines to Clinical Audit in Surgical Practice* in March 1989, recommending that one half session per week should be allocated to it. By March 1990, the DoH had instructed District Health Authorities (DHAs) to institute clinical audit as part of the NHS reforms – a very rapid roll-out.

As audit then became NHS policy, I warned our DHA that this would require the equivalent of half a day of clinicians' time per month, with a corresponding loss of outpatient and operating sessions. Our recently retired senior surgeon was appointed to manage medical audit, though he had never attended a surgical audit meeting! The official emphasis was on the detailed audit of a single diagnosis or procedure leading to changes in practice and further data collection 'to complete the audit cycle'. This was vastly different from my objective of comprehensive surgical audit. It did not provide the comparative results for hospitals and individual surgeons, which were developed in Scotland and later introduced in England in the second decade of the 21st century. Despite the district policy, we continued with the weekly audit of all general surgical admissions.

NATIONAL AUDITS

In 1990 Brendan Devlin, on behalf of NCEPOD, initiated the first of a series of national surgical audits and I volunteered to represent the Association of Surgeons in the first of them. A small committee of consultants convened to steer the topic, appointing a research fellow to do most of the analysis of the data, usually collected from three NHS regions. We then worked together to finalise the report. The first audit was on the repair of groin hernias. This led to the production of guidelines in 1993 and later a systematic review of the literature that was published in 1998[21], to each of which I contributed.

The Royal College of Physicians of London and the RCS jointly initiated an audit of endoscopy for upper gastrointestinal bleeding, for which I was again the ASGBI representative. The research fellow Tim Rockall used the data to produce the Rockall scoring system for predicting the risk of re-bleeding, and this became the standard guide for management.

PROGRESS

The inaccuracy of routine hospital data was repeatedly pointed out in connection with clinical audit, emphasising that surgeons need to take responsibility for its capture. Surgeons were concerned that publication of individuals' results could have disadvantages. Those undertaking operations in higher-risk patients might be discouraged from doing so. We therefore needed a system of risk adjustment. Not until the second decade of the 21st century was this problem overcome, following the successful release of cardiac surgeons' individual risk-adjusted results.

Throughout the development of surgical audit there has been a difference of opinion between the value of the detailed examination of a limited topic and the comprehensive audit of the work of a unit or individuals. The former lends itself to completion of the audit cycle, particularly if it relates to process.

---

21 Cheek C, Black N, Devlin B, Kingsnorth A, Taylor R, Watkin D. Groin hernia surgery: A systematic review. *Ann R Coll Surg Eng* (Suppl) 1998: 1.

Trainees are told to participate in audit but, to complete a project within their short timescale, a study of process is probably the only option. On the other hand, a comprehensive audit of outcomes is the best measure of quality, but for specialties, such as oncological surgery, it has a long timescale. Sensibly, both approaches should be employed in tandem.

33

THE SPECIALIST ADVISORY
COMMITTEE IN GENERAL SURGERY

Before describing my participation in the supervision of surgical training nationally, it is necessary to explain the background to the organisation. In the British Isles there are the four royal colleges of surgeons: of England, Edinburgh and Glasgow (also encompassing physicians) and *in* Ireland. In 1968, the four colleges cooperated to establish the Joint Committee on Higher Surgical Training (JCHST), a body covering the nine surgical specialties. This in turn set up a Specialist Advisory Committee (SAC) for each of the nine specialties, including general surgery, to supervise the training posts for senior registrars (SRs). There was no examination to mark completion of higher surgical training, just a minimum duration of four years in an approved post.

The membership of the General Surgical SAC comprised five surgeons nominated by the colleges, five nominated by the ASGBI, three from the Association of Professors of Surgery[22], a representative from the armed forces and a trainee, with a term of office of five years. The committee elected its own chairman, from among the members, for a three-year term. It met three-monthly in London at the Royal College of Surgeons and was supported by a lay secretary who did most of the administration.

---

22 The Association of Professors of Surgery merged with the Surgical Research Society to form the Society of Academic & Research Surgery (SARS) in 2004.

In 1991, there was a vacancy for an ASGBI representative. I was interested in training, put my name forward to the council and was appointed. The SAC determined the criteria for training posts and refined these as the context changed. The main activity at that time was the approval of training posts. Members operated in teams of three. Each team was responsible for periodic visits to the hospitals in three health regions, including Scotland, Wales, Northern Ireland and Eire.

The visit usually covered two or three hospitals in the region. The team spent time inspecting the facilities, such as theatres and the library, which the local consultants were keen to show us. The important task was interviewing the consultants, SRs and other junior staff, though at that time we were not responsible for registrars' training. An impressive lunch was provided and, as we usually stayed overnight, we could discuss our findings over dinner. Subsequently a report was produced, approved by all members of the team. The reports were discussed at meetings of the committee, where they might be amended.

Following the publication of *Hospital Medical Staffing: Achieving a Balance* in 1987 (see chapter 30), registrar posts were reclassified as CR and VR. The SAC then included these registrar posts in its remit.

Between visits there was no contact with those running the training schemes, apart from the receipt of lists of names submitted for confirmation of completion of training and the distribution of occasional newsletters. It occurred to me that, as a team of three covered three regions, it would be appropriate for each member to liaise regularly with one of the regions and attend the regional general surgical training committee. I suggested this and the plan was promptly accepted and implemented. Understanding between the SAC and the regions was enhanced, and this system was adopted by some other SACs.

THE CALMAN REPORT

In 1993, *Hospital Doctors – Training for the future* (the Calman Report) reorganised specialist medical training. It recommended that there should be a curriculum for each specialty, structured training programmes and progression through training based on formal annual assessments of competence, leading to a certificate of completion of specialist training (CCST). The SR and registrar grades were to be merged as specialist registrars (SpRs), with the expectation that training would be shortened. But after consultation with the RCS a duration of six years was agreed for the surgical specialties – no change from the status quo. Trainees would carry a personal number, the issue of these being limited to match the expected number of consultant vacancies. The medical royal colleges and postgraduate deans would share in the planning and delivery of the new system, to start by the end of 1995.

A CURRICULUM FOR TRAINING IN GENERAL SURGERY

The Calman Report included a requirement for the content of training to be defined in a curriculum for each specialty. Surprisingly, this had never been attempted; indeed, the JCHST, on a date some time before 1974, had stated: 'It is thus impossible to map out a defined syllabus of training.' It fell to each SAC to produce this document and I was a member of the curriculum subcommittee, chaired by Tom Bates, the vice chairman.

There was discussion about whether this would be a curriculum or a syllabus. The dictionary definitions are:

Curriculum: A regular course of study at a school or (Scottish) university.
Syllabus:
1. A concise statement of the heads of a discourse... the subject of a series of lectures, etc.
2. A summary of the points decided, and errors condemned by ecclesiastical authority.

The document met the first two of these definitions by covering both the organisation and the content of training, but some views expressed during our discussions seemed more like an ecclesiastical debate. The organisation of training was not contentious, simply following the proposals in the Calman Report. However, there were two sources of difficulty in defining the detailed operative experience. First, senior surgeons wished to include every procedure they had ever undertaken, even though some operations had migrated to other specialties; for example, tracheostomy was by then mainly carried out by ENT surgeons.

Second, and more fundamental, was the tension between general surgery, particularly for emergencies, and the interests of the developing subspecialties. To some extent these difficulties applied to statements of the required clinical knowledge, but the differences focused on lists of operations. To resolve this, three levels of training were described: training in general surgery, including emergencies; essential subspecialty training, for those with an interest; and advanced subspecialty training for those planning to work in highly specialised units. The basic knowledge and operative competencies required at each level were listed. It was decided that all trainees should complete the first two levels, and most would add one subspecialty at the advanced level.

In the first two years SpRs would cover the general surgical items, usually in four six-month attachments, arranged to cover the full range of general surgery. Thereafter, they would have whole-year placements with units providing training in their chosen interests. Some years might be spent in highly specialised units, but a trainee needed at least four years' experience of general surgical emergencies. One year of research was encouraged for those who had not previously occupied a research post. Published in June 1996, the curriculum was valid until the end of 1997.

CHAIRMAN

Professor Alan Johnson was due to complete his term as chairman of the SAC in February 1995. Colleagues suggested that I should be a candidate to replace him, and the committee balloted to decide between me and another member. While sitting next to him on a train on the way to a meeting of the SRS I learned that I had been elected. I decided to resign as treasurer of the ASGBI, one year short of the full five years and was followed in that job by Tony Giddings (who subsequently was president of the ASGBI for 1997/8).

Early in 1995, I was asked whether general surgery was ready to pioneer the Calman changes and the SAC agreed to take up the challenge. The regional training committees had to rearrange the existing registrar and SR rotations to fit the Calman system and decide into which year of SpR training each trainee should be assimilated. By the end of that year the process was well under way.

To monitor training, I asked the chairman of each regional training committee to complete an online form annually, listing the trainees in each year of their programme, the hospital in which they were placed and their subspecialty interest, if decided. Each year this collected much of the information formerly produced only at three-yearly intervals during an SAC visit.

I thought it would be informative to see how the other surgical SACs operated, so I invited myself to the meetings of two of them. I was welcomed, though they seemed surprised because no one had ever done this before. In fact, their procedures were like ours, although I discovered that no other SAC limited the ratio of SpRs to consultants as we did, apart from not allowing more than one-to-one.

While I was chairman of the SAC the first revision of the curriculum was required. In view of its importance, I opted to chair the subcommittee of six myself. We aimed to make the syllabus more explicit and align it with the Intercollegiate Board Exam (see chapter 34). Over many productive meetings, we expanded the listings of competencies and identified a few 'index procedures' that might be counted to measure experience. I pressed for greater prominence to be given to emergency surgery. This edition, effective from March 1998 to the end of 2000, ran to 32 pages – an increase of 220 per cent. By the 2016 version it had expanded to 352 pages, 35 times longer than the first edition.

NEWSLETTERS

Throughout my three years I wanted to explain the changes in training to all our surgeons, and to adjust policies in response to feedback from the regions. I produced an SAC newsletter twice each year, as my predecessor had done, but extended its circulation from just members of the SAC to all consultants. We also held meetings with the chairmen of the regional general surgical training committees. Copies of the newsletters provided an overview of the work of the SAC.

The first newsletter explained the Calman changes, including the introduction of the curriculum and the possible changes in the number of SpRs. The ratio of SpRs to consultants was a thorny topic. Originally it was limited by the SAC at one-to-two, though historically this was often exceeded. The ratio was justified partly to ensure a good volume of surgical experience and partly to match career prospects. The number of consultant appointments was increasing in response to the reduction in juniors' hours and the development of subspecialisation. The ASGBI had already adopted a target of one consultant to 30,000 of population, representing an increase of up to 66 per cent in some regions. To meet this demand, an increased allocation of SpR numbers was expected. The ratio was therefore relaxed to allow two SpRs to three consultants provided the training opportunities justified it. Regional training committees were asked to identify where this might apply.

The SAC held an away day to refine our objectives and discuss problems, for example the inclusion of university lecturers in the continuum. For highly specialised experience, trainees often needed a period of secondment to a unit in another region. To facilitate this, we agreed a national date of October 1st for the rotation of SpRs around training posts. Some consultants who were allocated level one trainees felt undervalued, so it was emphasised that levels of training referred to what was expected of a trainee, rather than the quality of surgery in a unit.

Subsequent newsletters considered whether a trainee should be able to offer a second subspecialty and whether such training could be accommodated within the six years. This was less difficult for the combination of upper and lower gastrointestinal work, which had much in common. Other possibilities for a secondary role were children's surgery and thyroid operations; SpRs often lacked experience in these activities as they pursued their interests in the main subspecialties. Concurrently these patients were becoming the subject of turf wars, respectively with the specialties of paediatric surgery and ENT.

BORDERLINE SUBSPECIALTIES

The surgery of neonatal congenital abnormalities and other work in infants, together with the management of malignant disease, was already concentrated in regional paediatric units. Older children with straightforward conditions such as appendicitis and hernias were cared for by the general surgeons in DGHs. An argument developed that all children should be in paediatric surgical units, but it would be ridiculous for a child with suspected appendicitis (often proving not to require an operation) to be sent to a hospital 50 miles away. The matter hinged on appropriate training, because many SpRs lacked experience with children. The solution would be to introduce a second interest of 'general paediatric surgery', but logistically it proved difficult to establish this and the trainees were rarely interested in it.

Many general surgeons did thyroid operations, which are relatively numerous, but no other endocrine surgery. Surgeons with a declared endocrine interest (whose work included other less common operations) were the only subspecialty which offered training in thyroidectomy, so this tended to be confined to the small number of trainees who wished to be endocrine specialists. When the present surgeons retired, thyroid surgery might cease in many hospitals. Additionally, the ENT surgeons, rebranded as 'head and neck surgeons', considered that the thyroid lay in their territory. I tried to get training in thyroid surgery a place as a subsidiary interest for more of the trainees, but again I was unsuccessful. Both issues were still under discussion during my later presidency of the ASGBI.

Another difficulty was training in gastrointestinal endoscopy. These procedures, using flexible instruments, were carried out by both gastroenterological physicians and surgeons, but formed a larger proportion of the physicians' workload. As training became more formalised, the physicians sought to monopolise training and the reduction in hours made it difficult to fit it into surgeons' programmes. A Joint Advisory Group (JAG) was set up to manage the interface, but it was difficult to agree the amount of experience required. The physicians wanted much larger numbers of procedures to certify competence, while the surgeons considered that the transferability of some of their skills (particularly from laparoscopic surgery, which operates 'on screen') enabled them to achieve competence sooner. It remained an uphill struggle to include endoscopy in the training for upper and lower gastrointestinal surgeons.

COMPLETION OF TRAINING

There was much discussion between the respective merits of the established time-based training and a competence-based approach. In principle, the latter is right, but the assessment of operative ability lies with individual consultants, and it was difficult to ensure consistency.

We suggested, as a partial solution, defining required numbers of index operations performed with and without direct supervision. The number of procedures needed to achieve competence in a procedure provoked considerable discussion, mainly because individuals progress at different rates. Also, the figures were often influenced by availability. For example, diagnostic colonoscopy was said to require experience of 90, but only 15 were felt necessary for the complex (but much less numerous) procedure of pancreatico-duodenectomy. Did this mean that the former is six times more difficult than the latter? Surely not! At the end of my chairmanship, we were still relying on the duration of training.

Consideration of operations performed requires individual record keeping by trainees and the means for the training scheme to analyse this data to compare training posts. Trainees were already keeping their own logbooks in various formats, showing procedures performed and assisted at.

A national computerised logbook was being developed by Tom Bates, which would enable analysis of the volume of operative training achieved within regions and nationwide.

CONSULTANT STAFFING

As chairman, I became involved in manpower issues. Additional consultant appointments were being made in response to the reductions in trainees' hours and in the exercise of the hospital trusts' new freedoms. As a result, trainees were being snapped up as soon as they were qualified, and a shortage of candidates was developing. The number of SpRs was increasing but these would only be ready six years hence. Some of the gaps could be filled by those in non-consultant career grades, provided they had sufficient training. A subgroup of the SAC and the RCS was set up to sift through 130 such applicants and assess who was appointable or could be approved subject to a year's training, assessment by their consultants and passing the Intercollegiate Board Exam. In the longer term, as the phase of consultant expansion slowed down, there were likely to be fewer vacancies so the number of SpRs would then need to be reduced. This was discussed with yet another national committee, SWAG (the Specialist Workforce Advisory Group).

CONTROVERSIES ABOUT SUBSPECIALISATION

Throughout my time with the council of the ASGBI and the SAC, subspecialisation within general surgery was a recurring topic. In 1998, I published an article entitled *Can there be too many surgical specialties?*[23]. I identified 61 specialties and subspecialties across the whole of surgery, the criteria being the existence of a society and a journal. Subspecialties tend to divide further; for example, a coloproctologist may concentrate on inflammatory bowel disease or pelvic floor problems.

In the context of subspecialisation, there are problems in the provision of emergency surgery as exemplified in chapter 28. The elective workload would not justify the number of consultant posts necessary to provide an acceptable (one-in-six) duty rota separately for each subspecialty, nor would this be economically possible unless the hospital was extremely large. All trainees should therefore achieve competence to be on general surgical take.

---

23   Watkin DFL. *Ann R Coll Surg Eng* (Suppl) 1998; 80: 105-108

As only a small percentage of patients within general surgery require such specialised care, it may be appropriate to staff DGHs with surgeons with a broad range of skills. Highly specialised work could then be concentrated in fewer hospitals. The 2013 *Shape of Training* review (Greenaway) recommended moving away from extreme specialisation and encouraging generalists instead. Simon Stevens as NHS chief executive also expressed this view.

Subspecialisation has implications for the curriculum. What experience of general surgery is required of the future subspecialist and what proportion of training should be devoted to the subspecialty? The crucial factor is the future involvement of the individual in the general emergency rota. This balance must be reflected in the Intercollegiate Exam.

CONCLUSION

In my last SAC newsletter, in 1998, I identified challenges for the future: meeting the needs of the service for emergency care; ensuring the appropriate balance between general surgery and the subspecialties; and improving training, despite the reductions in hours. The latter would include maximising the opportunities for supervised operating – 'every case a teaching case' – and the expansion of courses and simulation facilities. We needed to move from time-based to competence-based training.

In 1998 Tony Giddings was chosen to succeed me at the SAC, at about the same time as I was elected as his successor-but-two as president of the ASGBI.

34

THE INTERCOLLEGIATE SPECIALTY BOARD IN GENERAL SURGERY

Until the 1990s, once a trainee had passed the fellowship examination of one of the royal surgical colleges (FRCS), completion of training was defined only by its duration, in approved posts. The FRCS had become just an entry requirement for higher surgical training. It represented surgery in general and no longer covered the knowledge and skills required for practice in the range of surgical specialties. As early as 1979 the Royal College of Surgeons of Edinburgh held specialty examinations in neurosurgery and orthopaedics. Then in 1984 the four Royal Surgical Colleges agreed that there should be an intercollegiate exit examination in each of the nine SAC-defined surgical specialties, to mark the completion of training.

Examinations commenced in plastic surgery (1986) and urology (1987), plus three further specialties by 1991. Each was managed by an Intercollegiate Specialty Board, under the overall supervision of the Joint Committee on Intercollegiate Examinations (JCIE). Initially the administration was sited in an office in the Edinburgh College because of its prior experience, and it has remained there ever since. The specialty board meetings and examinations rotate around the territories of the four surgical colleges.

During this period, European specialty examinations were also launched, including the European Board of Surgery Qualification (EBSQ) in general and cardiovascular surgery. They were not accurately matched to the specialties recognised in the UK and very few British trainees took these qualifications.

The Royal Surgical Colleges agreed that the 'old' Fellowship should be renamed the Membership (MRCS), incidentally bringing this into line with the physicians' MRCP. Those passing the Intercollegiate Examination were then awarded the 'new' FRCS with a specialty suffix (Gen Surg in our case). The subspecialties wanted recognition in the Medical Register, but the GMC would not accept that.

GENERAL SURGERY

A specialty examination in general surgery was first discussed in 1987, but the idea was not popular. On passing the FRCS in the English College, we had all been told: 'you have now achieved the highest qualification in surgery', so why was another test required? After some contentious discussion, the ASGBI agreed that general surgery should participate, lest it be regarded as second class. An Intercollegiate Board was set up and the first examination was held in April 1991, with two candidates who both passed. I was recruited informally to the Board and as an examiner in 1992.

This new examination was unpopular with the trainees, who did not relish sitting another exam. It was therefore presented as 'not really an exam, more a friendly chat'. The initial regulations were for 'The Specialty *Assessment* in General Surgery'. I participated in the second session, for which there were four candidates, one of whom failed. This must have put him in a very lonely position, much worse than being one of a percentage of failures in a large group. The number of candidates increased more rapidly once it was announced that from 1st January 1995 a pass would be a requirement for the Certificate of Completion of Surgical Training (CCST). By then there were about 60 candidates for each of two annual diets[24]. The cumulative pass rate settled at around 85 per cent.

Candidates had to have passed the 'old' FRCS or the 'new' MRCS, have had a satisfactory assessment at the end of their fourth year of HST and produce their logbook of operations. The format comprised clinical cases and three vivas: emergency surgery with critical care, general surgery including the candidate's special interest (if declared) and an 'academic' viva. The latter involved critiquing three papers (provided in advance), and reviewing three

---

24   A 'diet' is a Scottish usage for a sitting of an examination.

abstracts of the candidate's published or presented papers. Each viva lasted 30 minutes with two examiners, so as the numbers increased, we needed more examiners, who had to be available for two days.

The whole group of examiners met at the end of the second day to review the marks, discuss marginal candidates and award the ASGBI medal to the best candidate. Examiners and successful candidates then mingled for a drink. A candidate was allowed only four attempts, though I do not recall anyone reaching that limit.

ORGANISATION OF THE EXAMINATIONS

In the spirit of intercollegiate cooperation, the exam moved around the fiefdoms of the four royal colleges in strict rotation. The exams for all nine surgical specialties were managed from the office of the JCIE in Edinburgh. The office negotiated which hospitals should host the clinicals on the first day and where to hold the vivas the next day. The exam is quite disruptive for a hospital. In England and Wales, the burden was moved around the teaching centres, but there was less scope for this in Scotland and Ireland.

During the 1990s, the format was adjusted to accommodate subspecialty interests in the short cases and in one of the vivas, and the academic viva was modified several times. Training for examiners was introduced and after some initial scepticism it was welcomed. As appeals against examination results, and even litigation, became increasingly common in medicine, we had to formalise the viva questions and even the follow-up questions. Many of us regretted this development and felt that it reduced our ability to identify either the outstanding candidates or the weakest ones. I understand that there are now (in 2019) question banks, their specialty-specific managers accounting for half of the staff at the JCIE, which has grown from four to 18. Presumably, some knowledge of these questions accumulates among trainers and trainees.

Each diet of the examination was accompanied by a dinner for the examiners – a most convivial occasion. Memorably in Dublin in 1995, our host Professor Niall O'Higgins, in lieu of a speech, delivered a poem of 50 lines ending:

Whether you've driven, flown or were bussed
From each far-flung corner of the NHS Trust
From Leicester, from Glasgow, from Sheffield or Bristol

From Canterbury, London or places more distal
To the intercollegiate health I propose
To shamrock, to thistle, to leek and to rose.

The last two lines became the regular after-dinner toast.

I completed my term as an examiner in 1998. It had been an interesting experience, particularly because, unlike most of my colleagues, I had not been an examiner for the old FRCS.

In 2000, 143 candidates passed the exam. It had come a long way since the first two sat and passed it in April 1991. The development of the Intercollegiate Examinations, with the training of examiners and their assessment is comprehensively described in: *To Shamrock, to Thistle, to Leek and to Rose* by Eleanor Winton, who was head of Intercollegiate Specialty Examinations for 18 years up to her retirement in 2011.

35

PRESIDENT

In January 1998 Tony Giddings, then president of the Association of Surgeons, phoned to ask if I would be prepared to be a candidate in the election for president for the year 2000–2001. I had been approached twice in earlier years and each time had declined, considering that I was not capable, so to be consistent my initial response on this occasion was the same. However, on reflection and after discussion with Elisabeth I changed my mind. I concluded that experience as chairman of the Specialist Advisory Committee and my prolonged membership of the council of the ASGBI would enable me to do the job. Confident that I could manage the politics, I was concerned about my lack of international contacts to produce speakers for the annual meeting. I phoned him back the same evening and was included in the election.

There were two other worthy candidates but at the next council meeting I was chosen, to my great surprise, with an overall majority in the first round of the ballot.

I then had two years to make my plans. Manchester had been booked for the annual meeting, but the conference centre was still being built and it was apparent that it would not be ready in time. We then switched to the International Convention Centre (ICC) in Birmingham. This had been an excellent venue in 1993 but the costs had become challenging. I did my best to raise some independent sponsorship, but I was unsuccessful apart from a very generous donation from one Leicester company, two directors: of which had been my patients. I think Leicester firms would have been more likely to contribute if the meeting had been held locally. There was also the possibility of an autumn meeting and there were numerous matters requiring discussion by council.

ORGANISATION

The informal meetings of the president, vice president, honorary secretary and treasurer had been replaced in the mid-1990s by an executive, which additionally included the vice-president elect and the chairmen of the Specialties Board and the Education Committee. The executive met monthly, usually for an afternoon, followed by dinner. A link surgeon had been identified in each hospital, as an aid to gathering and disseminating information. They had supplied up-to-date figures on consultant staffing, and in my year they participated in surveys of emergency workload and duty rotas.

The nine surgical specialties were each represented on the council of the Royal College of Surgeons of England (based in London) by an 'invited' member, usually their president. However, if he or she was already an elected member, the specialty was allowed another representative. That had been the situation during my predecessor Bernard Ribeiro's presidency, so the honorary secretary had acted up. When I became president, the newly appointed hon sec expected that he would represent us at the RCS. I felt I should fill this role, both to advocate for the Association and to ensure that I was well informed. I had to put this view quite forcefully before it was accepted.

Attendance at the council of the RCS was an interesting experience. The president conducted proceedings standing and members stood to speak. The elected members sat in a large oval with the invited members at tables in the centre, so that when speaking, I always had my back to half the members, detracting from the impact of my remarks. A single year was a short time in which to adapt to the environment, while elected members were there for six to 10 years, so my effectiveness was limited.

I was present for the election of the president and two vice-presidents of the college, though as an invited member I did not vote. Every elected member was a candidate unless he or she declined, which rarely happened. Ballot papers were collected by the secretary during a council meeting. In the first round the votes were widely spread. Then the member with the fewest votes was eliminated and the procedure was repeated until a member had an overall majority. All that was missing was a puff of smoke.

The Association had outgrown its offices, due to the need to accommodate the subspecialties, each with its own paid secretary. Tony Giddings, as president in 1997/8, had masterminded the conversion of the former laboratories on the top floor of the RCS into a large, open-plan office. There were also some smaller rooms and the Moynihan Room, which served as the council chamber. It was convertible to theatre-style seating and it was hoped that income from letting would offset the increased rental payments to the college. The cost of this conversion and its furnishings had consumed much of the Association's accumulated reserves, so the annual meetings over the following years could not risk substantial losses.

In the preceding year, I had embarked on a project to visit all the regional surgical societies. Their members were general surgeons and the societies had evolved to provide a forum for trainees' research papers. I managed to attend meetings of most of the active societies in England and Wales, recognising that the surgical colleges in Scotland and Ireland provided the focus there. I was always received cordially and found that the activity of and enthusiasm for the regional societies was proportional to their distance from London. Of the four metropolitan regions, only the north-eastern had a functioning society, doubtless because the Section of Surgery of the Royal Society of Medicine served a similar purpose. I think these visits may have helped to increase the membership of the Association from 64 to 72 per cent of consultants. This was still below what we hoped for; it was likely that many surgeons by then regarded their subspecialty society as their home.

I continued the practice of producing a president's newsletter, three times each year, and it was distributed to all fellows of the ASGBI. Most of the topics in the following sections of this chapter were discussed in the newsletters.

During the year, my successor Chris Russell proposed the appointment of a chief executive, in place of the administrator of the Association, to enhance leadership, though doubtless at increased cost. There was the opportunity to do this after the administrator went on maternity leave in September 2000 and the change was implemented in June 2001, just after I demitted office.

THE NHS PLAN

The NHS Plan: A Plan for Investment, A Plan for Reform was published in July 2000, introducing commissioning by 'primary care groups' to replace GP fundholding. As yet another reorganisation, it was received with scepticism.

However, it did promise an increase in funding of one-third over five years and a further 2,500 consultant posts, but there were no additional resources for training.

One detail, requiring consultants to not undertake private practice for their first seven years, was divisive and unfair to new appointees. Nevertheless, we agreed that it would be unwise to object publicly, as this would surely be represented in the press to give a negative image of consultants. Fortunately, after quiet negotiation by the royal colleges, the seven-year ban was dropped.

The plan proposed changes in the consultant contract, and I would have liked this to reflect workload more accurately, including a sessional allowance for time on call. In line with other occupations, full-time should be 10 (not 11) half days. As for time for private practice, I suggested that when one or more sessions were allocated for on-call duties, the corresponding number of daytime sessions might be available for private practice; alternatively, a consultant not interested in private practice might be paid for more than 10 sessions. Those with a larger private practice should be able to negotiate a reduced number of NHS sessions.

Around this time there had been a spate of articles questioning consultants' commitment to the NHS. My proposals would have neutralised these claims and I think would have been fair. I did not manage to gain support for these ideas within the executive and the contract negotiations extended well beyond my year as president.

SPECIALTIES WITHIN GENERAL SURGERY

The rapid development of subspecialties within general surgery during the 1990s caused tension in the Association. The subspecialty organisations had developed over the preceding 25 years, starting with the Vascular Surgical Society in 1966. The British Transplantation Society was set up in 1971 to support surgeons engaged in organ transplantation, but they were only a small group. There was then a long gap before the Association of Coloproctology was formed in 1990, raising the possibility of a future breakup of general surgery. The breast surgeons were represented as the British Breast Group within the British Association of Surgical Oncology and some of them were also members of the British Association of Endocrine Surgeons, but these affiliations did not seem to threaten separation.

As these groups began to flex their muscles, the surgeons with oesophago-gastric and hepatobiliary interests realised that they lacked representation, so in 1996 they formed the Association of Upper Gastrointestinal Surgeons. In parallel with these anatomically based groups, two technical organisations had developed: the British Surgical Stapling Group and the Society of Minimally Invasive General Surgeons. These merged in 1994 to become the Association of Laparoscopic Surgeons. The new associations adopted the suffix 'of Great Britain and Ireland', emphasising their affinity to the ASGBI.

The creation of the new suite of offices had provided accommodation for secretaries employed by the subspecialties, which also benefitted from shared administrators for membership and subscriptions. They each ran their own scientific conferences, to some extent in competition with the Association's annual meeting. Understandably, they sought greater independence, while the ASGBI aimed to accommodate them under its umbrella, rather than see them separate completely. They wished to have their representatives included in our council, but it was already large, comprising 26 full members and 10 observers. They also disliked being described as *sub*-specialties.

After repeated discussions, it was agreed that the presidents of these societies would be invited to join the council of the ASGBI, and that the approved terminology would be 'specialties within general surgery'. I doubted whether these compromises would hold in the long term. This indeed proved to be the case as the vascular surgeons and the coloproctologists later set up independent offices.

The government was most reluctant to recognise an increased number of specialties, so these groups remained within the ambit of the general surgical SAC. (In 2012 vascular surgery was granted its own SAC.). Inevitably, tensions arose between the requirements for the generality of training and training in each subspecialty. The trend to increasing specialisation among SpRs raised concerns about future competence across the wide range of emergency work. To draw attention to this I decided that the theme for the annual meeting should be 'Emergency Surgery'.

Two other subspecialty problems, considered when I was on the SAC, were still live: what children's surgery should continue to be performed by general surgeons; and who should do thyroid operations? Regional paediatric surgical units already did the complex operations required in neonates and for cancers. Appendicitis and operations for hernias and undescended testicles were handled by general surgeons. This surely should continue but by this time trainees often lacked appropriate training. The solution suggested was to encourage some SpRs to add general paediatric surgery (GPS) as a subsidiary interest. It was agreed that a six-month attachment to a paediatric unit would provide suitable training but very few trainees showed an interest. The ICB was unable to accommodate a second interest in the FRCS exam to validate this training. I suspect that general paediatric surgery remains an awkward issue.

Logically, thyroid surgery lies within endocrine surgery, where it is the most common operation. Some surgeons with another main interest also did a substantial amount of thyroid work, but no other endocrine surgery. However, in the 1990s ENT specialists, rebranding as 'head and neck surgeons', aspired to take over the thyroid. I tried to rally the general surgeons, but the thyroid did not fit into the emerging specialty structure within general surgery, and I concluded that it would gradually migrate to ENT.

STAFFING IN GENERAL SURGERY

In response to the reduction in trainees' hours and because of increasing specialisation, the number of consultant posts increased rapidly during the 1990s. In 1990 there were about 1,050 consultants in general surgery in the UK; by September 1999 there were 1,659 posts, of which 80 were without a substantive consultant. This was still short of the ratio of one consultant in general surgery to 30,000 population, recommended by the Association in 1991.

In 2000, in view of the reduction in junior support, the ASGBI increased its target for the number of consultants to one to 25,000. I developed a spreadsheet showing the number of trainees expected to gain their Certificate of Completion of Surgical Training (CCST) each year. It demonstrated that this would fall short of the number of consultant vacancies. Once the target was reached the number of SpRs might need to be reduced.

The SAC pressed the DoH to increase the number of SpRs, but it would take six years for the additional trainees to be ready to fill the consultant vacancies. To bridge the gap, associate specialists and overseas candidates were encouraged to apply for 'mediated entry' to the specialist register, subject to assessment of their training, a process managed by the SAC jointly with the royal college.

Vacancies for consultants with some subspecialty interests proved difficult to fill. To quantify this, I recorded the advertisements for consultant posts each year from 1998 and compared these with the distribution of interests among trainees passing the Intercollegiate Exam. There were shortages of candidates in breast and transplant specialties while there was a surplus in upper gastrointestinal surgery. There was no mechanism to align the supply of candidates with each subspecialty interest with the demand. All we could do was to point out the opportunities to the trainees.

I had been involved in manpower planning for several years while a member of the SAC and I concluded that it was nigh impossible. Changes in the NHS altered the requirement for consultants on a shorter timescale than the duration of training, so we could never catch up.

BRISTOL AND SHIPMAN

Two scandals in the late 1990s had profound effects. In 1995 high mortality rates were reported for infants undergoing cardiac surgery in Bristol. An anaesthetist had drawn attention to this as early as 1990 but was ignored and he had emigrated. The subsequent inquiry indicated 30–35 excess deaths between 1990 and 1995.

In January 2000 Harold Shipman, a single-handed GP in Hyde, was convicted of the murder of 15 of his patients, though the total number of victims was estimated at 250. It was extraordinary that his crimes had passed unnoticed over a 27-year period.

Council discussed these events and agreed that the effects would be seismic, but the national response developed only slowly over the following years. I digress from the year of my presidency to follow this through. The Healthcare Commission was set up in 2003 to monitor the performance of hospitals and was subsumed into the Care Quality Commission in 2009. It inspects hospitals, general practice and social services, but has had difficulty covering this large remit, despite an annual budget exceeding £200m.

After the inquiry into the Bristol paediatric cardiac surgery unit, revalidation of all doctors, under the supervision of the GMC, was proposed but its implementation was contentious and therefore delayed. A scheme was about to start in 2005 when the report on Shipman's murders criticised the plans as inadequate.

After several rounds of negotiation, the process finally started in 2012. Each doctor prepares a portfolio of practice and educational activities with feedback from colleagues and patients. He or she discusses it with the 'responsible officer' at annual appraisal, and a plan for professional development is agreed. Based on the appraisals, revalidation is decided by the GMC at five-yearly intervals. There is continuing inconsistency between two views of the purpose of revalidation: is it to weed out incompetent doctors or is it a formative educational process?

All this regulatory activity imposes a considerable workload on medical staff, competing with the time for clinical work and teaching. It remains to be seen whether it will be effective in preventing future scandals. So far it has not prevented the failures in the South Staffordshire Trust or a high neonatal mortality in the Morecambe Bay hospitals, in Shrewsbury and Telford or in Thanet. Perhaps the comprehensive reporting of the results for units and individual surgeons would provide better quality control.

SURVEYS OF THE EMERGENCY SERVICE

In cooperation with Graham Layer, ASGBI hon sec, I asked the link surgeons in all the hospitals to complete a 24-hour snapshot of the cases seen on take by the general surgical team. Seventy-one per cent responded, giving the numbers of patients seen in 197 hospitals on a specified day. On average, each hospital had 10 referrals, of whom 7.8 were admitted. Three emergency operations resulted, mostly appendicectomy, laparotomy or drainage of an abscess, with small numbers of operations for abdominal injuries and ruptured aortic aneurysms. From these results, we estimated that nationally over a million patients require emergency assessment by a general surgeon each year. The average consultant would be responsible for 181 emergency operations per annum.

We also surveyed consultant emergency rotas and facilities, with an 84 per cent response rate. There was a wide range of frequency: larger hospitals had less frequent duty days, but a heavier workload on those days. The median commitment was to be on take one day in five. Specialist cover for vascular surgery was available in only 46 per cent of hospitals and most vascular surgeons were in double jeopardy, also being on the general rota. A daytime theatre was reserved for emergencies in only 63 per cent of hospitals. When on take only about a third of consultants had daytime sessions free of fixed commitments. These requirements had been repeatedly emphasised in the reports from the National Confidential Enquiry into Patient Outcome and Death (NCEPOD) during the 1990s.

I presented these results in a symposium on the emergency service at the annual meeting. They provided ammunition in the campaign to get proper recognition of the needs of this service and were the subject of an interview on the BBC.

THE ISLE OF MAN

The last five presidents had organised small but enjoyable autumn meetings in Romania, Cape Town, Oslo, Belfast and New Zealand and I wondered how best to follow those, recognising that another expensive long-distance event would not be popular.

I was aware that surgeons serving small outlying populations faced special difficulties. Their average catchment could support only two very general surgeons, whose duties might include fractures and caesarean sections. They were on call one-in-two, though at low intensity, and diagnostic services were limited. This set-up could not support higher surgical training. It was difficult to recruit replacement consultants, or locums to cover leave. These surgeons met annually as the Viking Surgeons' Club. To hear their concerns at first hand I invited myself to their meetings, in Coleraine in 1998, and Elgin in 1999. I considered that their problems applied to other small remote hospitals in places such as Haverford West and Penzance. This generated the idea of a meeting themed around the surgical service in smaller hospitals.

A holiday in the Isle of Man suggested that it would be an appropriate site for such an event, while also introducing our members to an island that few of them knew. Preliminary visits secured the enthusiastic cooperation of the three local surgeons and identified suitable hotel and conference accommodation. We devised a social itinerary for accompanying persons during the surgical sessions and for everyone on the following day. The meeting was held at the end of September 2000. About 60 surgeons attended, many accompanied by their wives (there were no female surgeons in this group). The challenges and limitations of surgical practice in small and remote hospitals were discussed, but no solutions to their difficulties were identified.

A month later I was due to attend the American College of Surgeons in Chicago and then go on to represent the ASGBI at the South African Association of Surgeons. As described in chapter 27, I suffered a major bleed from a duodenal ulcer and had to cancel both visits. This precipitated retirement from my residual two day-case sessions at the LRI.

PLANNING THE ANNUAL MEETING

The conference had usually been given a general theme such as 'Safer Surgery'. I had become increasingly concerned about the problems of the emergency service in the context of increasing specialisation, so I decided on 'Emergency Surgery' as the title for the meeting in April 2001. I aimed to incorporate as many emergency topics as possible, within the limitations of the established format and I maximised the president's role in devising the programme. Each specialty expected to produce its own sessions and not all were amenable to including emergency topics. There were four lectures in the gift of the royal colleges while the Surgical Research Society would occupy three of the five lecture theatres for much of the first day.

An early request, in February 2000, for contributions to a symposium on emergencies produced a good response and I managed to include many other sessions and individual items on emergency topics. At the suggestion of Graham Layer, the hon sec, we added a category of mini poster, in which unusual or instructive emergency cases could be reported; this drew 89 offers of which we selected 57 for display.

Surgical history had long been an interest of mine, since I investigated the origins of operations for duodenal ulcer and prostatic obstruction when I was an SHO in Bristol. Most publications have been on surgery prior to the advent of anaesthesia, neglecting recent history. I exercised my prerogative to include three lectures on the history of emergency surgery: for intestinal obstruction (which I gave), appendicitis and the complications of peptic ulcer.

I was keen to include a session on the repair of incisional hernias, for which high recurrence rates were reported. Professor Andrew Kingsnorth kindly recruited an international faculty. Despite my colleagues' prediction that it would be of limited interest, the session proved extremely popular, filling the lecture theatre to standing room only.

I also wanted to feature the work of Professor Kehlet from Copenhagen. He had responded to the shorter hospital stay after laparoscopic operations by redesigning perioperative care for open procedures. I heard this programme described at a conference in Sweden, with the length of hospital stay for major operations rivalling that after laparoscopic surgery. Unfortunately, I did not manage to persuade either of the gastrointestinal societies to find time for him in their sessions. This 'enhanced recovery programme' was subsequently widely adopted. I should somehow have found space for it.

I was anxious that I lacked overseas contacts that I might invite to give some of the named lectures. Colleagues very kindly suggested suitable professors whom I then visited in Paris and Leiden and recruited them. Elisabeth and I expanded these trips into brief holidays. I wrote to another speaker from South Africa, as a visit would have been an extravagance. In accordance with the emergency theme one of them came as the Moynihan

Travelling Fellow to look at emergency surgery in three UK hospitals and report on this at the meeting. Another spoke on damage limitation surgery for trauma, then a new concept in the UK.

PRACTICAL ARRANGEMENTS

The Association's very experienced administrator had done much of the detailed preparation for the recent annual meetings, but in October 2000 she went on maternity leave. One of the specialty managers acted up as administrator and we appointed a locum to work on arrangements for the meeting. She was a very capable organiser, but it became clear that she had difficulty in dealing with crowds. She then solved that problem in December 2000 by finding a new job as a company secretary, so we were left in the lurch.

With the workload increasing, it was too late to recruit another locum. The acting administrator and one of the specialty managers volunteered to work overtime to organise the meeting and we gladly provided a suitable financial bonus. With their efforts and my spending extra days in London we completed the complex programme and made all the other arrangements. I remain eternally grateful to those two individuals.

Elisabeth and I selected the Birmingham Botanical Gardens for the Association's annual dinner and arranged for the council dinner to take place at a stately home. Meanwhile, with advice from colleagues in Birmingham, we devised a social programme for the accompanying persons. This traditional feature had been attracting diminishing support in recent years as fewer spouses attended the meeting, perhaps because more wives and partners were working. The uptake on this occasion was poor; a few years later it was discontinued.

BIRMINGHAM 2001

The meeting attracted just over one thousand surgeons, a 13 per cent increase on the previous year, and ran without any significant problems. For the first time we used PowerPoint digital projection, from a centrally serviced system, avoiding the malfunctions which may occur with slides. Nearly everyone kept to time. All the exhibition space was sold to 68 exhibitors, but two-thirds of the proceeds went to pay the cost of the hall and other expenses.

Elisabeth and I attended three official dinners and I had to give speeches at two of these, though to be precise there are no speeches at the council dinner, just 'remarks'. I had the opportunity to be interviewed by the BBC when I

With Elisabeth at the Annual Dinner at Birmingham Botanical Gardens in 2001

made the case for consultant expansion and emphasised the importance of the emergency workload.

The annual black-tie dinner attracted 331 people, including guests, and Professor Jim Drife (formerly of Leicester) gave a most entertaining speech. I still have the notes for my final contribution. I started with a wordplay on the 'Association', which to me, as a sailor, was the name of Sir Cloudesley Shovell's 90-gun ship which was wrecked on the Isles of Scilly in 1707, leading to a competition to produce a chronometer to determine longitude.

Despite being a student on the firm of one president (Sir Clement Price Thomas) and SHO to another (Professor Milnes Walker), I was ignorant of the ASGBI until I was a senior registrar; I suggested that it was now much better known. I described attending my first meeting, to give a paper, in 1971 and produced the tiny booklet to indicate the limited programme.

The Association had met in Birmingham on five previous occasions, the documents charting its steady growth. I welcomed the guests, reviewed the activities of council over the year and thanked the participants and the staff. I then lightened the mood by suggesting how, in the event of defeat in the forthcoming general election, members of the Cabinet might retrain for various appropriate surgical roles. Finally, I installed Chris Russell as president using the grandiose formula devised by Lord Moynihan. 'Mr President, I place upon your shoulders The Badge of Office, The Emblem of Leadership, The Reward of Service, A Tribute from your Colleagues.' I placed the very grand presidential jewel around his neck and in return received my past president's medal. Thus ended a memorable and at times difficult year.

I was pleased with how the meeting turned out and later was glad that, despite the high hire costs, we made a small surplus. With this meeting I had completed my varied surgical career. Elisabeth and I then went to Venice for a week to recuperate.

RETIREMENT

36

FAREWELL TO MEDICINE

I had planned to retire in mid-1998, when I reached the age of 63, and Elisabeth arranged to do likewise in 1999, though she was concerned about how she would occupy herself. Then early in 1998 I was unexpectedly elected to be president of the ASGBI for 2000/1 and therefore felt that I should remain in my hospital post (then only six sessions per week) until 2000. I explained my situation to the chief executive of the LRI Trust and it was agreed that I should continue to January 2000 and then reduce to just two day-case sessions. The medical school was keen for me to continue teaching but I was tired after my presidency, so I declined. I did not teach again until 2016.

We had few friends apart from hospital colleagues, most of whom were younger and still working. There had simply been no time to cultivate other contacts. In retirement, Elisabeth did some Open University courses, though she did not aspire to another degree. Taking the lead in branching out, she trained as a guide at the University Botanic Garden and through a conversation with a neighbour discovered NADFAS (the National Association of Decorative and Fine Arts Societies), which led on to other activities (see chapter 37). We enjoyed concerts – the Philharmonia and those organised by the Leicester International Music Festival.

Some of our colleagues moved after retiring, either to a Leicestershire village or the coast. That didn't appeal to us as we felt it would disrupt friendships and disconnect us from medical contacts should we need them. We did wonder whether to downsize. However, we were attached to the house and liked being able to accommodate the whole family. I was devoted to the large garden and could care for it more meticulously now that I had the time. Consequently, we decided to stay put!

We were fortunate in both having generous final salary pensions, topped up by annuities from my private practice. A cushion of capital was provided by lump sums from our NHS pension funds and bonuses from the endowment policies guaranteeing the mortgage, which we had paid off by the 1990s. So, anything was possible.

TRAVEL

We'd already visited many faraway places: Pakistan, India, Thailand, Malaysia, the USA (four times), Canada, New Zealand (twice) and Australia, but we still had ambitions.

I had wanted to take the Norwegian Coastal Voyage since one of my anaesthetists described it in the 1980s, and we finally did so in 2004. On the return journey we stayed for three nights on the Lofoten Islands. It was a most memorable trip. This whetted our appetites for cruising in smaller ships – in Russia, the River Douro, the Hebrides, the Riviera, the Galapagos and in a fully rigged ship around the Azores.

Other travels were land based, including to most European countries from Scandinavia to Italy and Spain. We often toured in a hire car until I had an unpleasant, though not serious, clash with a truck in Sweden in 2008. Thereafter we joined group tours.

REDESIGN

I did a course in garden design and chose as my project the redevelopment of our front garden at Knighton Rise; we implemented the plan in 2002. My long-standing interest in architecture then came into play, remodelling the large sitting room and replacing the flat garage roof with a ridge. Elisabeth had suggested that a lean-to greenhouse behind the garage would provide an interest for me. We decided to proceed with these projects in 2003. I did the rewiring myself to reduce the cost – that was just before it became illegal for an unqualified person to do such work.

We all agreed that the sitting room had been transformed, while the extra storage in the garage loft enabled us to keep even more junk. We continued to live there comfortably until 2015 when we decided to downsize (see chapter 40).

SURGICAL PUBLICATIONS

During my consultant career, I had my name on 24 clinical papers in peer-reviewed journals, though latterly most of the work had been done by my trainees. Often, I had suggested the project but in a few instances an SR had added my name as a courtesy, a practice which is now rightly condemned. Conversely there were articles for which I had suggested the idea or advised on presentation, but I declined to be listed as an author as I didn't think my involvement justified it.

In 1978, RM (Gerry) Kirk had published *General Surgical Operations*, a practical book which proved immensely popular. In the late 1990s he asked me to revise the chapter on hernias for the fourth edition. I was happy to write it, subject to the new laparoscopic approach being in a separate chapter. I did an extensive revision, eliminating several obsolete techniques of repair for inguinal hernias and emphasising the place for day-case operations and local anaesthesia.

Walford Gillison, a retired surgeon from Kidderminster, who had succeeded me as SR in Sheffield, proposed a multi-author book on *Pioneers in Surgical Gastroenterology*[25]. He had heard my historical lecture on intestinal obstruction at the ASGBI meeting in Birmingham and asked me to be co-editor. Flattered, I initially agreed but after some discussion I concluded that our approaches were not sufficiently aligned and withdrew amicably. He later recruited Professor Henry Buchwald from Minnesota who was a better choice, both in widening the contacts for the various chapters and commercially. I contributed two chapters: 'The challenge of intestinal obstruction', and 'Intestinal reconstruction'. Published in 2005, all one thousand copies had been sold by 2016.

Thereafter my medical contributions were limited to occasional letters to the *BMJ* or *The Times* on issues of surgical training or manpower.

PROFESSIONAL ACTIVITIES

Although I had intended to do no professional work once I'd retired, I did get involved in the first two years. As a former SAC chairman, I was asked to

25   ISBN 1-903378-35-4

lead a Training Interface Group on cleft lip and palate surgery. Cleft surgery was in the training curricula for four specialties: ENT, plastic, maxillofacial and paediatric surgery, being performed by different specialties in different regions. To maximise quality the service was to be rationalised into about eight specialised units and there would be an average of one consultant vacancy per annum. It was absurd for all the trainees in the four specialties to be expected to have experience of cleft surgery. The curricula needed to be reorganised to reflect this, and a special pathway established for training in cleft surgery for a few individuals. I failed to get agreement among the vested interests, and after two years handed over to another chairman.

In 2016, I heard of a Leicester Medical School project on 'clinical diagnostic reasoning'. The increasing specialisation of hospital units and the emphasis on protocols was leading to tunnel vision among students. This did not encourage a search for the diagnosis across the whole field of medicine, particularly important for patients with confusing stories or suffering from multiple pathologies. A short programme of discussion of case presentations was designed to help with this. Retired doctors, who had practised in a less structured system, were recruited to teach clinical diagnostic reasoning in these sessions and I enjoyed taking part. I now regret declining the invitation to continue teaching medical students early in retirement.

37

CLUBS AND SOCIETIES

W e had been so absorbed in our busy jobs that we had few outside contacts and little involvement in other organisations. On retirement, we made a conscious effort to engage.

FRIENDS OF THE BOTANIC GARDEN

When she retired, Elisabeth responded to a request for guides to take groups around the University of Leicester Botanic Garden in Oadby. Following training sessions by the director, new guides took groups around the garden, describing its history and pointing out plants of interest. A few years later I also became a guide.

In 2002, the chair of the Friends of the Garden suggested that the guides should be represented on the committee and recruited Elisabeth for this. Later she was asked to be the next chair and we then realised that retired professionals are much in demand for committee jobs. At the end of her three-year term no one from the committee was prepared to take over, so she reluctantly continued for a fourth year. Six months later the job was still vacant, so I reluctantly stepped in.

A thriving organisation with about 850 members, the Friends runs a fund-raising plant fair and family day and arranges gardening lectures and garden visits. It also supported the start of an excellent programme of school visits. The Garden's substantial running costs of around £200,000 were met by the university, but this was increasingly difficult to justify as traditional botany had become a much less prominent subject. Leicester's is unusual in being one of only two of the eight university botanic gardens in England not charging for admission.

As chairman, I advocated a change in policy to charging for entry. There were 50,000 visitors per year; at £4 per head this could have covered the running costs. It would have required a café and a shop, costing about £200,000. The Garden's priority was replacement of the display greenhouses, raising the capital cost for the combined scheme to an estimated £500,000. An application for lottery funding was unsuccessful, so the project lapsed.

The only way I could find a successor as chairman was by exchanging jobs with the treasurer. Then after three years, he found a treasurer to replace me. I had already retired as a tour guide and volunteer gardener and thus ended my formal involvement in the Friends.

A previous treasurer had organised an annual four-day garden tour. When he withdrew, I offered to take over. After the first year, I decided to arrange the tour without using a tour company. The most difficult part was finding a hotel of suitable quality and at an acceptable cost, which could accommodate a group of 50. The choice of gardens was easier, aided by an enjoyable reconnaissance. Elisabeth and I organised tours of gardens in Kent, North Wales, Devon, and the Lake District and then handed over to a small subcommittee.

U3A AND NADFAS

The University of the Third Age (U3A) is a national organisation for those who no longer work. Local societies each comprise many groups run independently and often meeting in members' homes. The groups cover topics ranging from philosophy to table tennis. Elisabeth joined and was a member of the photography group for several years. When a friend died, she inherited leadership of the needlework and knitting group which now meets monthly in our house, and I join in for tea. Elisabeth later joined the crosswords group.

Chatting to a neighbour, Elisabeth learned of the National Association of Decorative and Fine Arts Societies (NADFAS)[26]. We joined the local society (LDFAS) and enjoyed its high-quality monthly lectures and occasional day trips. Douglas Smith, a retired architect, also arranged overseas visits, which

---

26   NADFAS rebranded as The Arts Society in 2017.

took us to the Netherlands and Bilbao. Elisabeth booked the lecturers for three years.

I became treasurer and later Elisabeth was persuaded to do two years as chair. Her predecessor had organised a three-day visit to Cardiff. Elisabeth decided on Chichester, and we went back into travel agent mode, as we had for the Friends of the Botanic Garden. On an exploratory visit we tested two hotels, followed by hard bargaining for the better one. The trip was a good mixture of cathedral, art gallery, sculpture park and theatre.

LDFAS has a sub-group of church recorders who make an extremely detailed record of the church interior, a process that takes a couple of years. The descriptions from the eight specialties are compiled into a single volume. Elisabeth joined the group to record textiles and shortly afterwards the member responsible for compiling the complete record resigned for family reasons. As the most computer-literate member, Elisabeth took over as compiler, a considerable task. The completed record was distributed to English Heritage, the V&A, Historic England, the Church-Care Library, the local record office and the church itself.

After compiling for three churches, Elisabeth decided that she had done her share and handed over to others, while continuing as a recorder.

ART AND DESIGN GROUP
Douglas Smith invited us to join the Leicester Art and Design Group (ADG). The group has about 50 members with various backgrounds, and does day visits to notable, often recent, buildings and some interesting factories. We also went to Valencia, New York, Montpellier, Lyons and Turin. The treasurer was ageing, and I took over from him for seven years and then handed over to a younger colleague.

THE LEICESTER LITERARY AND PHILOSOPHICAL SOCIETY
The Lit and Phil was founded in 1835 by two medical practitioners, and in 1849 was instrumental in the establishment of the city museum and art gallery. It lobbied for the formation of the University College in 1921. The main ongoing activity is a series of fortnightly lectures on a variety of topics as wide as its title indicates. We originally joined in the 1980s, but our membership had lapsed. We rejoined in retirement, finding that the membership included many of our friends from LADFAS and the ADG, but remarkably few medics.

THE HALDANE SOCIETY

Named after the first visitor to the then Leicester, Leicestershire and Rutland College[27], The Haldane Society was formed to link town and gown. There are three lectures per year on a variety of topics, often given by national experts and each lecture is followed by a dinner. The lectures are always thought-provoking and the company at the dinners is interesting – we take pot-luck rather than booking a group for a table. Unfortunately, the membership now consists largely of the retired, both academics and others – not the original objective.

LEICESTER ANTIQUES SOCIETY AND LEICESTERSHIRE YACHT CLUB

Among the local clubs, we joined the Antiques Society. We knew several members, but there was a waiting list – we joked that we were not antique enough. Finally, our turn arrived, and shortly afterwards active recruitment became necessary. There were monthly lectures in the winter and a few day visits in the summer. The topics overlapped with those at LADFAS. By 2017 it became impossible to find new officers, the membership was falling and as a result the expenses were exceeding income. Regretfully the society closed in 2017.

A chance conversation at the Antiques Society with the hon sec of the Yacht Club resulted in an invitation to join in 2016. The title is a misnomer; it is really a dining club. About 50 members meet at the Leicestershire Golf Club for a three-course dinner followed by a talk on a sailing or related topic. Some members are, or have been, owners of cruising boats. Having chartered in the past and being elderly, we are not out of place, and I contributed one lecture on 'My Sailing Boats'.

KEEPING GOING

We have gained a lot from participating in these various organisations, both intellectually and socially. We have made many friends and our retirement has been enriched in sundry ways.

Both of us have done a fair share of the work of running the societies as committee members and officers. However, it is becoming increasingly difficult to find chairmen, honorary secretaries and treasurers. Membership is

---

27   Founded in 1921, this became the University of Leicester in 1957

falling because the following generation are less inclined to join, so the long-term future of many of these organisations is uncertain.

38

FAMILY RETROSPECTIVE

In retirement, it is a time to reflect on our lives as a family since moving to Leicester in 1971, including animals, sailing and holidays. We look back with pride on the lives of our three children. They are quite different, and each decided that medicine was not for them, saying: 'You both work far too hard.' Nevertheless, they worked hard in their various careers.

OUR PARENTS

Elisabeth's father, Jack Appleby, was suffering from angina before I first met him, and this became increasingly troublesome over the years. What a pity that coronary artery bypass had not yet become available. In 1974, while getting out of the driver's side of his parked car, he was hit by a passing van and died in hospital of multiple injuries a few hours later. He was only 66.

Elisabeth's mother, Bertha, lived on in their house in Edgware. In 1985, she broke her femur and after the operation she came to stay with us to convalesce. She made a good recovery and returned home. Three years later she fractured her other femur. After convalescing with us, she again went home to Edgware. Some months after that she suffered a myocardial infarction followed by intractable heart failure and died in our house a few months later aged 84.

My father, Frank Watkin, having had no serious illnesses, developed dementia in 1975. It was very sad – I am sure he was aware that he was not coping. My mother looked after him devotedly for two years and then he suddenly deteriorated physically and died in hospital the following morning. He was 76 and had had a good life until dementia struck. At his wish, he was buried at Montgomery. The mourners then lunched at The Dragon, where his grandfather had been the landlord.

Mary (Mollie), my mother, stayed on in the Wrexham house, though she was very lonely. I brought her to stay in Leicester after two episodes of illness, but each time after a few weeks she chose to return to her home and beloved garden. In April 1980, she collapsed while belatedly pruning the apple trees, and died of a ruptured aortic aneurysm. She was 80 years old. A few months earlier she had said that if she developed a 'tumour' she would like it to be allowed to take its course. I wonder if she had felt the aneurysm.

All four parents had done their very best for us educationally and had launched us into our medical careers. For religious reasons, they had not been happy about our marriage, but once that had happened, they forgave us and were fond grandparents.

OUR SCIENTIFIC FIRSTBORN

Andrew had a scientific bent from infancy. He was fascinated by electrical equipment and his first word was 'plug'. He took his time learning to read, solved by Enid Blyton: Elisabeth would read one chapter and to find out what happened next, he had to read the following one. At Beauchamp College, our local comprehensive, he gained 'A' grades in double maths, physics and chemistry.

He went on to Christ's College, Cambridge to read physics and gained a First. Simultaneously he had sponsorship from Marconi, which provided a paid gap year and interesting paid work in the vacations. He worked there with Simon Salter, a fellow student. While staying with Simon in Rotherham, he met Liz Price and they became firmly attached. He was offered a postgraduate place to work for a PhD but chose to start a job at Marconi.

Andrew worked on the control mechanism for a tank gunsight, to keep it on target as it travelled over uneven ground, and he stayed with Marconi for three years while Liz qualified as an occupational therapist. They married in 1986 and then set off in a Land Rover on a honeymoon trip to Nepal. They had a fantastic time, returning after nine months. Andrew had resigned from Marconi – he did not want to spend his life in armaments.

They stayed with Liz's parents in Rotherham until he found a job with Servelec, a control engineering firm near Sheffield, and Liz got a post as an occupational therapist in child psychiatry. They bought a house in Rotherham that had been split into two flats and spent the next four years completely restoring it, developing skills in carpentry, plumbing and electrical work. Their daughters Ruth and Laura were born in 1990 and 1993. They moved to Chesterfield to a larger house, with an acre of garden, and have gradually improved both.

Meanwhile, Simon had returned from working on the Antarctic survey and together they created a company producing maritime software, gaining contracts with the Hydrographic Office. As the business grew, they acquired secure offices and recruited staff, reaching a complement of about 20.

Andrew and Simon had always planned to retire from the business in their fifties. In 2017, Simon wanted to start touring the world with his partner in a giant motorhome, and Andrew was also happy to retire. A specialist firm helped them to market the company and after much deliberation, CherSoft was sold to a Danish firm with which they had already been working.

Ruth graduated in theatre design from Nottingham Trent University and has a business making theatre and historical costumes. Laura got a First in English and drama at Derby and went on to 'Teach First'. She teaches English for GCSE and A-levels.

OUR LITERARY MIDDLE CHILD

Sally was completely different. She taught herself to read at the age of three and was always adept with words. She wanted to write, so she did a diploma course in media studies at Birmingham Polytechnic. Sally started work with an unpaid internship at *Options* magazine while living with Grandma in Edgware. After a month, she was given a substantive job and worked in magazines as a writer and sub-editor for more than 30 years.

During this time, she bought her first flat in Finsbury Park, then moved to Mortlake before buying a terraced house in Crouch End. With Ian she had Molly (1997) and then Jasper (2000). In 2003 at Ian's suggestion, they moved to Güéjar Sierra, a village in the mountains near Granada, Spain, and let her London house.

They bought a shell of a house on the understanding that Ian would complete it while Sally continued writing articles for magazines. Ian made little progress and became increasingly difficult, so in 2005 Sally brought the children back to England and settled in South Brent, Devon, near to Polly, a friend from the poly. Ian died a few years later.

Sally advertised in *The Guardian*: 'Mermaid seeks Rock' and met Josh. They were happily married in 2012 at a quirky country house hotel in Devon, with their families and friends around them. In 2016, they decided to move to Penzance and bought a Grade II listed house there. It needed a lot of work, but it was ready for them to move in by September 2017.

Molly was a keen horsewoman with her own pony and won many rosettes. She was undecided about what to do after A levels and chose not to go to university. With Josh's help, she got a two-week placement with Foresight, a venture capital firm in London. They were so impressed that she was offered a job and is now working as an analyst. Jasper has settled into life in Penzance and gained a triple distinction in his sports science course. He has a job as a waiter and is considering his options for the future.

OUR ANIMAL-LOVING YOUNGEST

Clare followed the same path as the others through the Oadby schools. She was uncertain what she wanted to do after A levels and decided not to go to university, partly influenced by responsibility for her pony. She got a job at the headquarters of the Alliance & Leicester Building Society, which at that time was in Oadby.

She also volunteered in an RSPCA shop, from which she was recruited as secretary to its regional director. Subsequently she set up and managed the regional control centre, which was open 24 hours a day, 365 days a year, to provide a service relating to animals in distress. She bought her first house, in Leicester, and worked happily at the charity for 12 years.

Continuing in the animal charity sector, Clare then took a job as head of supporter care at WWF at its headquarters in Godalming. She next became manager for the PDSA's (People's Dispensary for Sick Animals) PetAid hospitals in Leicester and Coventry. More recently she has worked for a variety of charities including the British Red Cross, LOROS, and Age UK.

Clare lives only 10 minutes' walk from the downsizing house, which she found for us, and keeps a kindly eye on her elderly parents.

ANIMALS

Elisabeth had pets as a child, but I had none. We started with a cat in Sheffield at Sally's request, and subsequently we had two more, who overlapped, when a stray kitten adopted us. We got our first dog at Andrew's suggestion in 1972, a basset hound. Two golden retrievers followed at intervals. The second one, shared with Clare, visits an old people's home each Monday morning.

Once we'd moved to Knighton Rise, all three children had riding lessons. Inevitably this led to a wish for a pony by Sally and Clare. Shyboy was an attractive roan and a good jumper. Unfortunately, while being led along the main road to be shod, he was spooked by some debris in the hedge, bolted and died in collision with a car. Fearing that he might reach us via the food chain, Clare decided to become a vegetarian and Sally followed, in solidarity. Clare remains a strict vegetarian but after eight years the smell of bacon proved too tempting for Sally. Conversely, years later Elisabeth adopted a veggie diet. After an interval, Clare acquired another pony and had success at Pony Club events.

DINGHY SAILING

We had brought the GP14 dinghy with us from Sheffield and had to decide where to sail it. We learned that a 3,000 acre reservoir was being created in Rutland and fancied being in at the start of the club there. I signed up and paid my debenture of £100.

The Rutland Sailing Club opened in 1976 when the reservoir was half full, and the first phase of the clubhouse had been built. Racing started, the GPs being fewer than many other classes. We bought a Mirror dinghy for the children and Andrew and Sally came in first in a race for juniors. There was a demand for training for children, so I volunteered to organise a week-long course in the first summer holidays; it attracted about 20 kids, and everyone enjoyed it.

Before helping with future courses, I felt I should get a qualification, so I did a day boat instructor's course at a Leicester College. However, the club wanted the courses to run for the whole of each Saturday, which was more time than I could spare, and I did no further formal instructing.

After a couple of years, we decided that the dwindling GP14 class was not satisfactory for racing and changed ours for a Kestrel. This 15ft 6in boat was the first dinghy designed to be built in fibreglass. It is a moderate racing machine with a spinnaker but not a trapeze. Andrew and I raced it regularly (with Elisabeth sometimes deputising) until he married and moved away from Leicester. We then sold the Kestrel and I retired from the club.

We slung the Mirror in the garage in anticipation of future interest from grandchildren, but that did not materialise. I finally sold it on eBay in 2015 for £285, much more than expected and more than it had cost.

FAMILY HOLIDAYS

In our busy professional lives, holidays were important. For our first two years back in Leicester in the early 1970s, we rented a cottage at Newton-by-the-Sea in Northumberland, towing the GP14 to sail in the bay. Next, we travelled by car ferry to Guernsey and then Brittany with a mixture of beach and sightseeing. As the children got older, beach holidays gave way to activities. Over three summers, we stayed in Devon or West Wales with ponies included, all three children riding out over open countryside.

In other years, we hired sailing craft to cruise the Norfolk Broads or from Maldon on the east coast or took a motor cruiser on the river Nene. The last holiday with all three children was to Denmark in 1980. After that Sally and Andrew went away with friends, while Clare made one further trip with us, to Norway in 1982, before doing likewise. We had a final family sailing holiday on the south coast of Brittany in 1985.

Once the children had grown up, we embraced air travel, escaping from the shadow of the loss of four Westminster students in an air crash in 1959. We visited many places at home and abroad as described in chapter 36.

39

OUR TURN TO BE PATIENTS

Apart from the episode of septicaemia in 1964 and a bleeding duodenal ulcer in 2000 I'd had no significant illness. Otherwise, I had missed only a few days' work in 40 years. Then in 2004, I was found to have an abdominal aortic aneurysm.

For those not familiar with this condition, an abdominal aortic aneurysm (AAA) is a dilatation of the main artery in the abdomen extending downwards from just below the vessels supplying the kidneys. It usually causes no symptoms until it ruptures, resulting in bleeding into the adjacent tissues. Many patients then fail to make it to hospital and of those who do only about 50 per cent survive after an emergency operation to replace it with a synthetic arterial graft. The survivors then usually need a prolonged stay in the intensive care unit.

In the 1990s there were two major advances in the management of AAAs. The risk of rupture was shown to be related to size, as measured by ultrasound, becoming significant when the diameter reaches 5.5cm. This led to a national screening programme; an elective operation is advised once an AAA reaches that size. Concurrently, minimally invasive techniques were developed, in Leicester and other places, to insert a graft from within the artery, via an incision in the groin. This replaced the open operation for most patients.

PERSONAL EXPERIENCE

My aneurysm was monitored with ultrasound scans at six-monthly intervals. It progressed steadily and I predicted that I would need the operation in 2009 and this proved accurate. In preparation, a CT scan showed the presence of three (rather than one) arteries supplying the right kidney. The large lower right renal artery was arising from the neck of the aneurysm. As I had only 60 per cent of normal kidney function it was particularly desirable to preserve this artery. The supernumerary renal arteries therefore precluded the minimally invasive method of repair.

After appropriate discussion I was booked for operation on 9th November 2009. I had great confidence in the vascular unit. Professor Rob Sayers, whom I had known since he was a trainee, had vast experience of the open operation and would be supported by a very experienced team. The Leicester unit had the UK's joint lowest mortality for elective AAA surgery of 0.9 per cent. Nevertheless, the four-week wait for the operation was an anxious time. I occupied myself in getting the autumn work in the garden fully up to date and making sure that our financial affairs were clearly documented. I was also prompted to write an account of my early years, a project later expanded to become this book.

OPERATION

We arrived on the ward at 7am on the day planned for the operation. At about 7.30 my surgeon came to tell me, most apologetically, that there was no ICU bed available, so the operation would have to be cancelled. We went home again, expecting that it might be weeks before there was another slot. However, later that day there was a phone call giving a new date only three days later. On 12th November, I phoned in at 7am, but the position was still uncertain. Fortunately, an ICU bed proved to be available, with my operation second on the list, inevitably with a different anaesthetist from the one I had met at pre-clerking.

I was welcomed to the central operating department by Sue, who had managed my theatre. She had seen my name on the list and had kindly arranged to do the honours. I was wheeled into the theatre and put to sleep. At about 6.30pm Elisabeth received a phone call to say the operation had been completed successfully.

I was oblivious until about 7.30 the following morning when I awoke in the ICU, still with an endotracheal tube in place. Initially I was uncertain whether I was in the LRI, the Hammersmith Hospital or a hospital in Sweden! The endotracheal tube was removed and I gradually worked out where I was. I had many tubes (at least six) and the next two days passed in a blur, punctuated by visits from Elisabeth and Clare.

Rob Sayers explained that he had connected the anomalous lower right renal artery to the graft. I spent the following two nights in the adjacent high dependency unit (HDU). The medical and nursing care on the ICU/HDU was exemplary.

I was moved to a single room on the vascular ward, gradually having the various tubes removed. The plasma creatinine (a measure of kidney function) had peaked at 288 but came down to the preoperative value, indicating that both kidneys were functioning, including the lower part of the right one. I passed wind and then had some diarrhoea and was relieved of the nasogastric tube. The arterial pressure line and the central venous line in my neck (particularly awkward) were removed, as was the urinary catheter.

Five days postoperatively the epidural catheter was taken out. Pain relief was then by patient-controlled analgesia (PCA), giving a small intravenous dose of morphine when I pressed the button. I did not find it easy to control the pain by this means; it seemed necessary to give the next increment just *before* the pain returned.

On 20th November Rob Sayers said that there was a suspected case of *Clostridium difficile* infection on the ward and suggested that the safest course would be for me to go home immediately, about two days ahead of schedule. I readily agreed to this and by midday was in my own bed, supplied with regular paracetamol and tramadol (an opiate analgesic of intermediate potency) and with an intravenous drip for the first three days, supervised by Elisabeth.

RECOVERY AT HOME

I slept right through that first night but subsequently found that pain woke me every few hours. I became severely constipated due to the oral analgesic (tramadol). After discussion with Professor Nick London, who had assisted at the operation and visited daily on his way to the LRI, tramadol was replaced by pethidine, given intramuscularly by Elisabeth and I started on lactulose for the constipation.

The following two weeks were gruelling. I came downstairs for part of the day and for meals, but I continued to lose weight to a total of about 18 pounds. The nights were interrupted by the need for the next dose of paracetamol and two injections of pethidine. When neither was due, some distraction was provided by Classic FM, but I don't know how I would have got through it without Elisabeth's encouragement. By 2nd December (day 20) I was able to miss out some doses of pethidine and by the 8th I did not need it at all.

ELISABETH'S FRACTURE
Then on 10th December disaster struck. Elisabeth fell when walking our golden retriever Fred along a quiet road about a quarter of a mile from home. Fortunately, an acquaintance was about 50 yards behind her and came to the rescue. She was confused and reluctant to get up but holding firmly onto the lead. A neighbour in a car joined in and they brought Elisabeth home. She was bleeding from a wound on her chin and repeating: 'What happened? Is Fred all right?' 'I've got a Colles' fracture.' She had no memory of the fall, indicating that she had blacked out before falling.

I explained that we were in difficulty as I could not drive and one of her rescuers kindly offered to take us to A&E at the LRI. A helpful A&E registrar (a former house surgeon of mine) assessed the situation, and X-ray confirmed a Colles' fracture. She was seen by the orthopaedic registrar and a temporary plaster applied.

Elisabeth was then admitted to the acute medical unit for assessment of the cause of the transitory loss of consciousness. An ECG and cardiac enzymes were normal (excluding a myocardial infarction), and she was transferred to a bed which happened to be on the infectious diseases unit. The orthopaedic theatre was busy, so the fracture could not be reduced until the second day. We were able to take her home that afternoon in Clare's car.

The problem then was that neither of us could drive. Friends were generous with their offers of help, enabling me to get to Waitrose for supplies. We also ordered bulky items through the Ocado delivery service. Thankfully, my health gradually improved: I regained a little weight and by mid-December I no longer needed painkillers at night.

As there had been no progress in investigating the cause of Elisabeth's fall, I phoned the physician to whose ward she had been transferred, but he said it was out of his hands and we should consult our GP, and furthermore he had too few junior staff. The GP requested a 24-hour cardiac tape, but there was a delay in getting an appointment. At this stage, I visited the vascular unit for a follow-up check and incidentally met Professor Ross Naylor, a leading authority on internal carotid artery stenosis as a cause of mini-strokes. He immediately arranged for Elisabeth to be seen in the stroke unit. A thorough consultation was followed by a tilt-table test, which showed carotid sinus hypersensitivity, a probable explanation for the fall.

Meanwhile we had downgraded Christmas Day to a simple lunch with Clare. We put the chicken we had ordered in the freezer. Sally, Jasper and Molly were due to stay for two nights on 28th–30th and Andrew, Liz and Laura came down for the day. Helped by the visitors, I roasted the chicken with all the trimmings, and everyone had an enjoyable time.

Elisabeth's accident had the beneficial effect of expediting my rehabilitation, as I had to take on many of the domestic tasks and look after the dog. In the snow after Christmas, I was able to walk him across the golf course. By early January, my guts had returned to normal, and I had regained most of the weight. By mid-January, after a test drive with Clare, I was permitted to drive the car again, and began to do some work in the garden. By the time I saw Rob Sayers on 2nd February, I was fully recovered apart from some low-grade aching across my lower ribs posteriorly, probably related to the epidural infusion.

After removal of the plaster on 18th January, Elisabeth's wrist was inevitably more painful, but it gradually improved, and she regained function over the following four weeks. Reflecting on our combined disabilities, the timing could have been much worse. If Elisabeth had fallen soon after I came out of hospital, we would have been in very great difficulty.

This experience of life as a patient would have been invaluable during my clinical career. It reinforced my previous light-hearted suggestion to the SAC that every surgical trainee should undergo an operation.

MORE EVENTS

Elisabeth has a long history of asthma, well controlled with inhalers. In retirement, chronic obstructive pulmonary disease (COPD) was diagnosed, though she has never smoked. Despite this, she manages very well apart from shortness of breath on steep hills.

Following her fracture, we were careful to always carry a mobile phone when dog walking. In January 2014, she fell while crossing a muddy field, with Fred running free, and fractured her right femur. She phoned me and I drove there and called an ambulance. The fracture was 'pinned and plated', and she was discharged home on the fifth day, on crutches. We had booked a holiday in Bavaria for May and wondered whether this would be possible. However, Elisabeth recovered well, so we went as planned. The only real difficulty was walking up the long hill to mad King Ludwig's Neuschwanstein Castle.

Over a period of two years, I'd had occasional episodes of dizziness, particularly when standing around on a guided tour of an art gallery. My pulse rate was sometimes as low as 48 per minute and I'd have to sit down for a while to recover. A 24-hour ECG showed only a slight abnormality, not considered to need treatment. Then in March 2018, I suddenly became very dizzy and lay down to recover, my pulse rate having dropped to 35 due to complete heart block. I was admitted to the cardiology unit and had a pacemaker inserted. I haven't had any further dizzy bouts.

As we get older, we are careful about our activities. We always use the handrail when going down the stairs and have installed grab rails for bath and shower. Long car journeys are interrupted by stops for coffee and lunch, while visits to Penzance are by train.

40

DOWNSIZING

In 2013 we began to consider whether we should downsize. Our six-bedroom house was much larger than we needed. Should we reach a stage when there was only one of us, he or she would feel lost in it and would not then be in a good state to manage a move. The garden, which I had loved caring for, was beginning to seem burdensome and was likely to be more so in the future. We discussed the idea with the children, who agreed it was sensible, but we made no progress beyond scanning the *Leicester Mercury* property supplement.

Clare was out walking her dog one day in September 2014, when she noticed a house for sale that she felt would suit us. It was only about a mile away, and we went to look straightaway. It was one of six houses built 15 years earlier in a cul-de-sac off a road of Edwardian terraced houses. We viewed it with the agent a few days later and decided to buy it.

We were fortunate in being able to buy before selling. After a little negotiation, a price was agreed, below the original asking figure, as it had been on the market for six months. We completed the purchase at the end of January 2015.

SELLING

Next, we had to sell our very well-cared-for Edwardian house, in a much sought-after road, and reduce the volume of our belongings to fit into a smaller one. Three estate agents gave quite disparate valuations, one £100,000 below the highest. We appointed the agent who suggested the highest asking price, perhaps unwisely, and the sale was advertised in February 2015.

A total of 26 parties viewed the house, six of whom came back for a second look. We had expected criticism for the lack of en suite bathrooms. We had not expected that parking would be a problem – there was a two-car garage plus room for five on the drive, but for many multigenerational families this was not enough! Whereas we had considered the wide quiet road highly desirable, many wanted their prestige home to be on a busier thoroughfare. I suspect that the large garden may have been a negative factor, not an asset.

After several offers, a sale was agreed in April. The survey was satisfactory and, with matters proceeding over the next six weeks, we went on a previously booked holiday in Croatia. On arrival back at Gatwick, we picked up a text message that the purchaser had withdrawn the previous day. We put the house back on the market and in July we accepted an offer from a couple of young consultants from the LRI. Six weeks later they also backed out. In neither case was any reason given and they did not seek a price reduction. It was all very disappointing, but we tried to remain stoical.

Almost immediately, we had a further offer from a family living just along the road. They had been interested but could not commit until they had a buyer. Out of the blue, Leicester City Football Club then sought to buy their home for the club's new manager, provided the whole thing could be settled in three weeks. We agreed a price and met the deadline, moving on 22nd September. Leicester City went on to win the Premiership in 2016 and we claim that this was only possible because our purchaser's house was available for their manager.

MOVING

Our new home needed some minor improvements: new carpets downstairs, some kitchen cabinets and bookcases. We are unusual in keeping cars in the garage, so we wanted the luxury of electrical door openers. These tasks were completed in time for our first expected sale.

More difficult was reducing the amount of stuff to fit into a smaller house, though as our grandchildren commented: 'It's not much of a downsize.' But there are four bedrooms rather than six and a much smaller garden. At Knighton Rise, because the rooms were large, we had bought large furniture, but we managed to accommodate most of it. Books were a problem, despite a generous supply of bookcases, so we made many visits to charity shops. I gave my 'black and white' darkroom equipment to a photography student who was interested in the old techniques.

The remaining task was to sort out the garden. It had been professionally landscaped but was overgrown – maybe the previous owners had lost interest once they were planning the building of their new house, a process lasting about three years. Once the undergrowth was cleared, I enjoyed replanting, experimenting to see what would tolerate heavy shade from the trees, which were subject to preservation orders. We also had the paving modified to create a bed for a loganberry, to compensate for leaving our extensive fruit and vegetable garden.

We settled in well and are pleased that we have made the move. There is still room to accommodate the whole family, subject to two sleeping at Clare's house, only a few minutes' walk away. We hope never to move again; if stairs became impossible, we could contract into the downstairs rooms with only minor alterations.

41

PAST, PRESENT AND FUTURE

I was fortunate throughout my training, progressing through good posts without gaps or marking time. This was due to support from past consultants, who took the trouble to phone colleagues and put in a good word for me. That would not now be permissible. I had so much more experience than millennial trainees, particularly operatively. But by modern standards I had received little training. I fear some patients may have experienced suboptimal care while I was making my way up a steep learning curve. I was short of research and publications until the move to a lecturer post in Sheffield corrected this.

My objective had been to become a consultant in a good hospital; I did not think it had to be a teaching hospital. Nevertheless, it was exciting to be appointed to Leicester just as the medical school was being launched, and to become clinical sub-dean organising the start of clinical teaching. I was very keen to give my juniors better training than I had experienced and to provide the support in the emergency work that had been lacking when I was a trainee.

Reflecting on what had attracted me to general surgery, there were two factors: the variety and the challenge of coping with diagnostic uncertainty. Things are so different now. When I started as a consultant my operations ranged from thyroidectomy to gallstones and breast and rectal cancer. Subspecialisation narrowed surgeons' elective work and I became a coloproctologist. The quality of care for defined conditions is enhanced, but perhaps the capacity to handle the unexpected is impaired. In the assessment of abdominal emergencies, the power of gastrointestinal endoscopy and the ready availability of cross-sectional imaging have reduced uncertainty but can delay reaching a decision.

I thoroughly enjoyed my surgical career but am unsure what I would do if I were qualifying now. Would I choose surgery? I think I might opt for general practice, provided the current problems of under-resourcing were overcome.

As a trainee, I had no idea of the variety of non-clinical activities that I would later undertake. I had attended two management courses for SRs and accepted that there was a duty to contribute to decisions about the surgical service and the hospital in general, but I had never envisaged the extent of my participation in the management of the LRI or the District Health Authority. It was inconceivable that I should become regional adviser, a member of the council and then an officer of the ASGBI, chairman of the SAC in general surgery and finally president of the ASGBI. Yet all these things happened. In each case I was either asked to take on a role or persuaded to have my name put forward in an election. In the 21st century, such posts would be advertised, and appointed after a formal interview. I doubt whether I would have applied under the present system.

CHANGES IN GENERAL SURGERY

Hospitals changed hugely over the 40 years that I worked as a surgeon, particularly during the 1990s. Notable advances in rectal surgery were introduced, culminating in the formation of the Association of Coloproctology in 1990. Laparoscopy transformed gastrointestinal surgery. These are two of the factors which encouraged subspecialisation in the last decade of the 20th century. As a result, I mutated from a truly general surgeon into a coloproctologist by day, though still a generalist out of hours.

The greatest change in the wards was the shortening of patients' stay, while many more operations were done as day cases. Effective prophylaxis was developed for thromboembolic complications and wound infection. Mass closure of vertical abdominal incisions eliminated the 'burst abdomen'. Intensive care units, in the operation of which I was much involved as a junior, progressed to save the lives of critically ill patients.

The management structure of the NHS scarcely changed until 1974, following which there were repeated reorganisations. Consultant involvement increased gradually and, with the creation of NHS trusts, medical directors for hospitals and clinical directors for specialties were appointed. As I approached retirement many trusts were amalgamated and I feared that the managers might become too remote.

As a house surgeon at the Westminster, I was resident continuously for six months, but once I was no longer working in a London teaching hospital, more reasonable rotas operated. I was resident when on call until I became an SR. As a consultant I was mostly on call one-in-six. The hours for trainees began to be reduced in the 1990s, and this evolved into shift working after I retired. The 'firm' structure was thereby undermined, with negative consequences for morale and training. As the juniors' hours reduced, the intensity of their work increased in inverse proportion. The fewer juniors on duty and the limited experience of middle-grade staff required a much more frequent consultant presence, to support them in the emergency work. This and subspecialisation prompted an increase in the number of consultants. There were nine general surgical consultants in Leicester in 1971, then also covering urology, paediatric and vascular surgery; by the millennium, they had been replaced by a total of 30 in these specialties. I believe the total has increased since then.

The national output of medical graduates trebled between 1970 and 2002, but still we were short of doctors, while the proportion of females rose from 15 to 60 per cent. Teaching medical students in hospitals became more difficult as the range of work covered by each firm narrowed and the pressures to meet contractual targets reduced the time available. The limitations on the trainees' hours of work and the pressure on theatre time restricted our ability to deliver surgical training.

During the 1990s, rising public expectations, increasing litigation, the high paediatric cardiac surgical mortality in Bristol and the Shipman murders increased the pressure on medical staff. Hospital inspections by the Care Quality Commission followed and, after a long gestation, revalidation of individual doctors began. It remains to be seen whether these regulatory measures will prevent major failures. Comprehensive audit of care might be more effective.

THE NHS IN 2019

I cannot resist final comments on the NHS as observed in 2019, based on perusal of the medical journals and conversations with colleagues. There are clearly difficulties in recruitment to general practice and the most acute hospital specialties – accident and emergency, acute medicine and psychiatry. Press reports indicate that only half of the graduates completing their two foundation years are promptly applying for further training in general practice or hospital specialties. It is difficult to see what the other half are doing: some are emigrating; some are opting for life as locums, for which the pay has escalated due to the vacancies; and some are leaving medicine. I just don't know the proportions. I hope many will return to the mainstream after an interval.

Those in the hospital training grades are very unhappy. This has been attributed to pay and conditions of employment, but there are more fundamental problems. Doctors now feel under valued and are under excessive pressure in terms of workload, regulation and the risk of litigation. Hospital doctors, both junior and senior, suffer from the effects of shift working for the trainees. That has seriously disrupted the comradeship which used to develop under the 'firm' structure.

Teaching of medical students in hospitals is constrained by narrow specialisation and is under pressure from service targets. More teaching should be in general practice, but that too is overstretched. Postgraduate training likewise struggles as it competes with service pressures. The curriculum is increasingly congested, and whenever a problem in the NHS is reported in the media, medical schools and postgraduate training schemes are urged to insert more coverage of that topic.

The background is of underfunding of the NHS and even more so of social care, with a difficult interface between them. The solutions currently proposed involve reconfiguration of services, with transfer into the community of much of the care of the elderly and of specialist consultations. The plans express the hope that these changes will help to control costs; it remains to be seen whether this will happen. Certainly, these services would need to be created before hospital facilities can be cut, and the transitional phase is likely to prove more expensive. Major and intermediate surgical operations and other complex interventions will surely still be based in hospitals.

Despite all of this, there is much excellent care. If you have a single well-defined problem, there is a pathway to deliver the evidence-based solution. But for those with vague and confusing symptoms, or with multiple morbidities, the subspecialty-orientated hospitals do not always cope well.

WORK-LIFE BALANCE

As I draw this account to a close in 2019, I reflect that my other interests often had to take second place. Consequently, our work-life balance was frequently out of kilter, particularly in the last decade. Nevertheless, old enthusiasms had periodically re-surfaced. Participation in the planning of two hospitals reminded me of my early idea of becoming an architect. It was possible to continue my interest in sailing, on Rutland Water and by chartering cruising boats. Overseas visits with surgical organisations widened our horizons. I am a hereditary gardener and enjoyed managing and partly redesigning our gardens. In retirement we branched out into other activities and further travels.

Most of all, there is my family: three children and four grandchildren, all now independent. Elisabeth supported and encouraged me throughout my career, while pursuing her own successful work as a consultant radiologist. She continues as my companion in retirement.